Avionics:
Beyond the AET
Navigation, Communication, and Installation

Tom Inman

Production Staff
Designer/Photographer Dustin Blyer
Designer/Production Coordinator Roberta Byerly
Production Artist David Gorton
Lead Illustrator Amy Siever

International Standard Book Number 1-933189-29-0
ISBN 13: 978-1-933189-29-1
Order # T-AVBAET-0101

For Sale by: Avotek
A Select Aerospace Industries, Inc., company

Mail to:
P.O. Box 219
Weyers Cave, VA 24486
USA

Ship to:
200 Packaging Drive
Weyers Cave, VA 24486
USA

Toll Free: 800-828-6835
Telephone: 540-234-9090
Fax: -540-234-9399

First Edition
Second Printing
Printed in the USA

www.avotek.com

Dedication

*This book is dedicated to Sheila, whose pleasant
enthusiasm encouraged me right to the very end.*

Additional Thanks:

*I would like to thank my parents, Jerry and Carlene, for
instilling ambition within me, without which, I would
not have considered taking on this project.*

*Thanks to Dr. Bradley Hayden who taught me how
to write in an above average manner.*

*Thanks to my colleagues, both past and present, from
whom I've learned greatly.*

*Thanks to the students of the aviation department at
Pennsylvania College of Technology who
provide inspiration every day.*

Preface

This textbook is intended for those individuals who are working toward their National Center for Aerospace and Transportation Technologies (NCATT) certification and want to pursue a career in avionics. The material covered in this book goes beyond the basics. It is assumed that the reader has a thorough knowledge of aviation electronics and preferably holds a Federal Aviation Administration (FAA) Airframe and/or Powerplant certificate or an NCATT Aircraft Electronics Technician (AET) certification. An AET certificate will open the door, and this text will let the student take a step into the rewarding field of avionics.

Avionics: Beyond the AET, the second book in Avotek's avionics series, extensively covers the material required for the NCATT AET endorsements: Radio Communication Systems, Dependent Navigation Systems and Autonomous Navigation Systems. I am confident a student studying this text will find earning these endorsements a simple matter.

Today's aircraft contain a diverse blend of systems. This text explains both new technology and, what some may consider, legacy technology. The extreme reliability of aircraft and their systems serves to keep avionics in operation for many years. A competent technician must have a broad knowledge of these technologies.

A student study guide is available for this book that provides a variety of questions presented in assignment format. Each page is designed so the assignment can be turned in individually.

Textbooks, by nature, must be general in their overall coverage of a subject area. As always, the aircraft manufacturer is the sole source of operation, maintenance, repair and overhaul information. Their manuals are approved by the FAA and must always be followed. No material presented in this or any other textbook may be used as a manual for actual operation, maintenance or repairs.

The author has, to the best of his abilities, tried to provide accurate, honest and pertinent material in this textbook. However, as with all human endeavors, errors and omissions can show up in the most unexpected places. If any exist, they are unintentional. Please bring them to our attention. ⇥

Email us at comments@avotek.com for comments or suggestions.

Avotek® Aircraft Maintenance Series

Introduction to Aircraft Maintenance

Aircraft Structural Maintenance

Aircraft System Maintenance

Aircraft Powerplant Maintenance

Avotek Aircraft Avionics Series

Avionics: Fundamentals of Aircraft Electronics

Avionics: Beyond the AET

Avionics: Systems and Troubleshooting

Other Books by Avotek

Aircraft Corrosion Control Guide

Aircraft Structural Technician

Aircraft Turbine Engines

Aircraft Wiring and Electrical Installation

AMT Reference Handbook

Avotek Aeronautical Dictionary

Fundamentals of Modern Aviation

Light Sport Aircraft Inspection Procedures

Structural Composites: Advanced Composites in Aviation

Acknowledgments

Aircell

Jim Akovenko — *JAARS*

Larry Bartlett, Lori Johnson, — *Duncan Aviation*

Bendix/King by Honeywell, Inc.

Steve Bradley — *Classic Aviation Services*

Greg Campbell, Sherman Showalter, Stacey Smith — *Shenandoah Valley Regional Airport*

Pat Colgan — *Capital Aviation*

De-Ice Systems International

Duncan Aviation

Jeff Ellis, Steve Hanson, Tim Travis — *Hawker Beechcraft*

Tom Eismin — *Purdue University*

Garmin International, Inc.

Raymond Goldsby — *AIA*

Virgil Gottfried, Harry Moyer — *Samaritan's Purse*

Lee Helm — *RAM Aircraft Corporation*

Honeywell, Inc.

David Jones — *Aviation Institute of Maintenance*

JRA Executive Air

Lilbern Design

Lufthansa

NASA

Select Aerospace Industries, Inc.

Select Airparts

Spectrum Technologies, PLC

Brian Stoltzfus — *Priority Air Charter*

Karl Stoltzfus, Sr., Michael Stoltzfus, Aaron Lorson, and Staff — *Dynamic Aviation Group, Inc.*

Ken Stoltzfus, Jr. — *Preferred Airparts*

Susan Timmons — *JRA Executive Air*

Contents

Basic Electronics Review

Avionics: Beyond the AET builds upon the knowledge a technician gains while earning an Aircraft Electronics Technician (AET) certificate through the National Center for Aerospace and Transportation Technologies (NCATT). AET certification prepares the avionics technician to work and advance in today's aviation world.

This volume will prepare the technician for the certification exams for the most frequent endorsements to the AET: the radio communication systems, dependent navigation systems, autonomous navigation systems, and installation and integration. Certification in these areas enables the technician to show his or her knowledge and proficiency in the areas that many avionics technicians work on a daily basis.

Before moving into those subjects, this chapter reviews important concepts from the AET standard. In addition, the chapter provides an overview of knowledge areas important for technicians, but not addressed within the AET curriculum.

Section 1

Solid State Devices and Circuits

Originally electronic devices were constructed using vacuum tubes and electromechanical devices. While they can still be found in a few older aircraft, most aircraft electronics no longer use these types of parts. Modern electronics are typically constructed using "solid-

Left: Today's advanced cockpits require that avionics technicians be able to work with a wide range of electronic systems.

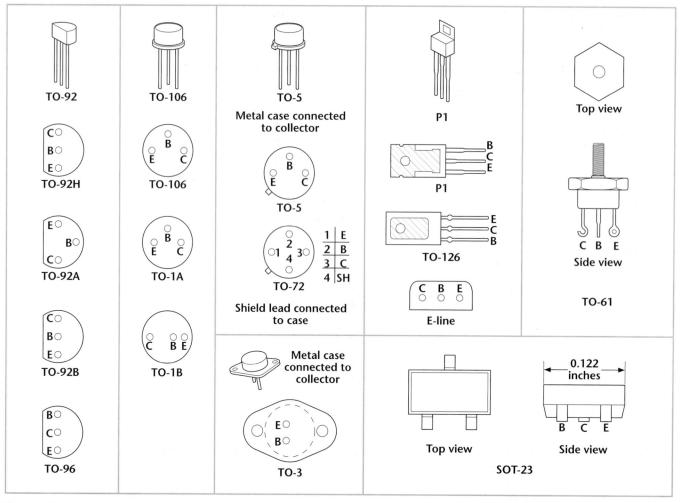

Figure 1-1-1. Types of bipolar transistors.

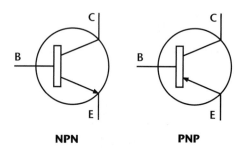

NPN   **PNP**

Figure 1-1-2. PNP and NPN transistor schematic symbols.

Bipolar Transistors

Bipolar transistors are semiconductor devices used in avionics equipment as switches, amplifiers, and variable resistances. As shown in Figure 1-1-1, bipolar transistors come in a variety of shapes and sizes, depending on use, and have three terminals. The two basic configurations of bipolar transistors are the NPN and the PNP. The schematic symbols for both transistors are shown in Figure 1-1-2.

Negative positive negative (NPN) refers to the emitter material, base material, and collector materials, respectively. In an NPN transistor the emitter material is constructed of silicon chemically doped to contain an excess of electrons, which is why the emitter is considered negatively doped. The base material is chemically altered or doped to have a positive charge and a shortage of electrons. Together the emitter and base are very similar to a diode. The collector in an NPN transistor, like the emitter, is negatively doped.

In either type of transistor a tiny amount of emitter-to-base current controls a relatively

state" devices. This means the components are made completely from a solid material, typically a crystalline semiconductor, that controls the electron flow without using mechanical means.

These solid-state devices can be assembled into complete circuits and systems that control, amplify, and direct electrical activity with no moving parts. This section reviews some of the common solid-state components that are found in modern circuitry.

large amount of emitter-to-collector current, as shown in Figure 1-1-3.

Forward biasing from emitter-to-base allows this current to flow. The polarity of the emitter to base bias depends on the transistor type. The base must be positive in respect to the emitter when using an NPN transistor, and the base must be negative in respect to the emitter when using a PNP transistor.

If the emitter base junction is forward biased properly, and if the proper collector bias is applied, then current will flow from emitter to collector. An NPN transistor requires that the collector be positive in relation to the emitter, and a PNP transistor requires that the collector be negative in relation to the emitter.

In many cases, bipolar transistors are used as switches in a similar way to solenoids and relays. In both solenoids and relays a small amount of current activates a coil, closing contacts that may be connected in a circuit carrying a larger amount of current. Forward biasing the base emitter junction of a transistor allows a tiny amount of current to flow, which then allows a much larger amount of current to flow from emitter to collector.

Bipolar transistors are more versatile than relays and solenoids because transistors have linear characteristics. As Figure 1-1-4 shows, a linear increase in base current results in a linear increase in collector current.

As shown at the lower left portion of the chart, the base voltage is not high enough to forward bias the emitter base junction, and no current flows. This condition is called cutoff because the current has been cut off and cannot flow. On the top right hand portion of the chart, the current flow is at maximum, and the emitter-to- collector current can no longer increase with a corresponding increase in emitter-to-base current. This condition is called saturation. The portion of the chart between cutoff and saturation is considered the linear region of the device. In the linear region, changes in emitter-to-base current are reflected in the emitter-to-collector current.

Field Effect Transistors

Like the bipolar transistor, the field effect transistor (FET) can be used as a switch or an amplifier. A simple FET has three leads, however, the leads have different names because field effect transistors work on a different principle than bipolar transistors. The schematic symbols for field effect transistors are shown in Figure 1-1-5. In an FET, a layer with a positively doped or negatively doped semi-

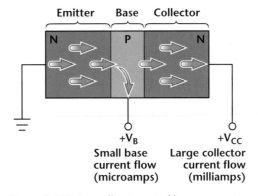

Figure 1-1-3. A small amount of base current allows a large amount of collector current.

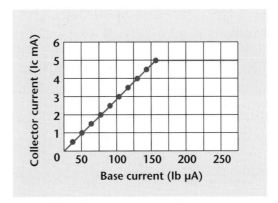

Figure 1-1-4. Base current vs. collector current.

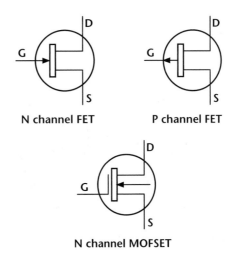

Figure 1-1-5. Field effect transistor symbols.

conductor is known as the channel, as shown in Figure 1-1-6.

FETs are divided into two general categories based on the channel doping. N-channel FETs have a negatively doped channel, and P-channel FETs have a positively doped channel. Layered on top of the channel is an area of material doped with the opposite charge. It is known as the source, since it works as the source of current into the channel. Another area

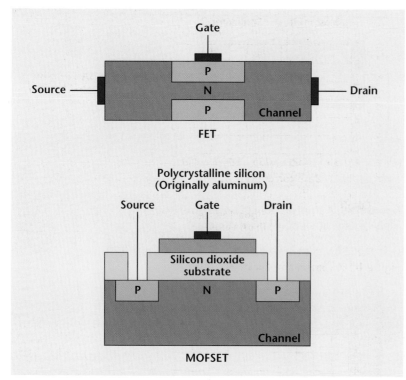

Figure 1-1-6. FET construction.

of material doped with the opposite charge is also layered onto the channel. This second area is called the drain, since current drains into this area from the channel. The third layer, or gate, resides between the source and the drain. During operation an electric field from the gate restricts current flow from source to drain through the channel. A small voltage change on the gate will cause a large change in channel current. Thus, amplification is possible with an FET. FETs may be constructed with multiple gates. This allows engineers to design circuits that can easily provide amplification and gain control in a single device. Figure 1-1-6 shows the construction of an FET and a MOSFET.

MOSFET is the acronym for *metal oxide semiconductor field effect transistor*. A MOSFET has a dielectric, or insulating, layer typically constructed of silicon dioxide between the gate and the substrate. The original MOSFETs were constructed with a metal gate, however, many gates are now constructed of polycrystalline silicon.

There are many types of FETs and most are very susceptible to electrostatic discharges. Some FETs and their descriptions are shown in Table 1-1-1. FETs of all types operate faster than bipolar transistors. FETs also have high input impedance and are used where this is important.

Like bipolar transistors, amplifiers based on FETs can be configured as Class A, B, or C and can be configured as common source, common drain, or common gate amplifiers.

It is important to use electrostatic control devices when handling an FET. Electrostatic control devices and procedures are discussed in more detail later in this text. FETs are packaged in conductive material and can have a shorting strap across the leads. A bench designed for electrostatic control has a conductive mat that is grounded and a grounded wrist strap for the technician to wear.

Amplifiers

Amplifiers are devices that use an external power source to increase the power of a signal. The amplifier takes the external power and matches the input signal to output at a larger amplitude. This allows a very low power input signal to be increased to the level required by components later in the circuit.

Classes of Amplifiers

The linear characteristic of transistors allows them to be used as amplifiers. Amplifiers are classed according to their biasing characteristics. If, when used as an amplifier, the base voltage and current remain within the linear range of the transistor, then the amplifier is considered a Class A system. Class A amplifiers have the least distortion and highest fidelity of any class of amplifier. However, when compared to other classes of amplifiers, the Class A amplifier is the least efficient. Figure 1-1-7 shows the amplifying curve of a Class A amplifier. The entire waveform is between cutoff and saturation. The signal induced variation in base current induces a corresponding variation in collector current. At no time does the base current fall to cutoff or increase to saturation.

Name	Full name	Description
MOSFET	Metal oxide semi-conductor field effect transistor	Constructed with an oxide layer between the gate and the channel
DGMOSFET	Dual gate metal oxide semi-conductor field effect transistor	A MOSFET with two gates
JFET	Junction field effect transistor	Separates the gate from the channel with a reverse biased PN junction
IGFET	Insulated gate field effect transistor	A broad description of several FET transistors with a layer between the gate and the channel

Table 1-1-1. FET types.

In a Class B amplifier, the base is biased at cutoff, and only one half of the wave is amplified. As a result, Class B amplifiers are often used in pairs in audio systems, with one bipolar transistor amplifying one half of the wave and the other bipolar transistor amplifying the other half of the wave. Class B amplifiers are more efficient than Class A amplifiers. The increased efficiency is a result of the transistor being off during 50 percent of the waveform. The price paid for this efficiency is loss of fidelity. The output resembles only half the input. Figure 1-1-8 shows the amplifying curve of a Class B amplifier with half of the waveform above cutoff.

When a bipolar transistor is used as an amplifier, the base is biased below cutoff and the amplifier is considered a Class C system. In a Class C amplifier only a small portion of the wave is amplified. As a result, Class C amplifiers can only be used to amplify sinusoidal waves. A tuned circuit can be used to recreate the rest of the wave. Figure 1-1-9 shows the amplifying curve of a Class C amplifier with less than half of the waveform above cutoff.

In addition to biased-based amplifiers there are three additional types of amplifiers made from bipolar transistors: common emitter, common collector, and common base. These are based on the transistor inputs and outputs. Each has its place in electronic circuitry. Since bipolar transistors have three leads, one lead is common to both the input and the output of the amplifier. The common lead identifies the amplifier type.

Common Emitter Amplifiers

Common emitter amplifiers (Figure 1-1-10) receive the input at the base and provide output at the collector. As the name implies, the emitter lead is common to both input and output. Common emitter amplifiers have high power gain and an output 180° out of phase with the input. Common emitter amplifiers are often used for small signal amplification.

Common Collector Amplifiers

Common collector amplifiers (Figure 1-1-11) receive the input at the base and provide output at the emitter. The collector lead is common to both input and output circuits. Common collector amplifiers have high current gain and an output with the same phase as the input. This type of amplifier has high input impedance and low output impedance. As a result, common collector amplifiers may be used as buffer circuits to protect high impedance circuits from low impedance loads. Common collector amplifiers are often used as DC amplifiers, where the transistor dissipates the power for

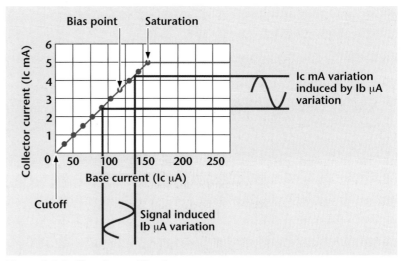

Figure 1-1-7. Class A amplification curve.

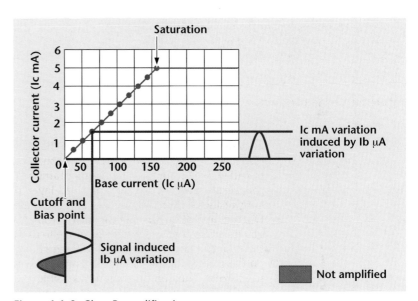

Figure 1-1-8. Class B amplification curve.

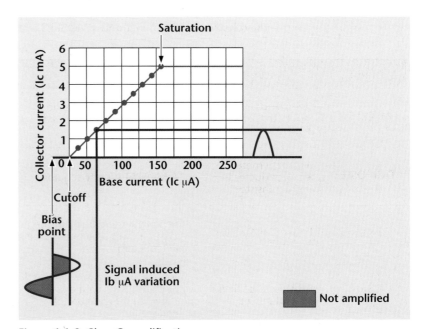

Figure 1-1-9. Class C amplification curve.

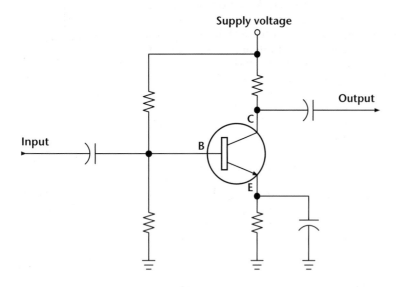

Figure 1-1-10. Common emitter amplifier.

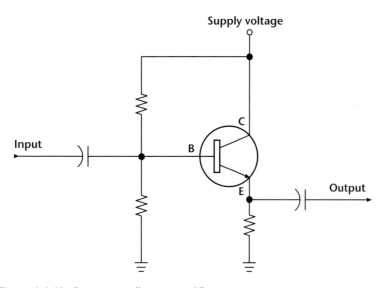

Figure 1-1-11. Common collector amplifier.

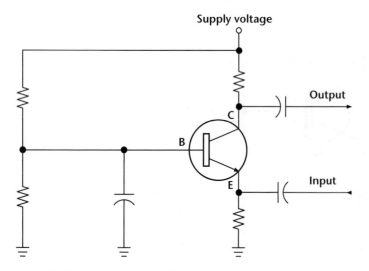

Figure 1-1-12. Common base amplifier.

a lighting dimmer circuit or a power supply regulator circuit.

Common Base Amplifiers

Common base amplifiers (Figure 1-1-12) receive the input at the emitter and provide output at the collector. Like common collector amplifiers, common base amplifiers have an output with the same phase as the input. This type of amplifier is known for high voltage gain, low input impedance, and high output impedance. Common base amplifiers may be found in RF circuits or in buffer applications, where the impedance must be changed from low to high.

Operational Amplifiers

An *operational amplifier* (op-amp) is a DC-coupled high gain amplifier with a differential input and, typically, a single output. An op-amp produces an output voltage that is typically hundreds of thousands times larger than the voltage difference between its input terminals.

Large numbers of transistors can be built into an integrated circuit designed to work as an operational amplifier. Operational amplifiers amplify the difference between the two input terminals. One terminal is connected to a reference, and the other terminal is connected to the signal to be amplified. If the signal is connected to the negative (–) terminal, then the output is inverted when compared to the input. The negative terminal is called the *inverting input*. If the signal to be amplified is connected to the positive (+) terminal, then the output is the same phase as the input. The positive terminal is referred to as the *non-inverting input*. The gain of an operational amplifier is controlled by providing negative feedback from the output to the inverting input. The gain can be determined by comparing the values of the feedback and input resistors as a ratio. With no feedback, an operational amplifier exhibits nearly infinite gain. Figure 1-1-13 shows an operational amplifier circuit.

Varactor Diodes

A *varactor diode* is a type of diode that has a variable capacitance depending on the voltage applied to it. These may also be referred to as varicap diodes, variable reactance diodes, or tuning diodes.

A varactor diode is designed to make maximum use of the inherent capacitance found within bipolar semiconductors. When forward

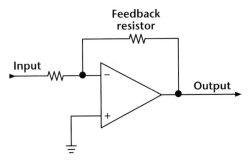

Figure 1-1-13. Operational amplifier circuit.

biased, a varactor diode passes current like any other diode, however, when reversed biased, the capacitance of the PN junction can be controlled by the amount of reverse bias voltage. This ability to control capacitance enables engineers to design filters and oscillators using varactor diodes to allow remote or automatic control of the circuit. Schematic symbols for varactor diodes are shown in Figure 1-1-14. Both symbols shown represent varactor diodes. The choice of which symbol to use is up to the engineer drawing the schematic. Using both types of symbols in a single schematic is extremely unlikely.

Oscillator Circuits

Oscillator circuits produce a repetitive electronic signal, commonly in a sine or square wave form. Avionics equipment uses oscilla-

tors as references to clock microprocessors in order for receivers and transmitters to operate. When engineers desire a stable frequency, such as those used for references or for microprocessor clocks, they design the system using a crystal controlled oscillator like the one shown in Figure 1-1-15. In this case, the quartz crystal exhibits characteristics of an LC circuit and can be placed in the feedback path of the oscillator.

When an oscillator must change frequency, engineers use an oscillator of either Hartley design (Figure 1-1-16) or Colpitts design (Figure 1-1-17). The main difference between the Hartley and Colpitts oscillators is the method used to obtain positive feedback. Colpitts oscillators tap into the capacitive portion of the LC resonant circuit, while Hartly oscillators tap into the inductive portion of the LC resonant circuit. Colpitts oscillators perform well at high frequencies but are easily effected by changes in load impedance. Hartley oscillators tend to produce more harmonics than Colpitts oscillators at higher frequencies. Engineers can design circuits in a way to negate the disadvantages of either circuit, therefore, the choice of oscillator tends to be determined by economics. In small manually tuned radios, Hartley oscillators have an advantage. In varactor tuned and synthesized radios, Colpitts oscillators have an advantage. Most often engineers use varactor diodes in the resonant circuit so that the circuit can be automatically or remotely controlled.

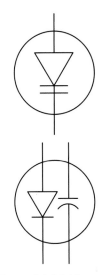

Figure 1-1-14. Varactor diode symbols.

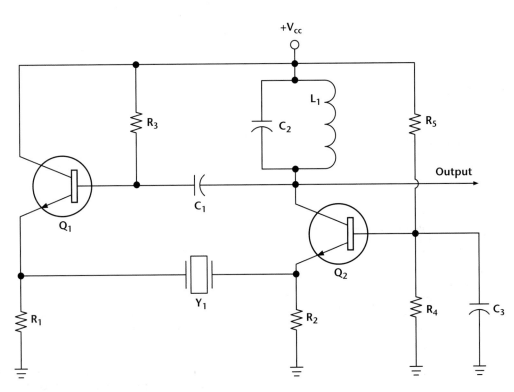

Figure 1-1-15. Crystal-controlled oscillator.

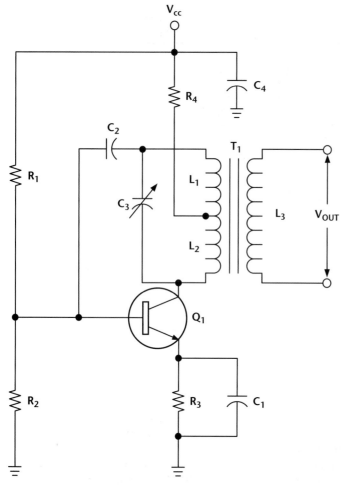

Figure 1-1-16. Hartley oscillator.

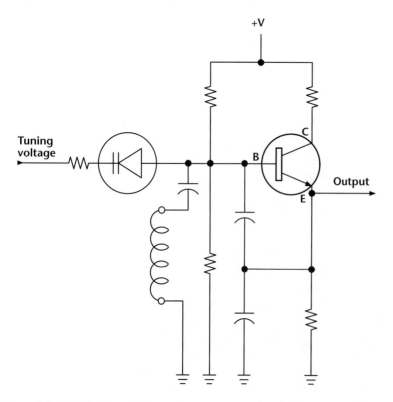

Figure 1-1-17. Colpitts oscillator using varactor tuning for frequency adjustment.

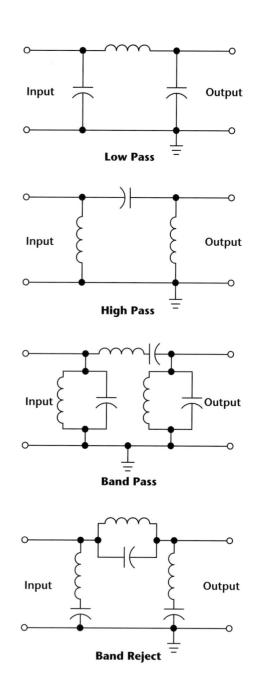

Figure 1-1-18. Pi-type filter configurations.

Filter Circuits

Filter circuits use a network of capacitors and inductors to filter in or filter out a certain frequency or group of frequencies. There are two key factors used to identify filter circuits. First, the technician must identify the input and output of the filter. Once the input and output are identified, the technician must identify the type of components or circuits through which a signal must pass while travelling from input to output.

Signals passing from the input through a capacitor or capacitors to the output identify the filter as high pass, since impedance decreases in a capacitor as frequency increases. If the signal

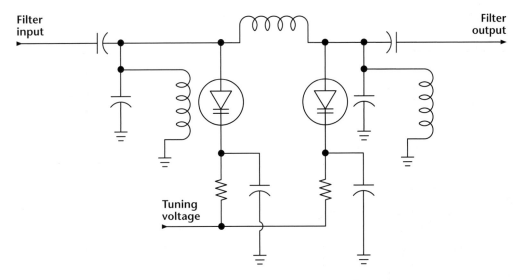

Figure 1-1-19. Preselector.

must pass through an inductor, the filter can be identified as low pass, since inductors decrease their impedance with decreasing frequency.

For band pass or band stop filters the technician must remember series resonant circuits pass current within a narrow range of frequencies, and parallel resonant circuits pass reduced current within a narrow band of frequencies. Band stop filters are also known as band reject filters. Various simple filters are shown and identified in Figure 1-1-18.

By adding varactor diodes to a band pass filter, as shown in Figure 1-1-19, engineers can create a circuit called a preselector, which can be controlled automatically from another part of the system. Aviation VHF receivers use preselectors at the input to filter in the desired channel and filter out interference.

Section 2

Basic Test Equipment

Voltmeters

Avionics technicians use a variety of both simple and complex test equipment. Voltmeters are one of the most common tools for troubleshooting. Examples of a handheld and a bench top digital voltmeter are shown in Figure 1-2-1. Voltmeters have a high input impedance and must be connected in parallel with the load. Attempting to connect a voltmeter in series renders the circuit under test inoperative, since the proper amount of current does not flow.

When using a manually scaled voltmeter to test an unknown voltage, set the voltmeter to the highest scale. If the voltage is known, set the meter to the appropriate scale.

A multimeter, also known as a VOM or volt-ohm meter, combines several measurement functions in one instrument, including the measurement of volts (like a voltmeter) or amps (like an ohmmeter). It may be used in place of these separate instruments. An analog multimeter may have several scales printed on the card behind the meter movement, as shown in Figure 1-2-2, so the technician should take care to read from the appropriate scale. If, for example, the multimeter in Figure 1-2-2 is used as a voltmeter and is set to the 250 VDC range,

A.

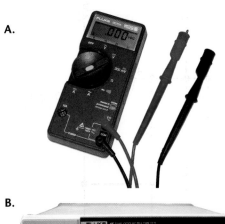

B.

Figure 1-2-1. Digital multimeters: (A) Handheld, (B) Bench top.

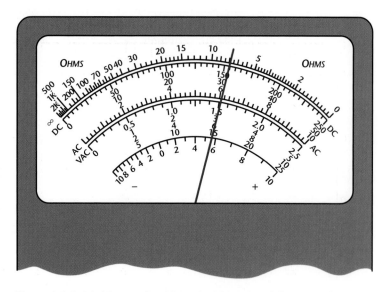

Figure 1-2-2. Multimeter faceplate showing nine different scales.

the meter indicates 155 V. However, if the meter is set to the 2.5 VAC range, it reads 1.5 V.

Ammeters

Most ammeters are designed to be connected in series or inserted into the circuit under test. Always select the appropriate scale, and if the amperage is unknown, start with the highest scale. Due to the high current load in high amperage applications, connecting an ammeter in series is not practical or safe. In these cases a clamp-type ammeter may be used. The clamp-type ammeter indirectly measures the current flow by measuring the strength of the magnetic field around the wire. Clamp-type ammeters do not work in low current circuits. Since the internal resistance of an ammeter is extremely low, never connect an ammeter in parallel because damage will occur to both the meter and the circuit under test.

Wattmeters

Both audio and radio frequency wattmeters are standard equipment in any avionics laboratory.

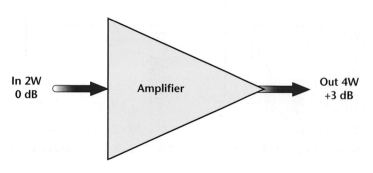

Figure 1-3-1. Output compared to input of an amplifier.

When using an audio wattmeter, the technician must ensure the appropriate load is used to prevent damage to the test equipment or the avionics equipment being tested. In addition, power readings will not be accurate unless the impedance is set appropriately for the system being tested.

When using a radio frequency wattmeter, the technician must ensure it is set properly to measure power on the frequency being tested. Some RF wattmeters have removable elements for different frequencies and power ranges. When using this type of wattmeter, the technician must ensure the appropriate element is installed. In addition, the technician must make sure the transmitter is properly loaded, otherwise damage to the transmitter under test may occur.

Ohmmeters

Ohmmeters are used to test resistance. The scale on most analog ohmmeters is labeled in reverse to the other scales, as shown in Figure 1-2-2. An ohmmeter uses an internal power source to create current. The current passes through the device under test. The amount of current is inversely proportional to the resistance of the device, and the meter is scaled to take this proportion into consideration. Portable meters use a battery as a current source. Since the ohmmeter creates its own current, it should never be connected to an energized circuit. Connecting an ohmmeter to an energized circuit produces unpredictable results that range from erroneous readings to ohmmeter or circuit damage.

Section 3

Decibels

Definition of Decibels

A *decibel* is a logarithmic unit that indicates the ratio of a physical quality, typically a power or intensity level, relative to a reference level. The reference level may be defined or implied. A ratio in decibels is 10 times the logarithm to base 10 of the ratio of two power quantities. A decibel can also be defined as one-tenth of a bel, where a bel is a base-10 logarithm of a power ratio.

The definition and usage of the term *decibel* is key to understanding the performance of any kind of radio, amplifier, or filter. Throughout this book, the term *decibels* is used to describe, estimate, and calculate values of voltage or power. Documentation for avionics equipment makes references frequently to decibels. Decibels are a useful tool to document the relationship between different measurements. Moreover, decibels can be used to make estimates of values. The abbreviation for a decibel is dB. Bell Laboratories coined the term to describe signal loss in telephone circuits.

What is meant by a power ratio? Figure 1-3-1 illustrates an amplifier with a 2 W input. The amplifier doubles the power and has an output of 4 W. This can be expressed as a ratio, such as power out/power in, or 4/2. The ratio could also be expressed as an equation:

amplification = power out/power in

or

$$2 = \frac{2}{4}$$

Ratios may also be used to express loss or attenuation. If we started with 4 W and our power was reduced by 2 W, then we would have a ratio of 2/4, or as expressed as an equation:

amplification = power out/power in

or

$$0.5 = \frac{2}{4}$$

Using the types of ratios described above work well, as long as the increase or decrease in power is small and as long as the person performing the calculations remembers fractional numbers represent loss.

Decibel Advantages

Decibels present some advantages over conventional reference numbers. Decibels are logarithmic, which means large increases or decreases in power can be expressed easily. A *logarithm* is the exponent necessary to raise a base number to another value. For example, the base-10 logarithm of 100 is 2. In other words, 10 raised to the power of 2 (10^2) is equal to 100. In contrast to normal numbers, logarithmic numbers, such as decibels, represent much larger increases in values, as shown in Figure 1-3-2. Furthermore, reductions of power are shown as negative numbers, which makes the identification of loss or attenuation easy to recognize.

Decibel Use

A key to understanding decibels is to remember that decibels always describe a compari-

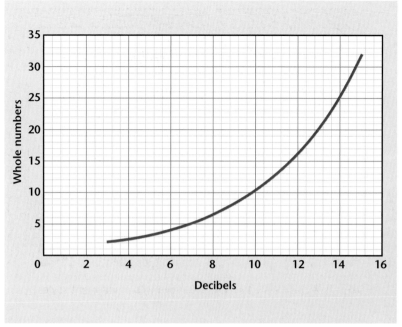

Figure 1-3-2. Whole numbers vs. decibels—a logarithmic change.

son or a ratio. For example, an amplifier may double the input power, as shown in Figure 1-3-1. In this case, the comparison would be from output to input and could be described as approximately +3 dB, or approximately 3 dB of gain.

Decibels are also used to compare the values before and after an action was taken, as shown in Figure 1-3-3, where turning a filter off increases the output by approximately 3 dB. In this case, a technician measures audio output level with the filter on, turns the filter off, and then measures again. With the filter on the technician measures 2 W. When the technician turns the filter off, the output increases to a new level of 4 W. This represents an increase of approximately 3 dB.

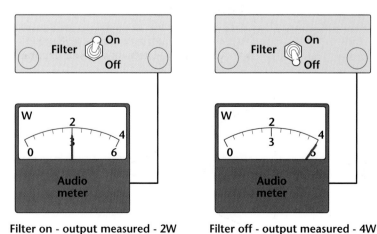

Filter on - output measured - 2W   Filter off - output measured - 4W

Figure 1-3-3. Decibel value before and after an action.

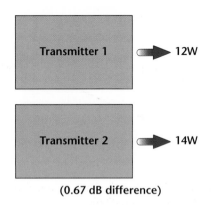

Figure 1-3-4. Two transmitter outputs.

Comparisons may also be made between two different points in a system, or even between two different systems, as shown in Figure 1-3-4, where a 0.67 dB difference exists between the output power of the two transmitters. Transmitter 2 has slightly more output than transmitter 1. When expressed as a dB ratio, the output of transmitter 2 is 0.67 dB more than the output of transmitter 1.

In the previous figures, the decibel figures calculated are considered relational because they describe a relationship between values: the relationship between input and output wattage (Figure 1-3-1), output wattage before and after an action was taken (Figure 1-3-3), and the wattage relationship between two different transmitters (Figure 1-3-4). Another common way to use decibels is to describe an exact value. In this case, the comparison is made to a standard reference value. There are many standard references. Whenever a standard reference value is made, an extra letter is added to the dB abbreviation. The International Electrotechnical Commission has adopted several standards values that can be used as a reference for decibels. Two of these standard values are used in the avionics industry. Avionics technicians use *dBm* to compare a value with standard value of 1 mW across a 50 Ω load. The *m* in dBm stands for a reference value of 1 mW. Avionics technicians also use *dBW* to compare a value with standard value of 1 W. The *W* in dBW stands for a reference value of 1 W.

Decibel Math

There are two formulas used to calculate decibels, one using power and the other voltage.

$$dB = 10 \times LOG_{10} \frac{POWER\ OUT}{POWER\ IN}$$

$$dB = 20 \times LOG_{10} \frac{VOLTAGE\ OUT}{VOLTAGE\ IN}$$

The basic power formula measures a ratio of power amplitudes and is 10 times the base 10 log of power out divided by power in.

$$dB = 10 \times LOG_{10} \frac{POWER\ OUT}{POWER\ IN}$$

$$dB = 10 \times LOG_{10} \frac{4W}{2W}$$

$$dB = 10 \times LOG_{10} 2$$

$$dB = 10 \times 0.301$$

$$dB = 3.01$$

This formula demonstrates how to calculate the dB difference between a 4 W output and a 2 W input. When calculating dBm, power in is replaced with 1 mW as measured across a 50 Ω load.

$$dB = 10 \times LOG_{10} \frac{POWER\ OUT}{1\ mW}$$

$$dB = 10 \times LOG_{10} \frac{2\ mW}{1\ mW}$$

$$dB = 10 \times LOG_{10} 2$$

$$dB = 10 \times 0.301$$

$$dB = 3.01$$

When dBm is used, then *power in* is replaced with 1 mW.

$$dB = 10 \times LOG_{10} \frac{POWER\ OUT}{1\ W}$$

$$dB = 10 \times LOG_{10} \frac{2\ W}{1\ W}$$

$$dB = 10 \times LOG_{10} 2$$

$$dB = 10 \times 0.301$$

$$dB = 3.01$$

While watts is a direst measure of power, voltage is not. As a result, if a technician is calculating decibels using voltage, then he or she must use a slightly different formula.

$$dB = 20 \times LOG_{10} \frac{VOLTAGE\ OUT}{VOLTAGE\ IN}$$

In the case of voltage, multiplying the base 10 log of voltage out over voltage in by 20 yields an accurate answer. Doubling the multiplication factor from 10 to 20 converts the voltage measurements to power measurements; dB is always a power ratio.

The formula for voltage works in a similar way. The following shows how the decibels of

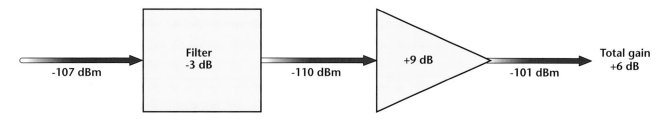

Figure 1-3-5. Algebraically adding decibels.

an amplifier producing 6 V output with 3 V input can be calculated.

$$dB = 20 \times LOG_{10} \frac{6V}{3V}$$

$$dB = 20 \times LOG_{10} 2$$

$$dB = 20 \times 0.301$$

$$dB = 6.02$$

Since decibels are based on logarithms, no matter what type of decibels are being used a technician may algebraically add them to determine total gain or loss. This is so because logarithms may be added and subtracted. Figure 1-3-5 illustrates a block diagram of a circuit with both loss and gain. By adding the decibel figures together, one may determine easily the total loss or gain.

Decibel Rules of Thumb

By using formulas, a technician may calculate exact values, however, the real power of decibels comes into play when estimating values. When troubleshooting, technicians often make estimates of values, which speeds up the troubleshooting process. Three is the magic number when it pertains to power. When a circuit exhibits gain, each 3 dB approximately doubles the power. Whenever power is doubled, the result of dividing the output by the input equals two. The base 10 log of 2 is approximately 0.301. Multiplying 0.301 by 10 equals 3.01 dB of gain. Three decibels always represent a doubling of power. The formula below shows how this is true no matter what wattages are used.

$$\frac{4}{2} = 2 \qquad \frac{10}{5} = 2 \qquad \frac{15}{7.5} = 2 \qquad \frac{24}{12} = 2$$

$$LOG_{10}(2) = 0.301$$

$$0.301 \times 10 = 3.01 \text{ dB}$$

While three is the main number for decibels using watts, six is the main number for decibels using volts. Six decibels always represent a doubling of volts as shown in the following

formula, multiplying the base 10 logarithm of 2 by 20 always yields 6.02 dB.

$$\frac{4}{2} = 2 \qquad \frac{10}{5} = 2 \qquad \frac{15}{7.5} = 2 \qquad \frac{24}{12} = 2$$

$$LOG_{10}(2) = 0.301$$

$$0.301 \times 20 = 6.02 \text{ dB}$$

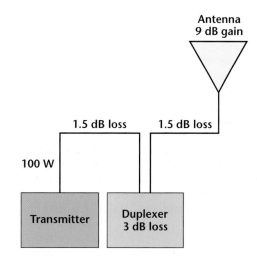

Figure 1-3-6. Transmitter system with gain and loss figures.

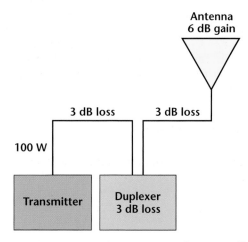

Figure 1-3-7. Transmitter system with an overall loss.

Figure 1-3-6 illustrates a communications system with a gain producing antenna, and it illustrates both the rules of thumb and shows the ease of algebraically adding decibels.

In this case, the total decibel figure is:

$$(-1.5dB) + (-3dB) + (-1.5dB) + 9dB = 3dB$$

The estimated power radiating from the antenna is double the input power, or approximately 200 W. If the antenna gain is 12 dB, then the power doubles twice and approximately 400 W is radiated.

When calculating loss, three is still the main number to use and represents the power being divided by half. Figure 1-3-7 illustrates a similar transmitter and antenna system with a lower gain antenna and more loss in the transmission line.

In this case, the total dB is:

$$(-3dB) + (-3dB) + (-3dB) + 6dB = (-3dB)$$

We have a total of 3 dB of loss, and the power radiating from the antenna is then approximately 50 W. If the duplexer loss in Figure 1-3-7 increased to 6 dB, the overall loss becomes 6 dB, and the power radiating from the antenna drops to approximately 25 W.

$$(-3dB) + (-6dB) + (-3dB) + 6dB = (-6dB)$$

The rules for adding, subtracting, and estimating apply no matter what type of decibels are being used. The rules apply to dB, dBm, dBW, or any other type of decibels.

Decibel Summary

Decibels, abbreviated dB, is a ratio of two power or voltage values. The formulae for decibels are:

Type of decibel	Power formula
dB	$dB = 10 \times LOG_{10}\left(\dfrac{POWER\ OUT}{POWER\ IN}\right)$
dBW	$dBW = 10\ LOG_{10}\left(\dfrac{POWER\ OUT}{1W}\right)$
dBm	$dBm = 10\ LOG_{10}\left(\dfrac{POWER\ OUT}{1mW}\right)$

Table 1-3-1. Types of decibels and their formulas.

$$dB = 10 \times LOG_{10}\frac{POWER\ OUT}{POWER\ IN}$$

$$dB = 20 \times LOG_{10}\frac{VOLTAGE\ OUT}{VOLTAGE\ IN}$$

An easy way to remember which formula has the 10 multiplier is to memorize the phrase, "powers of 10," since 10 is the multiplier for the power formula. Decibels may be added and subtracted to determine the total loss or gain of a circuit or system. Loss is represented by negative numbers and gain by positive numbers. In the case of voltage, values may be estimated by doubling the voltage for each +6 dB in the circuit or halving the voltage for each -6 dB in the circuit. In the case of power, values may be estimated by doubling the wattage for each +3 dB in the circuit or halving the wattage for each -3 dB in the circuit. Decibels with a letter added represent comparisons to a standard; dBW is a ratio comparison to 1W, and dBm is a ratio comparison to 1 mW, as shown in Table 1-3-1.

Section 4

Safety

Radio Frequency Radiation Hazards

Unlike nuclear radiation, radio frequency (RF) energy does not break down atoms. As a result, radio waves are considered non-ionizing radiation, but they still contain high levels of radio energy that can heat living tissue and cause damage. High levels of radiation can cause skin burns, cataracts, and internal burns. A technician exposed to high levels of radio wave radiation for a long period of time may suffer heat exhaustion or heat stroke. If the technician is working in close proximity to a radiating element, such as an antenna, then electrical shock is also possible. Radar systems radiate energy at incredibly high power levels for very short periods of time. As a result, the technician may not feel any sensation as the damage is occurring.

Limits for RF energy are published by The Occupational Safety and Health Administration (OSHA). At frequencies between 10 MHz and 100 GHz, OSHA recommends a maximum permissible exposure limit (PEL) of 10 mW per square centimeter of body surface averaged over a six minute period of time. In addition, weather radar manuals contain information regarding the minimum safe distance a technician must stay from a radiating radar antenna.

Weather radar systems can also induce arcs and sparks in metal structures; therefore, they should never be operated in the hangar or around other aircraft or ground vehicles.

Typically, radar is turned off while an aircraft is on the ground. The avionics technician may need to power up the radar to service it, however, in which case, caution must be taken to protect him or herself and others. An aircraft radar antenna is shown in Figure 1-4-1, and the radome, or nose cone, housing for the antenna can be clearly seen in the primed King Air 350 in Figure 1-4-2.

EMF Hazards

EMF hazards refer to danger resulting from close proximity to high voltage or electromotive force. On occasion, avionics technicians may work in close proximity to exposed circuits energized with high voltages. When near such circuits, the technician must use extreme care to ensure he or she is not grounded. Do not stand on a wet surface, keep metal tools away from the energized circuit and work with one hand. The other hand should be placed in a pocket to avoid grounding the circuit through the chest cavity. If at all possible, such circuits should be de-energized prior to performing any work.

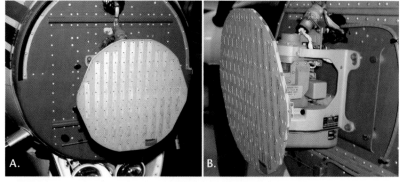

Figure 1-4-1. Radar antenna: (A) Front view, (B) Mechanism.

Figure 1-4-2. The black radome, or nose cone, housing for radar antenna is apparent on this primed, but not yet painted, Beechcraft King Air 350.

Section 5

Summary

Bipolar transistors are semiconductor devices used in avionics equipment. The linear characteristic of bipolar transistors allows them to be used as amplifiers. These transistors have three leads, known as the emitter, base, and collector. In most circuits, the base lead is considered the control lead. Like the bipolar transistor, the field effect transistor can be used as a switch or an amplifier. The basic FET has three leads: source, gate, and drain. In most circuits, the gate is considered the control lead. Large numbers of transistors can be built into an integrated circuit designed to work as an operational amplifier. The operational amplifier amplifies any difference between the two input leads and has its gain controlled by feedback from the output to the inverting input lead.

Avionics technicians use a variety of both simple and complex test equipment. Voltmeters are of relatively high impedance and must be used in parallel with the circuit under test. Ammeters are of very low impedance and must be used in series with the circuit under test. Wattmeters must be used with the appropriate load. Ohmmeters create their own voltage internally and must never be connected to an energized circuit.

The definition and usage of the term *decibel* is important for understanding the performance of any kind of electronic device. Decibels are a logarithmic ratio and can be strictly relational or related to a value, such as a milliwatt, as is the case with dBm. Decibels may be added or subtracted. In addition, technicians can use decibel rules of thumb to estimate values. When measuring power an increase of 3 dB is approximately an increase of double. Likewise, a decrease of 3 dB (-3 dB) is approximately a decrease of half. Using voltage, the double or half number is six.

Radio frequency energy is non-ionizing, however, high-power RF radiation can heat living tissue and cause various types of damage. Technicians may also encounter exposed circuitry energized at a high voltage. When working around high voltage circuits, a technician should use extreme care to ensure he or she is not grounded.

2

General Radio Communication Theory

Even in this era of modern aviation, much of the aircraft's avionics panel still relies on radio communication equipment. As a result, today's avionics technician must be well versed in general radio communication theory. This chapter provides the basic theory of how information is sent and received using radio. The devices that carry and broadcast radio energy and the basic troubleshooting of these devices are also examined.

Section 1

Radio Theory

Creating Radio Waves

When electrical current flows in a wire a magnetic field is generated around the wire. This field is known as *lines of flux* or *flux field* and flows perpendicular or 90° to the wire itself. To understand how lines of flux flow around the wire, technicians learn the right hand rule—hold the wire with the right hand and point the thumb in the direction of current flow; fingers that are wrapped around the wire point in the direction that the magnetic field is flowing. Not only does the current produce a magnetic, or H field, it also produces an electric field known as the E field. The E field flows parallel to the wire. (Figure 2-1-1) When an alternating current (AC) is applied to the same wire, the H and E fields are constantly changing with the frequency of the applied current. This changing field is called an *electromagnetic wave*, which radiates away from the wire at or near the speed of light. A radio wave is a type of electromag-

Left: Air transportation requires reliable, efficient radio communication.

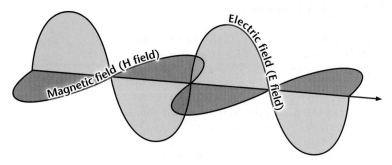

Figure 2-1-1. Electromagnetic waves.

netic wave. This radio wave will occur on any frequency.

Electromagnetic or radio waves have two dimensions. The first dimension is *amplitude*, which can be defined as power or strength of a wave signal. The second dimension is *wavelength*, which is the distance between any point on a wave and the equivalent point on the next wave. Therefore, each radio wave can be defined by its frequency, wavelength, and amplitude (Figure 2-1-2). Wavelength (λ) can be calculated by dividing the speed of the radio wave by its frequency (f). As we stated earlier, radio waves

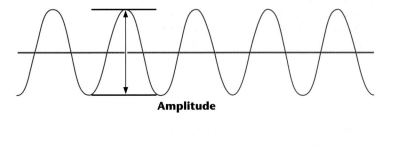

Amplitude

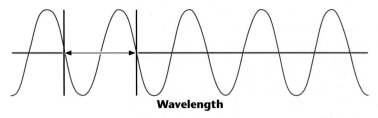

Wavelength

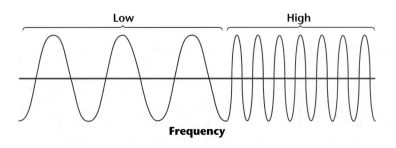

Frequency

Figure 2-1-2. Examples of radio waves showing amplitude, wavelength and frequency.

move away from the wire at approximately the speed of light (c), which is 300,000,000 meters per second ($c/f = \lambda$). Please note, the examples in Figure 2-1-2 demonstrate that as the frequency increases, the wave length decreases.

Radio Frequency Spectrum

The *radio frequency spectrum* is the world where radio communication and navigation reside. This spectrum includes frequencies from 1 Hz to approximately 428 GHz (Figure 2-1-3). The United States Department of Commerce National Telecommunications and Information Administration (NTIA) has divided up the radio frequency spectrum into different groups of frequencies called *bands*. These bands range from very low frequency (VLF) to extremely high frequency (EHF). The NTIA, along with the Federal Communications Commission (FCC), has allocated different frequency bands to various radio services. The NTIA publishes a chart showing how the frequencies are allocated. Portions of this *allocation chart* discussed in this section are shown in Appendix A. Avionics technicians and other technicians engaged in the repair and servicing of radio equipment need to have an understanding of these bands of frequencies.

Very Low Frequency

The *very low frequency* (VLF) band starts at 1 Hz and ends at 30 kHz with wavelengths from 0 to 10 km. This band of frequencies includes those in the audible range and below. Radio communication is possible at these frequencies over long distances on the earth, however, there are very few systems designed to work within this range. Although the frequencies from 9 kHz to 14 kHz in the VLF range are designated for radio navigation, no system is currently using them.

Low Frequency

The *low frequency* (LF) band starts at 30 kHz and ends at 300 kHz with wavelengths from 10 km to 1 km. Like the VLF band, radio communication is possible over long distances within this range. This range of frequencies contains a significant amount of weather related atmospheric noise. Aircraft electrical systems are also known to cause noise from electrical induction within this band of frequencies. Shielded wiring and noise filters are often used on avionic installations to prevent this noise from bleeding into the avionics signals. The LF bands from 190 kHz to 300 kHz are designated by the FCC for aeronautical radio navigation use. The only current aeronautical radio navigation system working within these frequencies is the automatic direction finder (ADF). Details of this system will be explained in later chapters.

Medium Frequency

The *medium frequency* (MF) band starts at 300 kHz and ends at 3 MHz with wavelengths from 1 km to 100 m. Like the LF band, communication over long distances is possible, however this band is also subject to a significant amount of atmospheric noise. Most of the frequencies from 300 kHz to 535 kHz are designated for aeronautical radio navigation. Frequencies from 535 kHz to 1.705 Mhz are familiar to many as the AM radio broadcasting band.

High Frequency

The *high frequency* (HF) band starts at 3 MHz and ends at 30 MHz with wavelengths from 100 m to 10 m. This band of frequencies is commonly known as the short wave band. The HF band is subject to a fair amount of atmospheric noise at the lower frequencies that becomes less noticeable near or at the higher frequencies. Communication over long distances is possible within the HF spectrum, however, reliable frequencies change from day to day and even from hour to hour. This change in reliability is due to the sun's affect on the ionosphere, which is discussed in more detail later in this chapter. The HF band contains a wide variety of amateur, mobile, fixed, and broadcasting allocations, including several frequencies reserved for aeronautical mobile.

When established, HF band wavelengths were considered short and the frequencies were considered to be quite high. At this time wavelengths shorter than ten meters were not considered usable. As technology has progressed, engineers have found ways to use much higher frequencies and shorter wavelengths. By today's standards, the HF wavelengths do not seem very short.

Very High Frequency

The *very high frequency* (VHF) band starts at 30 MHz and ends at 300 MHz with wavelengths from 10m to 1m. This band of frequencies is subject to very little atmospheric noise. Communication over long distances is not normally possible within the VHF spectrum, and communication is limited to line of sight. The VHF band contains a wide variety of amateur, mobile, and fixed allocations, including television broadcasting and FM stereo. Aviation navigation and communication use 75 MHz and frequencies from 108 MHz to 137 MHz.

Ultra High Frequency

The *ultra high frequency* (UHF) band starts at 300 MHz and ends at 3 GHz with wavelengths from 1 m to 10 cm. Like the VHF band, this band of frequencies is subject to very little atmospheric noise. Frequencies within the UHF band are considered microwave frequencies by at least one definition, which describes them as frequencies with wavelengths of one meter. Communication over long distances is not possible within the UHF spectrum, and communication is limited to line of sight. The UHF band contains a wide variety of amateur, mobile, fixed, and satellite allocations, including television broadcasting. Frequencies from 328.6 MHz to 335.4 MHz and 960 MHz to 1.35 GHz are used for aviation navigation and communication.

Super High Frequency

The *super high frequency* (SHF) band starts at 3 GHz and ends at 30 GHz with wavelengths from 10 cm to 1 cm. Like the VHF and UHF bands, this band of frequencies is subject to very little atmospheric noise. Communication over long distances is not possible within the SHF spectrum, and communication is limited to line of sight. The SHF band contains a variety of mobile, fixed, and satellite allocations. Aeronautical radio navigation frequencies within SHF are used mostly for weather radar.

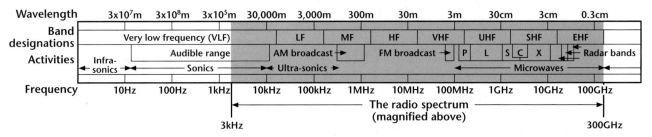

Figure 2-1-3. Radio frequency spectrum.

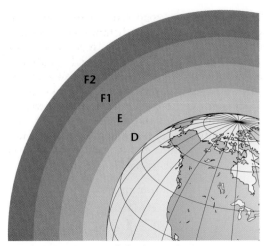

Figure 2-1-4. Layers of the ionosphere.

Extremely High Frequency

The *extremely high frequency* (EHF) band starts at 30 GHz and ends at 300 GHz with wavelengths from 1 cm to 1 mm. Like the VHF, UHF, and SHF bands, these frequencies are subject to very little atmospheric noise. Communication is limited to line of sight within the EHF spectrum. The EHF band contains a variety of mobile, fixed, and satellite allocations. None of the aeronautical systems described in this text use the EHF band.

Radio Wave Propagation

The movement of electromagnetic or radio waves through a medium, such as a wire, the atmosphere or space, is known as *propagation*. Radio waves propagate differently depending on their frequency and on atmospheric conditions.

Ionosphere

The ionosphere is a portion of the earth's atmosphere ionized by solar radiation. The ionosphere has a great affect upon radio wave propagation. All layers of the ionosphere impede the progress of radio waves. Knowledge of the ionosphere is important in understanding the various forms of radio propagation.

Electromagnetic waves and, in this case, radio signals, can be reflected or refracted by interactions with objects and the media through which they travel. These interactions cause the radio signals to change direction and affect the areas and directions in which the radio signals travel.

The sun has an enormous impact on radio signal propagation because of its affect on the ionosphere where most long distance radio communications occur. As a result, it greatly affects many forms of radio communications used by various types of mobile radio equipment. Radio propagation prediction constantly takes the state of the sun into consideration when it estimates the propagation conditions, so knowledge of how the conditions on the sun affect radio signal propagation is essential.

The ionosphere ranges from approximately 30 miles to 250 miles above the surface of the earth and is divided into three layers—D, E, and F (Figure 2-1-4). During the day, the ionosphere is subjected to solar radiation that causes the layers to expand. The F layer expands enough during the day to be divided into two layers, F1 and F2.

D Layer Characteristics. The D layer of the ionosphere is relatively weakly ionized. This

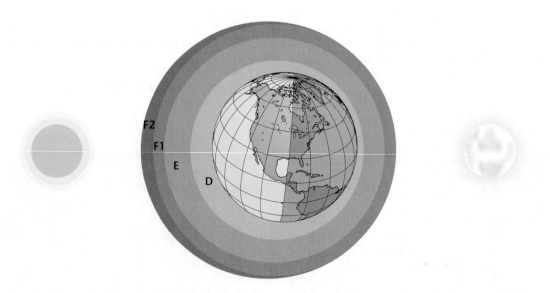

Figure 2-1-5. Ionosphere layers change during the day and night.

layer attenuates, or reduces, radio waves, but will not bend them enough to make them return to the earth.

E Layer Characteristics. Like the D layer, the E layer is weakly ionized and attenuates radio waves. In rare cases, extra ionization caused by a meteor or a sunspot-related burst of solar radiation will cause the E layer to refract radio waves enough to cause them to return to the earth. In these rare cases, long distance communications will be possible at much higher than normal frequencies and band widths. This condition is sporadic and lasts only for a short time at each occurrence.

F Layer Characteristics. The F layer is more strongly ionized and higher in altitude than either of the other layers discussed in this text. The F layer will reliably bend radio signals back to the earth, making long distance communications possible. The F layer changes from day to day and from hour to hour. At any given time there will be a maximum and minimum usable frequency for wave propagation. At night when the F layer is less ionized, like all the layers lower in altitude, as shown in Figure 2-1-5, both of these frequencies will drop. The minimum usable frequency during nighttime hours may extend into the MF band. During daylight both of these frequencies will rise, and the maximum usable frequency may approach the VHF band.

Propagation By Frequency

Radio waves at frequencies below the minimum usable frequency are trapped between the ionosphere and the earth, as shown in Figure 2-1-6. This type of propagation is known as *ground wave propagation*. These waves will not enter the ionosphere bur are forced to follow the curvature of the earth, thus allowing communication or navigation over long distances and beyond the visual horizon. Radio waves in the VLF and LF bands propagate reliably as ground waves.

During the day radio waves in the MF band are likely to radiate as ground waves. At night, however, as the overall altitude and ionization of the ionosphere decreases, the minimum usable frequency may fall into the MF band allowing sky wave propagation to occur. Like ground wave propagation, *sky wave propagation* allows long distance communication to occur, but there will be gaps on the earth where no signal can be heard. Skywave propagation is illustrated in Figure 2-1-7, which shows a radio wave refracting through the ionosphere and returning to the earth thousands of miles away.

The HF band is very reliable for sky wave propagation and long distance communication, since HF band waves enter the ionosphere, lose their polarity, and gradually bend enough to return to earth. Sky waves work best with signals that do not take much space within the radio frequency spectrum. These are known as *narrow bandwidth signals.* Bandwidth is described in more detail in the next section. Sky wave propagation is

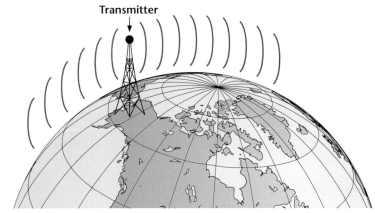

Figure 2-1-6. Ground waves work over long distances.

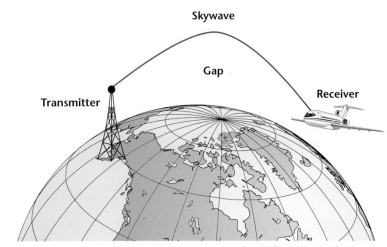

Figure 2-1-7. Sky wave propagation works over long distances with gaps.

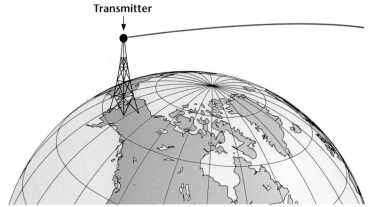

Figure 2-1-8. Space wave propagation does not return to or follow the curvature of the earth.

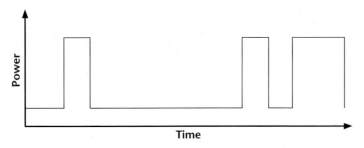

Figure 2-1-9. On/off-type pulses used to interrogate a transponder.

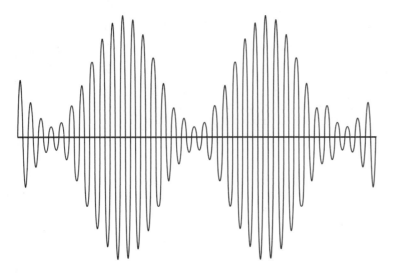

Figure 2-1-10. Amplitude modulated carrier.

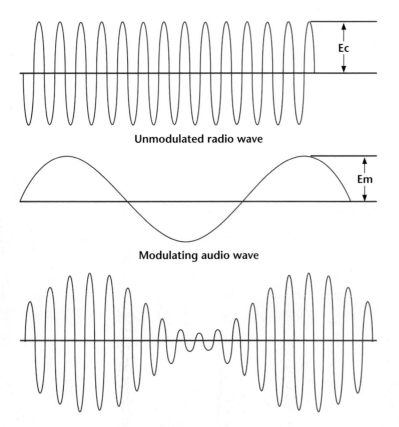

Unmodulated radio wave

Modulating audio wave

Modulated radio wave

Figure 2-1-11. AM measurements.

so reliable that long distance communication between continents is possible while radiating a signal of less than 1 watt.

Above the maximum usable frequency, sky wave propagation is not possible. Radio waves in the VHF band and above bend when they enter the ionosphere but not enough to return to earth, and the energy continues into space, as shown in Figure 2-1-8. This type of propagation is known as *space wave propagation*. These higher bands radiate energy in the form of space waves, thus making long distance communication impossible without the help of a relay station of some type. Although the radio horizon is slightly farther than the visual horizon, this type of radio communication works only as a line of sight, or as far as you can see.

Modulation

By themselves radio waves cannot carry any usable information; they are just an electromagnetic field. In order to make the radio wave usable for communication, it must be changed or given form. The term for this change is known as *modulation* or *mode*. There are several methods of modulating, or changing, a radio wave in order to carry information. Once modulated, the electromagnetic wave is referred to as a carrier wave, or carrier, because it carries information.

On/Off Keyed Carrier

The simplest and oldest form of modulation is to change the radio wave by turning it on and off. One of the first forms of the modulated signal was the telegraph. An experienced radio telegraph operator was able to send and receive information at 250 characters per minute—even the slowest computers today are is still more than 10 times faster than a telegraph. A variation of the on/off keyed carrier is known as pulse modulation. We see this type of signal modulation being used today primarily in aircraft navigation and tracking systems such as distance measuring equipment (DME) and transponders. These units send information by turning on and off the carrier at specifically coded intervals as shown in Figure 2-1-9.

Amplitude Modulation

Amplitude modulation (AM) was the invention that made radio broadcasting of voice possible. Amplitude modulation is produced by changing the power of the carrier wave, as shown in Figure 2-1-10. This change of power is accomplished by using a microphone to convert ordinary sound into an electric signal that is superimposed on continuous radio wave. The modulated radio waves, now matching the amplitude of the electric signal, are sent out over a transmitting antenna to a receiver where the radio waves are converted back into electric signals and demodulated; meaning the radio wave carrier is removed, leaving behind the audio signal that is then amplified and sent to a loudspeaker.

Amplitude modulated carrier waves can be measured by calculating *modulation index*, or *percentage of modulation*. To calculate the modulation index (m), divide the peak voltage of the carrier wave without modulation (Ec) into the peak voltage of the modulating signal (Em), or

Em/Ec = m

Multiplying m by 100 yields percentage of modulation: m x 100 = modulating percentage. Figure 2-1-11. shows the measurements used in the modulation index calculations.

If the modulation index is more than one, or the percentage is greater than 100 percent, then the information becomes distorted. As the percentage rises to percentages above 100 percent, then the information becomes distorted enough to become unreadable, as shown in Figure 2-1-12. Moreover, carriers modulated over 100 percent cause interference on other radio frequencies; therefore, modulation over 100 percent is not legal.

Since an audible frequency is used often to modulate radio frequencies, modulation is a form of mixing frequencies. Whenever two frequencies are mixed, four frequencies are produced. These frequencies are:

- Carrier frequency

- Modulating frequency

- Sum of the modulating frequency and the carrier frequency

- Difference between the modulating frequency and the carrier frequency

In practice, three of these frequencies become part of the electromagnetic radiation and can be detected using proper instrumentation. Figure 2-1-13 shows a spectrum analysis of an amplitude modulated carrier wave. A *spectrum analysis* is a presentation of frequency versus power. Present on the graph are the difference, sum, and carrier frequencies. The sum and the difference are called *sidebands*. The sideband created by the difference between the modulating and carrier frequencies is called the *lower sideband*. The sideband created by the sum of the modulating and carrier frequencies is called the *upper sideband*.

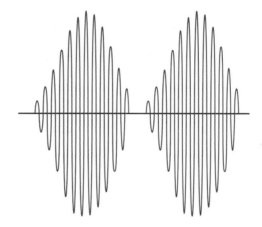

Figure 2-1-12. Overmodulated carrier.

The difference between the upper and lower sideband frequencies is known as the *bandwidth*. The higher the modulating frequency, the more frequencies are used and the bandwidth is greater.

The sidebands comprise one-third of the power radiated in an amplitude modulated transmission. VHF communication and navigation systems use amplitude modulation. The bandwidth for aviation VHF communication systems is 6 kHz.

Single Sideband

For high frequency, long distance communication systems that rely on sky waves, amplitude

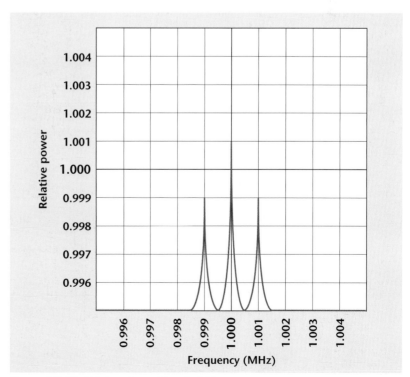

Figure 2-1-13. Sidebands and bandwidth.

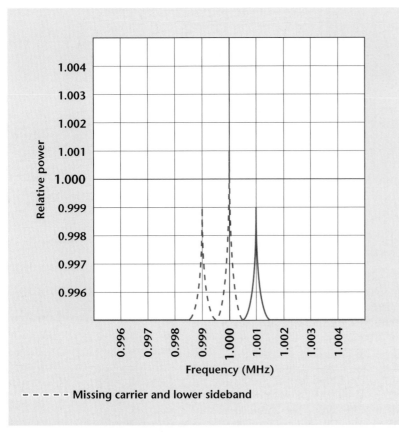

Figure 2-1-14. Single sideband.

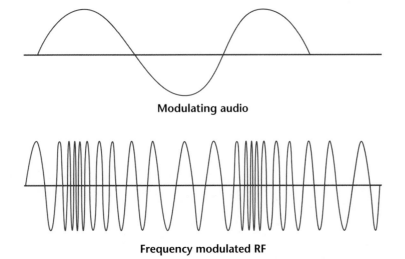

Figure 2-1-15. Frequency modulation illustrated.

modulation has too great a bandwidth for reliable transfer of information. For this reason high frequency systems are designed to use a mode of transmission derived from AM called *single sideband*. A single sideband transmission starts out as an AM transmission with both sidebands and the carrier wave. Before final transmission, the signal is fed through filters designed to remove the carrier wave and one sideband, as shown in Figure 2-1-14. The remaining sideband is then amplified and transmitted.

A single sideband transmission is not readable with a normal AM receiver. To receive a single sideband transmission, a receiver must mix a signal with the sideband to recreate the carrier and the other sideband. Single sideband receivers include an oscillator called a *beat frequency oscillator* (BFO). Often, this oscillator is adjustable by the pilot and is sometimes called a clarifier. BFO operation will be described in detail in the chapter on HF radio receivers.

Frequency Modulation

Another way of enabling the carrier wave to send information is by varying its frequency, as shown in Figure 2-1-15. This type of modulation is known as *frequency modulation* (FM) or *phase modulation* (PM). In a practical sense, the difference between phase and frequency modulation is very small. The transmitted signal in either case is identical, and the method of reception is the same. In the case of FM, the audio wave is used to control the frequency of an oscillator. As the audio frequency rises, so does the oscillator frequency. Like amplitude modulated signals, bandwidth increases as modulating frequency increases.

In FM systems the index (I) is calculated by dividing the modulating frequency (fm) into the highest frequency deviation from the carrier frequency (Δf) or $I = \Delta f/fm$. Bandwidth can be calculated by doubling the sum of deviation from the carrier frequency plus the modulating frequency, or $BW = 2(\Delta f + fm)$. In avionics systems, frequency modulation is used in some airborne telephones and as part of the VHF navigation system.

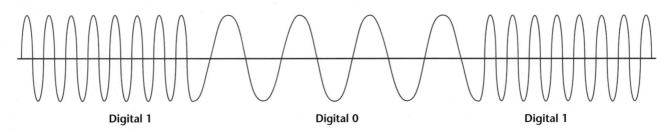

Figure 2-1-16. Example of frequency shift keying.

Frequency Shift Keying

Frequency shift keying (FSK) is a method of modulation used to send digital information. In this system, the carrier frequency is changed as it is in FM; however, the carrier only changes, or shifts, between two frequencies. The higher of the two frequencies is used to send a digital 1, and the lower frequency is used to send a digital 0, as shown in Figure 2-1-16. Some airborne telephone systems use FSK.

Phase Shift Keying

Phase shift keying (PSK) uses a 180° phase change in the carrier frequency to encode digital 1s and 0s, as shown in Figure 2-1-17. PSK has an advantage over FSK in that very little bandwidth is used, since the carrier never changes frequency. The received carrier is compared and synchronized with a reference signal at the same frequency. If the signals add, then a logic 1 is produced. If the signals cancel each other, then a logic 0 is produced.

In all modes of modulation, the radio frequency is changed in some way to send information. The change may be as simple as turning the carrier on and off, or it may be as complex as combining FM and AM together. In any case, the transmitter and the receiver must operate in the same modulating mode, otherwise no information is transferred.

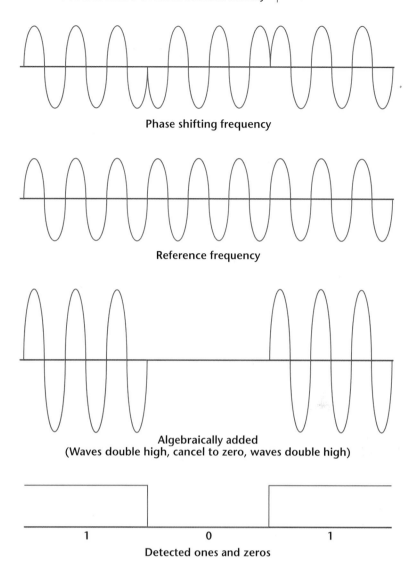

Phase shifting frequency

Reference frequency

Algebraically added
(Waves double high, cancel to zero, waves double high)

1 0 1

Detected ones and zeros

Figure 2-1-17. Example of phase shift keying.

Section 2

Antennas

An *antenna* is the component of a radio system that is used to send or receive a radio signal. A radio frequency (RF) signal that has been generated in a radio transmitter travels through a transmission line (such as a coaxial cable) to an antenna. An antenna is the device that releases RF energy in the form of an electromagnetic field to be sent to a distant receiver. The receiving antenna picks up the RF energy. As the electromagnetic field strikes the receiving antenna, a voltage is induced into the antenna, which serves as a conductor. The induced RF voltage is then used to recover the transmitted RF information.

Figure 2-2-1 displays a variety of navigation and communication antennas commonly used on small corporate aircraft, like the Piper Meridian pictured. Nearly all antennas used in aviation are a variation of three basic forms: *Marconi, Hertzian,* and *Yagi-Uda.* The basic

Figure 2-2-1. Aircraft use a wide variety of antenna styles and technologies to meet their communication needs.

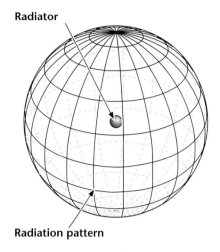

Radiator

Radiation pattern

Figure 2-2-2. An isotropic radiator.

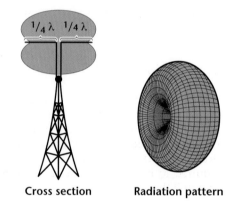

$^{1}/_{4}\lambda$ $^{1}/_{4}\lambda$

Cross section   **Radiation pattern**

Figure 2-2-3. Hertzian antenna.

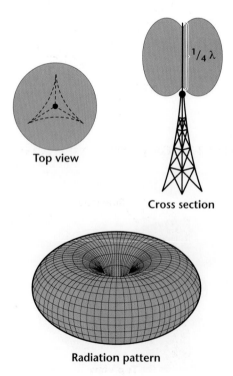

Top view

$^{1}/_{4}\lambda$

Cross section

Radiation pattern

Figure 2-2-4. Radiation pattern of a Marconi antenna.

antenna design consists of two one-quarter wave elements. In some systems, both quarter-wave elements are readily recognizable, in others they are not.

Antennas follow the *rule of reciprocity*. This rule states, "Whatever is true for transmission is also true for reception." For purposes of brevity, antennas in this text are discussed in terms of transmission. The reader should keep in mind the rule of reciprocity. For example, if an antenna transmits well in a particular direction, then it also receives well from the same direction.

When used in line of sight applications, antennas work best when the transmitting antenna and the receiving antenna are polarized the same. For example, if the transmitting antenna is vertical in relation to the earth, then for the best reception, the receiving antenna must be vertical in relation to the earth. Cross polarization will cause signal loss of up to 60 dB.

Isotropic Radiator

An *isotropic radiator* is a one-dimensional point in space that transmits energy equally in all directions in a spheroid pattern with 100 percent efficiency, as illustrated in Figure 2-2-2. Although not possible in the real world, an isotropic radiator gives a point (pardon the pun) of comparison with real-world antennas.

Hertzian Antenna

The *Hertzian antenna* is also known as a *dipole* and consists of two $1/4\lambda$ wires placed end-to-end, as shown in Figure 2-2-2. Hertzian antennas are balanced. In other words, each side must remain the same electrical distance from ground.

Hertzian antennas radiate well in directions perpendicular to the antenna; however, they do not radiate at all off the wire tips. Since the radiated energy is concentrated broadside to the wire, a Hertzian antenna exhibits 2.1 dB of gain when compared to an isotropic radiator. A Hertzian antenna exhibits a bidirectional radiation pattern evident when viewed from above. In other words, it radiates well in two directions. Hertzian antennas are used in VHF omnirange, localizer, and glideslope systems. Hertzian antennas used on board aircraft are horizontally polarized.

Marconi Antenna

The *Marconi antenna* is often referred to as a vertical antenna, since the vast majority of are vertically polarized. The Marconi antenna is designed as half of a Hertzian antenna. As a result, the Marconi antenna is 1/4λ long and the ground or the airframe comprises the other quarter wave radiating element. Like the Hertzian antenna, the Marconi antenna does not radiate well off its tip. The Marconi antenna radiates well in all directions, which is apparent when viewed from above, as shown in Figure 2-2-4, and it is considered to be an omnidirectional antenna.

When a Marconi antenna is mounted on a tower, a *counterpoise* may be added (Figure 2-2-5). A counterpoise acts as ground and as the second quarter of the radiating element. Aviation VHF and HF communication systems, transponders, distance measuring equipment, global positioning systems, and marker beacon systems use Marconi-type antennas on the aircraft.

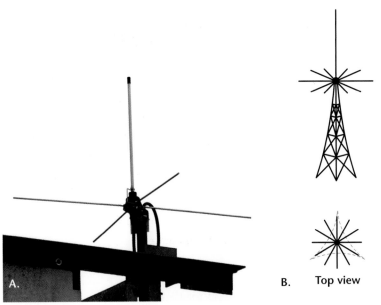

A.   B.   Top view

Figure 2-2-5. Marconi antenna with a counterpoise.

Yagi-Uda Antenna

The *Yagi-Uda antenna* is considered a unidirectional antenna. The Yagi-Uda focuses as much of the radiation pattern as possible in a single direction. This type of antenna starts with a dipole element called the driven element. The driven element is connected to the antenna feed line. Added to the antenna are *directors* and *reflectors*, as shown in Figure 2-2-6.

Directors focus energy toward the intended single direction. Reflectors bounce energy radiated in the wrong direction back toward the intended direction. Directors and reflectors are also known as parasitic elements, since they have no direct connection to the antenna feed line. Since the energy of a Yagi-Uda antenna is focused in one direction, it will exhibit approximately 8 dB of gain more than a Hertzian antenna.

A Yagi-Uda antenna has at least one director, which is approximately 96 percent shorter than the driven element (1/2λ). Each successive director is four percent shorter than the preceding director. Yagi-Uda antennas also have at least one reflector that is approximately five percent longer than the driven element. Each successive reflector is five percent longer than the preceding director. As reflectors and directors are added, gains up to 15 dB are possible when compared to a Hertzian antenna.

Yagi-Uda antennas are not 100 percent efficient. Energy will leak off the sides and the back of the antenna. The radiation patterns created by leakage are known as *side lobes*. Figure 2-2-7 illustrates the radiation pattern of a Yagi-Uda antenna with side lobes.

Antenna Variations

To meet different installation applications, the basic antenna forms may need to be physically changed. In aviation, many of the antennas have to be shortened to fit aerodynamically on the aircraft. As previously discussed, antennas are required to be a certain length to receive and transmit the desired frequency. In order to

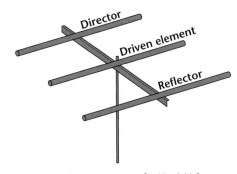

Figure 2-2-6. Components of a Yagi-Uda antenna.

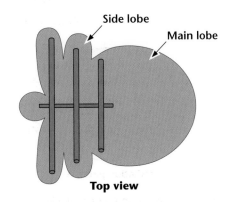

Figure 2-2-7. Yagi-Uda radiation pattern.

Figure 2-2-8. Dual frequency ELT antenna.

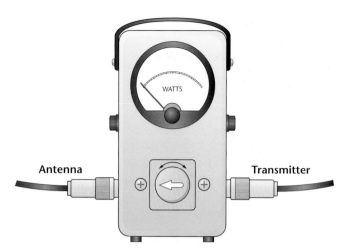

Figure 2-2-9. Through line watt meter.

make up for the loss of length, an inductance is added in the form of a *loading coil*—a coil that electronically lengthens an antenna while keeping it physically short. There are complex calculations to determine the size of the coil and the diameter it coils material in order to achieve the desired frequency. If the loading coil is placed directly on the antenna's radiator, then the antenna may be optimized for two separate frequencies. Figure 2-2-8 shows an emergency locator antenna with a loading coil on the radiator to illustrate this effect. Energy radiated on 121.5 MHz uses the entire antenna, and energy radiated on 243 MHz uses only the lower portion.

Another antenna variation is the *loop antenna*. A loop antenna is considered a Hertzian-type antenna with the wire ends connected. Loop antennas are shaped, as their name suggests, in a continuous loop. They have the ability to determine from which direction a signal is coming from; hence, they are also called directional antennas. Most have two or three separate coils of very thin wire that are wound at varying angles to form a round shape that is laid flat. The signal is received at different

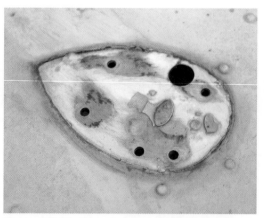

Figure 2-2-10. Corrosion on antenna mounting base.

strengths between the coils, and the receiver uses those different signal strengths to determine the direction from which those signals originated. In today's aircraft the ADF and lightning detection systems use the loop-style of antenna.

Since most aircraft antennas need to operate on a range of frequencies, one of the most common antenna variations utilized by avionics engineers is to change the diameter of the antenna because bandwidth increases as the antenna's diameter is increased.

Troubleshooting Antennas

The method used to troubleshoot an antenna depends on the system to which the antenna is connected, but all troubleshooting starts with a visual inspection. Look at the antenna carefully to make sure it is free of dirt or paint. In addition, check to make sure the sealant around the base is intact. Since most aircraft antennas are mounted externally, intrusion of an electrolyte, such as water, through a broken seal is common, often causing corrosion of either the mounting base or the connector. Figure 2-2-10 shows corrosion on the mounting base under the antenna. Corrosion of either will contribute to reduced effectiveness of the antenna.

A through line wattmeter installed between the transmission line and an antenna should be used when testing an antenna connected to a communications transmitter. If the antenna is bad, then it will reject power from the transmitter, reflecting it back into the transmission line and toward the transmitter. The through line watt meter shows the power moving forward toward the transmission line and the power reflected. Figure 2-2-9 illustrates a through line watt meter connected to an antenna system. The element within the wattmeter can be turned to measure power in either direction.

The reflected power will create *standing waves*. Standing waves can be described as power dissipating within the transmission line. A useful way to measure these waves is to calculate the *voltage standing wave ratio* (VSWR), which is a comparison of forward moving energy and reflected energy. To calculate VSWR, measure and record the power in each direction, then apply the following formula:

$$SWR = \frac{1 + \left(\sqrt{\dfrac{\text{reflected power}}{\text{forward power}}}\right)}{1 - \left(\sqrt{\dfrac{\text{reflected power}}{\text{forward power}}}\right)}$$

An excellent antenna has a VSWR of 1.2:1 or less. A standing wave of 1.5:1 is an indication that 4 percent of the output power is being reflected.

At 2.0:1, 10 percent of the output power is being rejected by the antenna and reflected into the transmission line. Not only does a high VSWR create transmitter losses, but it also will create a loss of reception that increases as VSWR increases.

For antennas connected to receivers, a through line wattmeter will not work. To troubleshoot these systems, disconnect the coaxial cable from the antenna and replace the antenna with a signal generator. Then test the system with the generator set for a low signal output to see if it works.

Section 3

Transmission Lines

In order to transmit and receive energy in the radio frequency spectrum, energy waves must travel between the radio and the antenna via a transmission line. The most commonly used type of transmission line in aircraft today is coaxial cable. A coaxial cable contains two wires sharing a common axis, as shown in Figure 2-3-1. The inner wire, known as the inner conductor, is surrounded by a special material called a *dielectric*. Surrounding the dielectric is a braided outer wire called the *shield*. The shield is then enclosed within an insulating outer jacket.

For aircraft use, the inner conductor is stranded to resist breaks. The dielectric is constructed of a foam or polyethylene insulating material. Unlike shielded wire where the primary characteristic is gauge and insulation thickness, coaxial cable is carefully engineered to allow radio energy to transfer, or propagate, along its length.

From the standpoint of the radio wave, the coaxial cable appears as an infinite series of resistors, capacitors, and inductors. These theoretical components have impedance known as *surge impedance*; therefore, coaxial cables are so rated. Aviation coaxial cable has a surge impedance of 50 Ω.

Since it takes time for capacitors and inductors to charge, the radio wave velocity of propagation is reduced when compared to its velocity in space. As a result, coaxial cable is also rated for velocity factor (VF), which is expressed as a decimal of the speed of light. For example, most aviation coaxial cable has a velocity factor of 0.66, which means the radio waves travel down the coaxial cable at 66 percent of the speed of light.

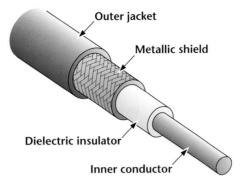

Figure 2-3-1. Coaxial cable.

The surge impedance and velocity factor of coaxial cable also translates into energy loss. Coaxial cable also will be rated by how much energy is lost over a certain length.

Troubleshooting

If the transmission line surge impedance is matched perfectly to the source and load, then the energy travels down the line, as shown in Figure 2-3-2. The current and voltage are in phase as shown, and the energy travels down the line at a fraction of the speed of light, as described above. Energy travelling in the correct direction is known as the *incident wave*.

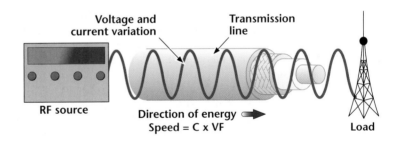

Figure 2-3-2. Energy propagation along a transmission line.

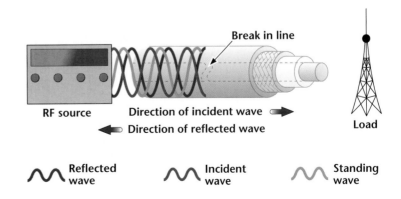

Figure 2-3-3. A break in the transmission line creates reflected and standing waves.

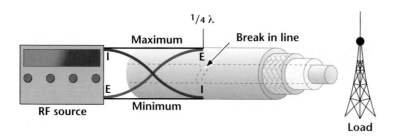

Figure 2-3-4. Reflected current maximum at the source.

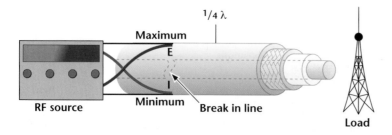

Figure 2-3-5. Reflected current is higher than reflected voltage but not at maximum and minimum values.

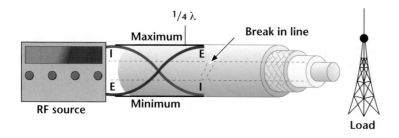

Figure 2-3-6. Reflected voltage is higher than reflected current but not at maximum and minimum values.

If there is a problem in the system, such as a bad antenna, then some of this energy is reflected back from the load into the transmission line. This reflected energy, called the *reflected wave* is added algebraically with the incident wave, creating a *standing wave*. Standing waves do not move along the transmission line. In other words, they are stationary. The energy from a standing wave will dissipate in the form of heat. Figure 2-3-3 illustrates a standing wave caused by a break in the transmission line.

A problem with the transmission line itself can cause a variety of symptoms, depending on the type and the location of the problem. Some of these symptoms can be surprising: a shorted or open cable may cause the coaxial cable to behave like an inductor, capacitor, or a resonant circuit. Since the symptom is determined by the type of problem and the distance in wavelengths from the RF source, it changes when the frequency is changed.

For example, if an open occurs at exactly 1/4λ from the source, then the incident wave at the open point is forced to maximum voltage; however, because the line is open, no current will flow. In addition, a sinusoidal reflected wave is generated at the open point and travels back to the source. The energy reaching the source is at maximum I value, as shown in Figure 2-3-4. As a result, the characteristics of a short circuit—maximum current, minimum voltage—are present.

A transmission line with a break before the 1/4λ point causes the reflected current to lead the reflected voltage, giving the appearance of a capacitor, as shown in Figure 2-3-5. Like the forward moving incident wave, the reflected wave is in sinusoidal form. Since this I wave reflected from the open does not have room to reach its maximum value, the reflected current is increasing, or leading, the voltage. Like the reflected current wave, the reflected voltage wave does not have enough space to reach its maximum value and is decreasing.

If the break occurs between 1/4λ and 1/2λ, then at the source the voltage curve will appear to lead the current curve, giving the appearance of an inductor. In this case, there is more room between the break and the source for the sinusoidal waves to travel. The current wave has room to reach its maximum value and begin to decrease. The voltage wave also has room to reach its minimum value and begin increasing again. The result is shown in Figure 2-3-6.

These conditions described above repeat, every 1/2λ along the transmission line. A converse condition occurs for a short in a transmission line. At the exact point of the short, current is at maximum and voltage is at minimum. If the short occurs at exactly 1/4λ, as shown in Figure 2-3-7, then at the source the current is at minimum and the voltage is at maximum, giving the appearance of an open. The behavior of the reflected waves in a shorted transmission line is the exact opposite of those in an open line.

If the short in the transmission line occurs before 1/4λ, then at the source the decreasing current appears to lag behind the increasing voltage, giving the appearance of an inductor. The current does not have room to fall to its minimum value, and the voltage does not have room to rise to its maximum value, as shown in Figure 2-3-8.

If the short occurs between 1/4λ and 1/2λ, then at the source the voltage curve wave appears to lag behind the current curve, giving the appearance of a capacitor. In this case, with more than 1/4λ of room, the reflected voltage wave has increased to maximum and begun to decrease again. The reflected current wave has room to decrease to minimum and begin increasing again, as shown in Figure 2-3-9. Like the open conditions described previously, these conditions repeat every half wave.

Shorts at 1/4λ, 3/4λ, and 1 1/4λ all exhibit AC characteristics of an open. Conversely, opens at 1/4λ, 3/4λ, and 1 1/4λ all exhibit AC characteristics of a short.

Table 2-3-1 shows the behavior of shorts and opens in a transmission line compared to its wavelength. If a short occurs exactly at a 1/4 λ interval, then the symptoms will imitate an open, which is exactly the opposite of the condition. The opposite occurs if the cable is open exactly at a 1/4λ interval. For example, a coaxial cable with an open at exactly 1/4λ causes a transmitter to behave as if it is transmitting into a short. If a technician connects an ohmmeter across this coaxial cable then he or she would measure an open. Shorts and opens in between 1/4λ intervals will behave like capacitance or inductance.

For transmission lines connected to communication transmitters, a technician may use a through line wattmeter to assist in troubleshooting. The wattmeter can be placed between the transmission line and the antenna and often between the radio and the transmission line. If full transmitter power is measured at the radio but not at the antenna, then something is wrong with the coaxial cable.

A *time domain reflectometer*, or TDR, may also be used to check any transmission line. The technician connects the TDR to one end of a transmission line. Once activated, the TDR sends a pulse into the cable then displays the reflection on a screen like that shown in Figure 2-3-10.

The TDR screen shows distance along the horizontal axis and impedance along the vertical axis. The display starts in the lower left of the screen, indicating 0Ω of impedance and 0 ft.

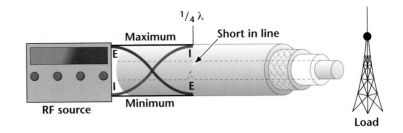

Figure 2-3-7. Reflected voltage at maximum and reflected current at minimum.

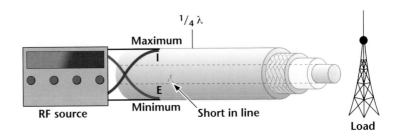

Figure 2-3-8. Reflected voltage is higher than reflected current but not at maximum and minimum values.

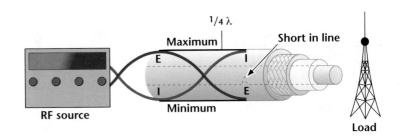

Figure 2-3-9. Reflected current is higher than reflected voltage but not at maximum and minimum values.

Continuing to the right, the line rises to the surge impedance value of the cable. If the other end of the cable is open, then the line will rise to a point representing infinite impedance. If the other end of the line is shorted, then the line will return to the low end of the screen, as shown in Figure 2-3-11.

Condition	Short	Short	Short	Open	Open	Open
Location	<λ	=λ	>λ	<λ	=λ	>λ
RF Behavior	Inductor	Parallel resonant circuit (open)	Capacitor	Capacitor	Series resonant circuit (short)	Inductor
DC Behavior	Short	Short	Short	Open	Open	Open

Table 2-3-1. Affect of shorts and opens at various locations within a transmission line.

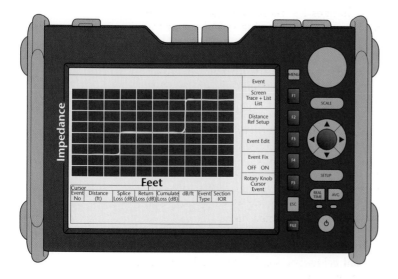

Figure 2-3-10. Time domain reflectometer screen showing an open cable.

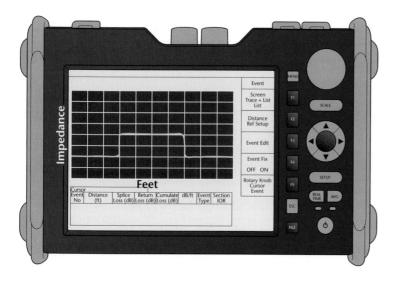

Figure 2-3-11. Time domain reflectometer screen showing a shorted cable.

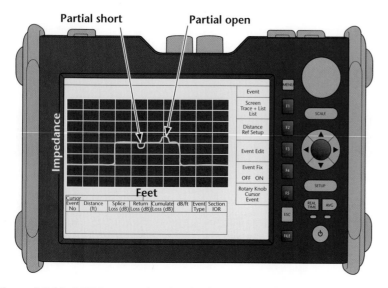

Figure 2-3-12. A TDR screen showing both a pinch and a fray.

Since the screen shows distance, the technician can determine the location of the fault in the line. For example, if the cable in Figure 2-3-2 is 20 feet in length and is disconnected from the antenna leaving the end open, and if the TDR is set to a resolution of 2 feet per division, then Figure 2-3-10 shows a open at 8 feet Not only will the TDR indicate what type of problem the cable has, it will also approximate the location. A well constructed TDR is sensitive enough to detect partial shorts and opens. These faults may be caused by frayed shielding or a pinched cable. Figure 2-3-12 shows both a partial short and a partial open. These partial shorts and opens would not be detectable with an ohm-meter, since pinches and frays only affect the impedance and not the DC resistance of the cable.

Pinched or partially shorted cable will force the impedance line toward the bottom of the screen. Frays or partial opens force the impedance line toward the top of the screen.

Section 4

Summary

When AC current is induced into a wire, it produces a magnetic H field and an electric E field. This changing E field is called an electromagnetic wave, which radiates away from the wire at or near the speed of light. When this electromagnetic wave comes in contact with another wire, a current is induced into the new wire from the wave. Each radio wave can be defined by frequency or wavelength and its power or amplitude. Wavelength (λ) can be calculated by dividing the speed of the radio wave by its frequency.

The radio frequency spectrum includes frequencies from 1 Hz to approximately 428 GHz, which is among the lowest frequencies of infrared light. The very low frequency (VLF) band starts at 1 Hz and ends at 30 kHz with wavelengths from 0 to 10 km. The low frequency (LF) band starts at 30 kHz and ends at 300 kHz with wavelengths from 10 km to 1 km. The medium frequency band (MF) starts at 300 kHz and ends at 3 MHz with wavelengths from 1 km to 100 m. The high frequency (HF) band starts at 3 MHz and ends at 30 MHz with wavelengths from 100 m to 10 m. The very high frequency (VHF) band starts at 30 MHz and ends at 300 MHz with wavelengths from 10 m to 1 m. The ultra high frequency (UHF) band starts at 300 MHz and ends at 3 GHz with wavelengths from 1 m to 10 cm. The super high frequency (SHF) band starts at 3 GHz and ends at 30 GHz with wavelengths from 10 cm to 1 cm. The extremely high frequency (EHF) band starts at 30 GHz and ends at 300 GHz with wavelengths from 1 cm to 1 mm.

The movement of electromagnetic radio waves through a medium such as a wire, the atmosphere or space is known as propagation. There are three types of radio propagation: ground waves, sky waves, and space waves. Ground waves follow the curvature of the earth. Sky waves bend through the F layers of the ionosphere and return to earth. Space waves continue into space. The F layer of the ionosphere expands during the day due to solar radiation, and the minimum and maximum usable sky wave frequencies increase. Sky waves predominate in the HF frequency band.

There are several methods of modulating, or changing, a radio wave in order to carry information. An on/off keyed carrier changes the radio wave by turning it on or off. Amplitude modulation changes the radio wave by changing power. Frequency modulation changes the radio wave by changing frequency. Frequency shift keying changes the radio wave to send digital information by changing the frequency between two set values. Phase shift keying changes the radio wave to send digital information by changing the phase of the radio wave.

Radio waves are broadcast through antennas. Hertzian antennas are balanced and measure a half wavelength from end to end. Marconi antennas are not balanced, require a ground plane, and measure one-quarter wavelength from base to tip. Yagi-Uda antennas are primarily unidirectional and have reflectors and directors. Antenna problems can be determined through inspection, substitution and, in some cases, measuring the forward and reflected power of a transmitter.

Transmission line, better known in aircraft as coaxial cable, is used to carry radio waves between antennas and radio transmitters or receivers. From the standpoint of the radio wave, the coaxial cable appears as an infinite series of resistors, capacitors, and inductors. Coaxial cable has a surge impedance rating, a velocity of propagation rating and a loss per 100 ft. rating in dB. Problems in coaxial cable can be determined using a time domain reflectometer or by measuring forward and reflected power. Due to phase changes within the coaxial cable, the symptoms of a problem can change with frequency.

3

Radio Receivers

Radio receivers are used in most aircraft navigation systems and all aircraft communication
systems. For a technician to be an effective
troubleshooter of these navigation and communication (NAVCOMM) systems, he or she needs
a good understanding of how radio receivers
function. The rest of this chapter describes the
three most common types of radio receivers—
direct conversion receivers, super regenerative
receivers, and super-heterodyne receivers—all
of which can be found in various NAVCOMM
systems.

Section 1

Direct Conversion Receivers

Direct conversion receivers obtain, filter, and
amplify radio waves, then convert the modulation to audio. In systems where only one
frequency needs to be received, engineers
may use this type of receiver. For example,
GPS receivers, like the Honeywell KLN94
pictured in Figure 3-1-1, are direct conversion
receivers. A block diagram of a simple direct
conversion AM receiver is shown in Figure
3-1-2.

The antenna in Figure 3-1-2 receives the radio
signal and passes it to the filter. The filter
rejects unwanted frequencies, while allowing the desired frequency to pass to the RF
amplifier. The most common filters are band
pass filters, band stop filters, or a combination of these two filter types. As shown in
Figure 3-1-2, the radio frequency amplifier
increases the amplitude or the power of the

Learning Objectives

DESCRIBE

- Operational theory
  of direct conversion

- Operational
  theory of super-
  regenerative radio
  receivers

- Operational theory
  of super-heterodyne
  radio receivers

- Operational theory
  of a stabilized
  master oscillator

APPLY

- Draw a block
  diagram of a super-
  regenerative radio
  receiver

- Draw a block
  diagram of a direct
  conversion radio
  receiver

- Draw a block
  diagram of a super-
  heterodyne radio
  receiver

- Draw a block
  diagram of a
  stabilized master
  oscillator

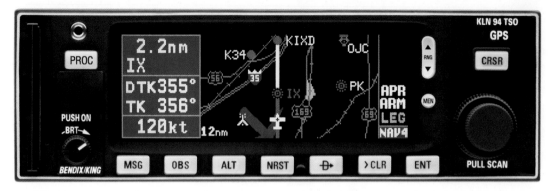

Figure 3-1-1. Most GPS receivers, such as this Honeywell KLN94, are of the direct conversion type.

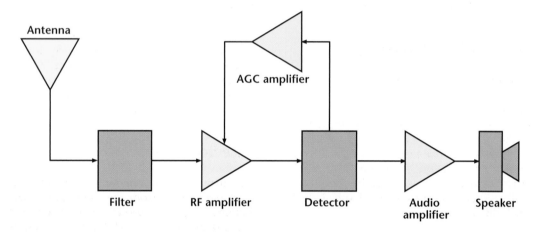

Figure 3-1-2. Block diagram of a direct conversion receiver.

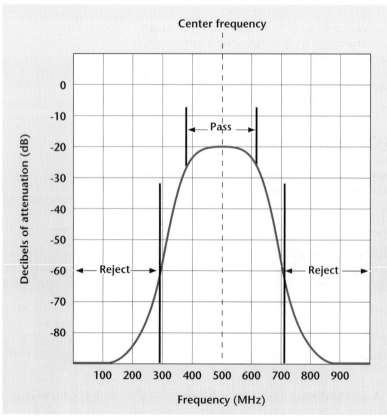

Figure 3-1-3. Radio frequency filter performance.

signal supplied by the filter. The amplification of this signal is often referred to as gain. This amplified signal is then passed on to the *detector*, which removes the radio frequencies and leaves the audio. Then the *audio amplifier* increases the power of the remaining audio frequencies to the point that they can be heard through a speaker or headphones. The *automatic gain control* (AGC) amplifier reduces strong signals, which might overload the detector.

Filter Operation

Radio filters are commonly constructed using capacitors and inductors configured as filters or a combination of filters. The net result of filtration is to allow the desired frequency through to the radio frequency amplifier. Band pass filters allow frequencies at or near the desired frequency to pass while rejecting unwanted frequencies. Band stop filters raise or lower radio signals that are significantly lower or higher than the desired (center) frequency until only the desired frequency is passed to the RF amplifier. This reduction of unwanted frequencies is called an attenuated signal and is illustrated in Figure 3-1-3.

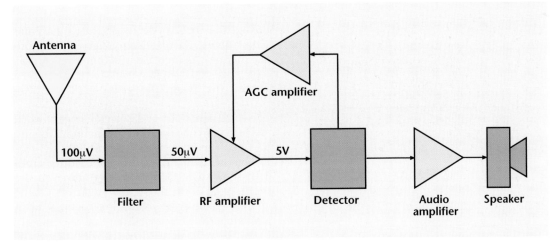

Figure 3-1-4. Direct conversion receiver with RF signal levels.

RF Amplifier Operation

Amplitude loss occurs when a radio signal passes through a filter; the purpose of a radio frequency (RF) amplifier is to increase the amplitude of the radio signal received from the filter. An ideal filter of the highest quality would allow a desirable signal to pass through it without any loss. But, we do not live in a perfect world, and we must abide by the laws of physics. Filters can cause a signal loss of .05 dB up to 3 dB or more.

For example, the antenna shown in Figure 3-1-4 picks up a signal of 100 μV. The filter causes a reduction of signal, perhaps 3 dB. This leaves approximately 50 μV for the RF amplifier. With 100 dB of gain from the RF amplifier, approximately 5 V are provided to the detector.

In order to avoid exceeding the capacity of the detector, the (AGC) will reduce the gain of the RF amplifier when strong signals are received. For example, if a 200 μV signal were received at the antenna, then the AGC would reduce the gain of the RF amplifier by approximately 6dB, in order to maintain a 5 V input to the detector.

The AGC acts as a form of power supply for the components within the RF amplifier. As the detector signal increases, the AGC amplifier reduces the voltage supplied to the RF amplifier, thus reducing its gain.

Detector Operation

The purpose of the *detector* is to extract the audio frequencies from the modulated radio frequency signal. A diode can be used as a simple detector. As the RF level increases, as shown in Figure 3-1-5, the diode rectifies more energy, supplying more current and voltage to the succeeding stages.

The variation in the detector output matches the variation in RF level, creating a varying DC voltage that takes the form of an audio signal. This signal, or waveform, is supplied to the AGC amplifier where it is further amplified and supplied to a speaker, headphones, or audio system.

AGC Amplifier Operation

AGC amplifier operation is nearly identical, regardless of the types of receivers discussed

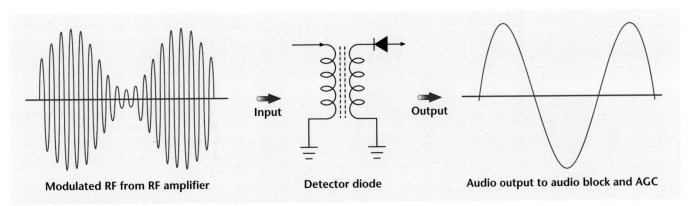

| Modulated RF from RF amplifier | Detector diode | Audio output to audio block and AGC |

Figure 3-1-5. A simple detector.

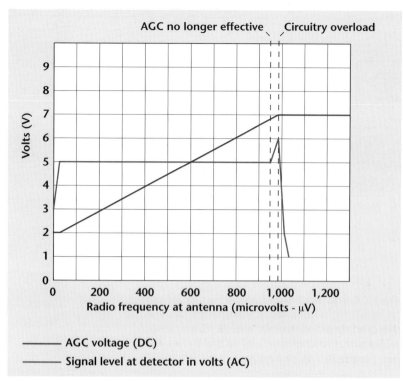

Figure 3-1-6. Comparison of RF level, AGC voltage and detector signal level.

an increase of signal causes an increase in DC voltage that, in turn, decreases the RF amplifier gain. Some AGC systems operate in the opposite manner: an increase in signal levels causes a decrease in DC voltage that in turn, causes a decrease in RF amplifier gain.

The AGC, amplifier, and detector stages form a stable loop. When operating properly, increasing RF signal levels cause a change in AGC DC voltage but not a change in detector output. Figure 3-1-6 shows the AGC action of a receiver. At low input signal levels, the AGC is not active. On the chart, the blue AGC voltage line remains flat at 2 V, while the detector output line rises rapidly toward 5 V. At approximately 20 µV, the AGC becomes active and begins to increase linearly with an increase in RF level. Once the AGC is active, the detector output remains steady. At a level just under 1,000 µV, the AGC reaches maximum value and will increase no more. As the RF level continues to increase, the detector output begins to increase again, but quickly, various components within the radio will overload, or saturate, causing the detector output to fall rapidly to very low values.

In some maintenance literature, the flat part of the red curve shown in Figure 3-1-6, ranging from 20 to 980 µV, is referred to as the *dynamic range* of the receiver. A radio is expected to work normally within its dynamic range. The AGC amplifier eliminates the need for listeners to continually adjust the volume control as the signal strengthens or weakens. In addition, AGC allows radio circuitry to operate properly over a wide range of input RF levels.

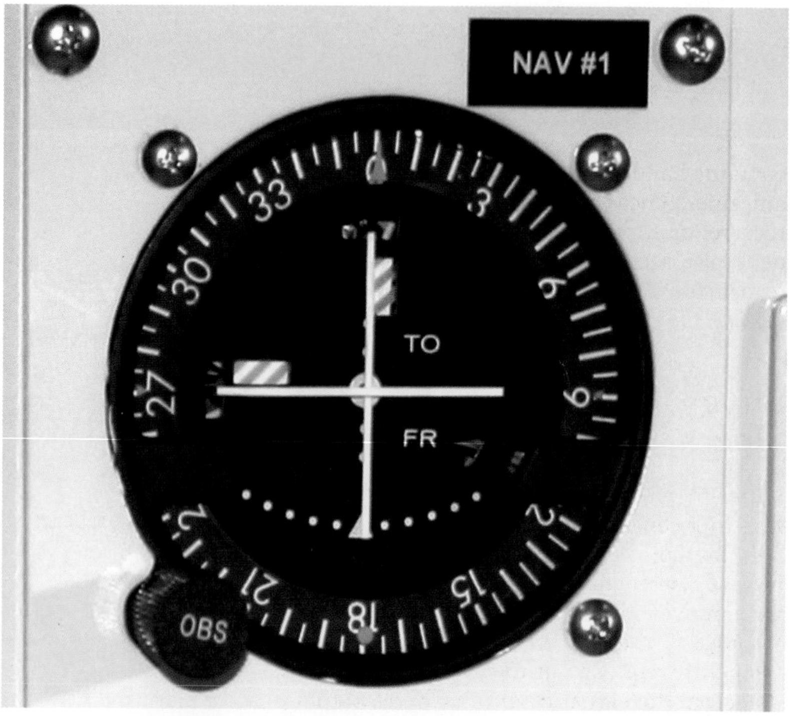

in this chapter. The AGC amplifier takes the varying DC voltage from the detector, filters it into a steady DC voltage, then amplifies this DC voltage to use as a control for the RF amplifier. As the amplitude of the detector output increases, the output from the AGC amplifier is used to decrease the gain of the RF amplifier. Engineers design many AGC systems so that

Audio Amplifier Operation

To understand how any amplifier works, a technician needs knowledge of the two major types of amplification, plus a third "derived" type:

- Voltage Amplifier: an amp that boosts the voltage of an input signal

- Current Amplifier: an amp that boosts the current of a signal

- Power Amplifier: the combination of the above two amplifiers

In the case of a voltage amplifier, a small input voltage is increased so that, for example, a 10 mV (0.01 V) input signal is amplified to achieve an output of 1 V. This represents a gain of 100, the output voltage is 100 times as great as the input voltage. This is called the *voltage gain* of the amplifier.

In the case of a current amplifier, an input current of 10 mA (0.01 A) may be amplified to give

Figure 3-2-1. The Honeywell KI214 indicator incorporates a super-regenerative glideslope receiver.

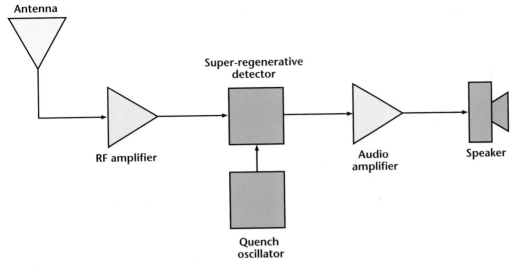

Figure 3-2-2. Diagram of a simple super-regenerative receiver.

an output of 1 A. Again, this is a gain of 100 and is the current gain of the amplifier.

If the two amplifiers are combined, then calculating the input power and the output power, measures the power gain. The audio amplifier uses one or more power amplifiers to increase the power of the audio signal from the detector to a level that can be used to operate a speaker, headphones or digital circuit. If the receiver has a volume control, then it will be part of the audio amplifier block in the form of a variable resistor. Most amplifiers are controlled by resistors. Like the AGC circuit, audio amplifiers operate in a similar manner in any of the aircraft receiver systems discussed in this chapter.

Audio amplifiers are designed to provide the highest fidelity possible and an appropriate level of power at the output. Typically, audio amplifiers designed to operate aviation headphones produce a maximum power output between 50 mW and 100 mW, when measured across a 500 Ω load. The typical audio amplifier designed to operate the speaker on the flight deck will produce between 5 W and 10 W when measured across a 3.2 Ω load.

Section 2

Super-Regenerative Receivers

Super-regenerative receivers obtain radio waves then convert the radio signal to an intermediate frequency above audio by using *regeneration*. After regeneration, the audio is amplified so that

the modulation can be heard. The Honeywell KI214 pictured in Figure 3-2-1 includes a super-regenerative glideslope receiver.

Regeneration is the process in which a tuned circuit oscillates at an intermediate frequency between audio and the received radio signal. This process continuously brings the detector into its most sensitive region at a rate that was higher than the audio frequency range (hence the term super as in supersonic) but lower than the radio frequency range. A block diagram of a super-regenerative receiver is shown in Figure 3-2-2. Engineers are able to design super-regenerative receivers that have high sensitivity, while using few parts when compared to other receivers.

RF Section Operation

The RF section of a super-regenerative receiver contains band pass filters and may contain an amplifier. Since this type of receiver is used to receive multiple frequencies, the bandwidth of the RF section is wider than those used in direct conversion receivers, as shown in Figure 3-1-2.

Super-Regenerative Detector Operation

Super-regenerative receivers can be modified to receive different frequencies, or channels, by adjusting the resonant frequency of the super-regenerative detector. When the user moves the channel selector to a new frequency, then he or she is changing the resonant frequency of the super-regenerative detector. The signal from the RF section triggers the super-regenerative detector into an oscillation called regeneration. The oscillation

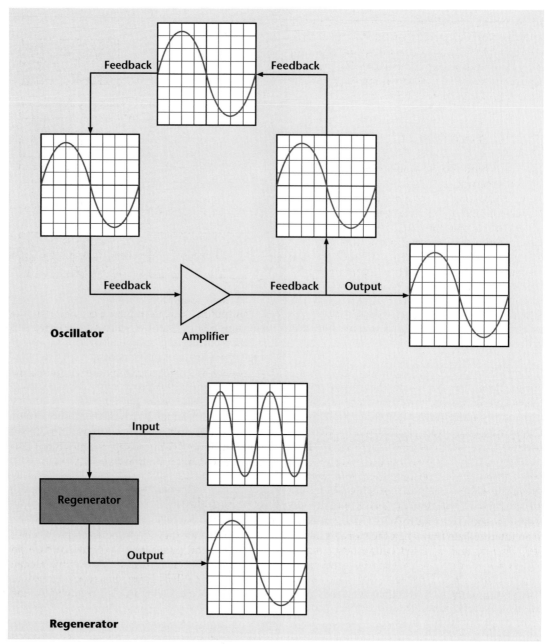

Figure 3-2-3. Oscillator regenerator comparison.

frequency is lower than the frequency of the received radio signal.

The oscillators reviewed in Chapter 1 operate with positive feedback. A portion of the output signal is continuously fed back into the input. The super-regenerative detector does not feed back. Instead, the input from the RF section excites the oscillations. Figure 3-2-3 shows a comparison between an oscillator system and a regenerator system.

The oscillator shown in Figure 3-2-3 has continuous, in phase feedback. Each positive swing in voltage helps the oscillation continue. In comparison, the regenerator input is at a higher frequency than the output. In the regeneration system shown, only every fifth

peak of the input helps the oscillation continue.

The super-regenerative detector oscillates with a relatively high energy output, around 100 dB more than the received radio signal. Moreover, the signal within the detector is complex, containing the RF signal, the super-regenerative signal, and the audio signal.

Quench Oscillator Operation

In order to prevent the super-regenerative detector from becoming unstable, it must be periodically shut down, or *quenched*. To accomplish this, a *quench oscillator* is used to rapidly turn the super-regenerative detector on and off. A quench oscillator may be as simple as a multi-vibrator circuit or as complex as a square wave output from a microprocessor. In any case, the process is the same. The quench oscillator turns on and off the super-regenerative detector, as shown in Figure 3-2-4.

Audio Amplifier Operation

The audio amplifier section of the super-regenerative receiver operates as described previously in the direct conversion receiver section. Audio sections of super-regenerative receivers include a low pass filter, so only audio frequencies are amplified. The audio amplifier uses one or more amplifying sections to increase the power of the audio signal to a level that can be used to operate a speaker, headphones, or digital circuit. If the receiver has a volume control, it will be part of the audio amplifier block.

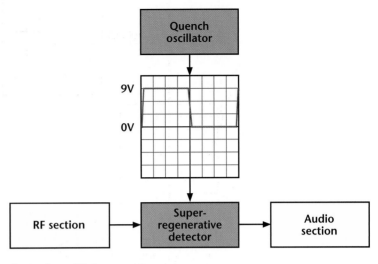

Quench oscillator:
Output at 9V, super-regenerative detector is on
Output at 0V, super-regenerative detector is off

Figure 3-2-4. Quench oscillator output turns super-regenerative detector on and off.

Section 3

Superheterodyne Receivers

Superheterodyne receivers obtain radio waves then convert the radio signal to an intermediate frequency above audio by using heterodyning action. A block diagram of a super-heterodyne receiver is shown in Figure 3-3-1. Once converted to an intermediate frequency, the signal is amplified, filtered, and detected before being amplified to a level that can be used by speakers or digital circuits. The super-heterodyne receiver is the most common type of radio receiver used in avionics. The multifunction Garmin GNS430 pictured in Figure 3-3-2 uses super-heterodyne navigation and communication receivers.

RF Section

The RF section of a superheterodyne receiver contains band pass filters and may contain an amplifier. RF sections containing amplifiers may be gain controlled. Since this type of receiver is used to receive multiple frequencies, the

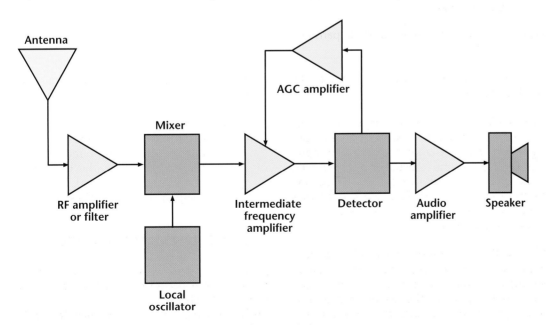

Figure 3-3-1. Block diagram of a super-heterodyne receiver.

Figure 3-3-2. The communication and navigation receivers in this multifunction Garmin GNS430 are of the super-heterodyne type.

Courtesy of Garmin

bandwidth of the RF section is wider than those used in direct conversion receivers. Compare the direct conversion receiver diagramed in Figure 3-1-2 and the super-heterodyne receiver in Figure 3-3-1. Some RF sections have tunable filters. If the RF section has a tunable filter, then technicians refer to it as a preselector.

Local Oscillator Section

The *local oscillator* (LO) produces a radio signal offset from the received radio signal. When a user desires to receive a different frequency and changes the channel selector, he or she is changing the local oscillator frequency. In simple receivers a knob connected to a variable capacitor or inductor, as shown in Figure 3-3-3, can tune the local oscillator.

As the capacitance or inductance changes, the frequency of the local oscillator changes. Modern aviation radios use frequency synthesizers as local oscillators. A frequency synthesizer creates a stable frequency and will be described later in this chapter.

Mixer Section

The *mixer section* is where the heterodyne action takes place. Heterodyne describes the mixing of different frequencies. Within the mixer section, four frequencies are present as the mixing takes place. These frequencies are:

- Radio frequency from the RF section

- Local oscillator frequency from the local oscillator

- Sum of the radio and local oscillator frequencies

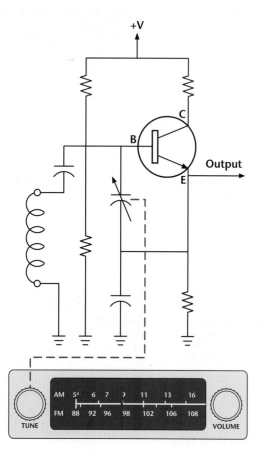
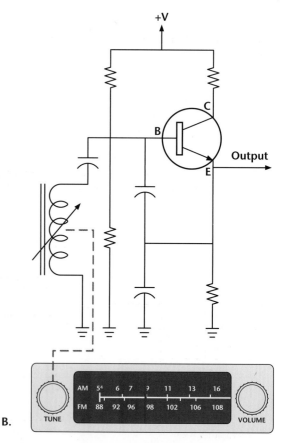

Figure 3-3-3. Schematic diagrams depicting a radio tuning knob connected to: (A) a variable capacitor, or (B) a variable inductor in the oscillator circuit.

• Difference between the radio and local oscillator frequencies

Usually, the difference between the radio and local oscillator frequencies becomes the intermediate frequency. A simple mixer section contains a dual gate FET with inputs from the local oscillator and the RF section on each gate, as shown in Figure 3-3-4.

High and Low Side Injection

Injection refers to the insertion of a local oscillator signal into a mixer. This term is used because local oscillator signals are said to be injected into the mixer. If the injection signal is higher in frequency than the radio frequency intended to be received, then the injection is referred to as *high side injection*. If the injection signal is lower in frequency than the radio frequency intended to be received, then the injection is referred to as *low side injection*. Some receivers may use a combination of high and low side injection, which varies by the frequency selected. The block diagram in Figure 3-3-5 shows examples of radio frequencies, local oscillator frequencies, and the frequencies created by the heterodyne, or mixing, action. Both examples in Figure 3-3-5 show a 30 MHz difference, which is used as the intermediate frequency.

Intermediate Amplifier Section

The *intermediate amplifier* (IF) contains band stop filters and amplifiers. The IF filters out all frequencies except the difference between the radio and local oscillator frequencies. Often this section is gain controlled and will increase the signal level by 100 dB or more. In many radios, multiple amplifier and filter sections are utilized like those shown in the schematic in Figure 3-3-6.

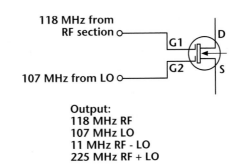

Figure 3-3-4. Diagram showing a simplified dual input MOSFET as a mixer.

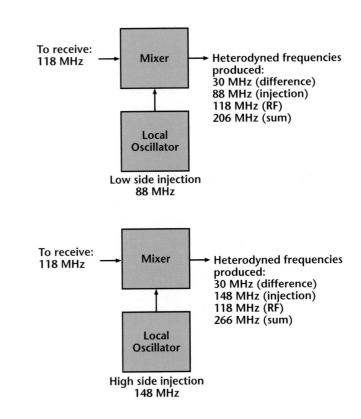

Figure 3-3-5. Diagram showing high and low side injection with frequencies created by heterodyning.

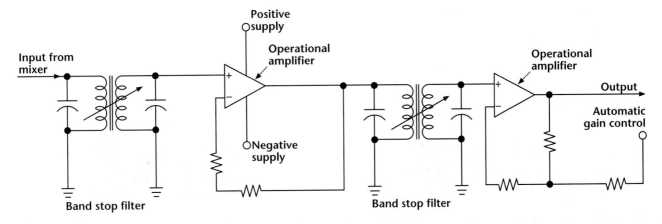

Figure 3-3-6. Schematic of an intermediate frequency section with two operational amplifiers and two band stop filters.

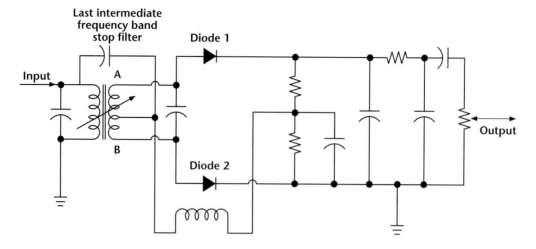

Figure 3-3-7. Schematic diagram of simple discriminator circuit.

Detector Section

The purpose of the *detector* is to extract the audio frequencies from the modulated radio frequency signal. The detector theory within a super-heterodyne receiver is the same as that for other receivers. A diode can be used as a simple detector. As the RF level increases, as shown in Figure 3-1-5, the diode rectifies more energy, supplying more current and voltage to the succeeding stages.

Radios designed to receive frequency modulated radio signals contain a discriminator, instead of a detector. *Discriminators* change the variation in the intermediate frequency into a varying voltage. Whether the receiver is for FM or AM, the result is the same. The detector or discriminator extracts audio from the radio signal for the audio section to amplify. A simple Foster-Seeley discriminator circuit is shown in the schematic in Figure 3-3-7.

In the Foster-Seeley discriminator circuit shown, the output winding of the band stop filter transformer is center tapped and, in this example, the other outputs are labeled A and B. When the IF is on center frequency, the outputs from A and B are equal. As a result, diodes 1 and 2 rectify equally and the circuit does not produce an output. If the IF deviates from the center frequency, then the A and B outputs differ causing diodes 1 and 2 to conduct differently and an output to occur. The output voltage is in proportion to the deviation of the IF from center frequency.

Automatic Gain Control Section

In order to avoid exceeding the capacity of the detector, the AGC reduces the gain of the IF or

RF amplifier when strong signals are received. The AGC theory in a super-heterodyne receiver is the same as that for other receivers discussed in this chapter. The AGC acts as a form of power supply for the components within the amplifiers. As the detector signal increases, the AGC amplifier changes the bias within the RF or IF amplifier, thus reducing its gain.

In some receivers, both the radio frequency (RF) and intermediate frequency (IF) sections are gain controlled, as shown in Figure 3-3-8.

Audio Section

The audio amplifier uses one or more amplifying sections to increase the power of the audio signal to a level that can be used to operate a speaker, headphones, or digital circuit. The audio amplifier theory of a super-heterodyne receiver is the same as that for other receivers discussed in this chapter. If the receiver has a volume control, it will be part of the audio amplifier block.

Dual Super-Heterodyne Receivers

Some radio receivers are designed with two or more mixers, local oscillators, and intermediate frequency sections. The most common type is a dual super-heterodyne receiver, as shown in Figure 3-3-9.

Dual super-heterodyne receivers work on the same principles as a single super-heterodyne receiver. In this case, the second local oscillator is at a fixed frequency, since the second mixer always converts the frequency from the first IF to the second IF.

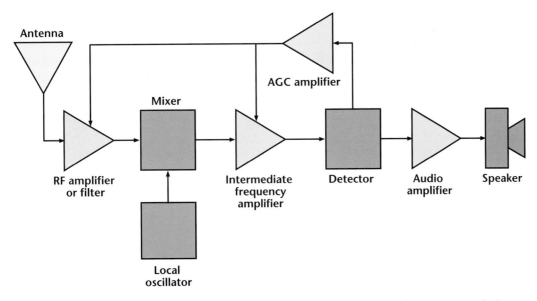

Figure 3-3-8. Block diagram of a super-heterodyne receiver with both RF and IF gain controlled.

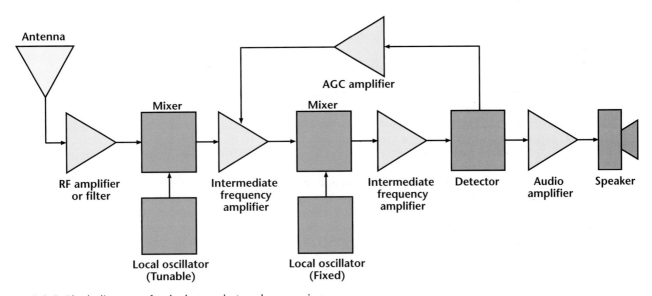

Figure 3-3-9. Block diagram of a dual super-heterodyne receiver.

Section 4

Stabilized Master Oscillators

The majority of tunable avionics receivers use a *stabilized master oscillator* (SMO) as a local oscillator. An SMO allows an adjustable oscillator to be as stable as a crystal-controlled oscillator. An SMO is a looped feedback circuit that uses mathematical binary division and comparisons to control the frequency of a voltage controlled oscillator (VCO), which is made possible by the use of a varactor diode to adjust capacitance. The *varactor diode,* in simple terms, is a voltage controlled variable capacitor. A simplified VCO is shown in Figure 3-4-1.

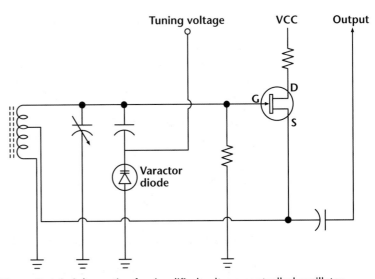

Figure 3-4-1. Schematic of a simplified voltage controlled oscillator.

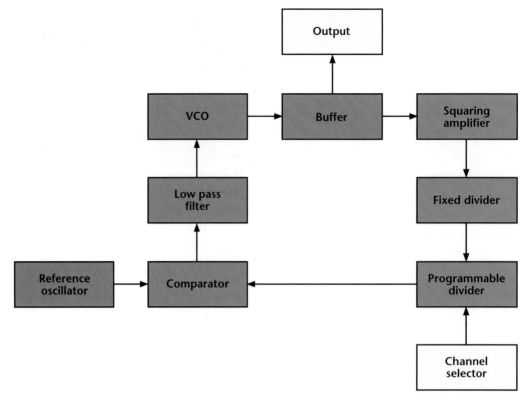

Figure 3-4-2. Simplified block diagram of a stabilized master oscillator.

The varactor diode shown in Figure 3-4-1 is part of the parallel resonant circuit within this modified Hartley oscillator. The oscillator can be identified as a Hartley by the center-tapped inductor. The tuning voltage changes the capacitance of the diode, which in turn changes the resonant frequency of the oscillator circuit. A SMO consists of a feedback path where the VCO frequency is monitored and compared against a crystal-controlled reference frequency. A simplified block diagram of an SMO is shown in Figure 3-4-2.

Reference Oscillator

The reference oscillator uses a crystal to create a very stable frequency. The reference oscilla-

tor signal starts out as a sinusoidal wave, but is converted to a square wave, as shown in Figure 3-4-3. In some equipment, the reference frequency is divided before the output. The frequency stability of both the receiver and the transmitter rely on the stability of this reference oscillator. Engineers design reference oscillators to operate at a frequency much lower than the output frequency of the SMO. This allows larger, thus more stable, crystals to be used.

Buffer

The *buffer* is a low or no gain amplifier, which prevents the mixer or the squaring amplifier from affecting each other or the VCO. Some stabilized master oscillators have multiple buffers, one for each output. Depending on design requirements, the amplifiers are a common collector, common emitter, or common base, as described in Chapter 2.

Squaring Amplifier

Squaring amplifiers use transistors or operational amplifiers biased so the sinusoidal input causes the amplifier to switch rapidly between cutoff and saturation, as shown in Figure 3-4-4. As the input sine wave shown goes positive, it drives the transistor from cut off to saturation very quickly. As a result, the output at the

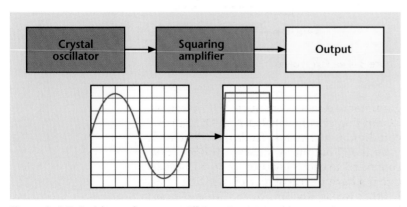

Figure 3-4-3. Inside a reference oscillator.

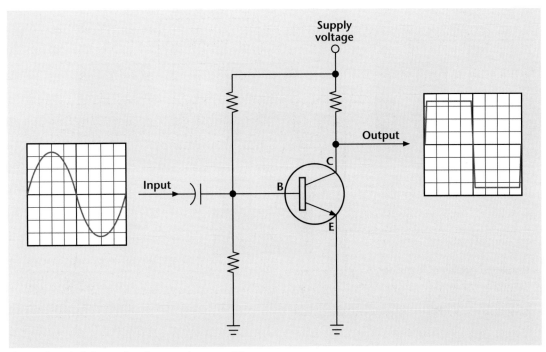

Figure 3-4-4. Schematic of a squaring amplifier.

collector drops rapidly to ground potential or 0 V. As the input waveform drops, the transistor cuts off and the collector rises quickly to the supply value. In this way, the sinusoidal wave gets transformed into a square wave having the same frequency.

The squaring amplifier converts the sinusoidal output of the VCO to a square wave, as shown in the diagram in Figure 3-4-5. This square wave is viewed by subsequent stages as a continuous series of 1s and 0s. The squaring amplifier may consist of an operational amplifier or a transistor amplifier driven rapidly between cut off and saturation, as shown in the schematic in Figure 3-4-4.

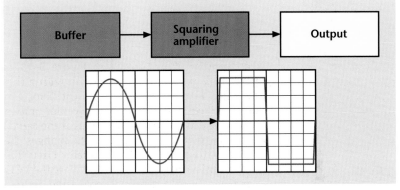

Figure 3-4-5. Squaring amplifier.

Fixed Divider

The *fixed divider* divides the output of the squaring amplifier by a fixed amount. Figure 3-4-6 shows a fixed divider using a D-type flip-flop. The divider section may consist of a flip-flop circuit, a multivibrator circuit, or a counter circuit, depending on engineering requirements.

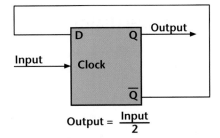

$$Output = \frac{Input}{2}$$

Figure 3-4-6. Fixed divider.

Programmable Divider

The *programmable divider* divides by a number necessary to yield the same frequency as the reference oscillator. The channel or frequency selector connects to and presets the programmable divider. This section of the stabilized master oscillator consists of a series of counting circuits, which are preset by the frequency selector. Figure 3-4-7 depicts a simple pro-

grammable divider constructed of presetable JK flip-flop circuits labeled A to D. Each circuit divides by two and feeds the next circuit from the Q output. A binary monitor is also connected to each Q output. Four JK flip-flop circuits have the capability of counting to or, in other words, dividing by 16. This is the case because each individual flip-flop divides by

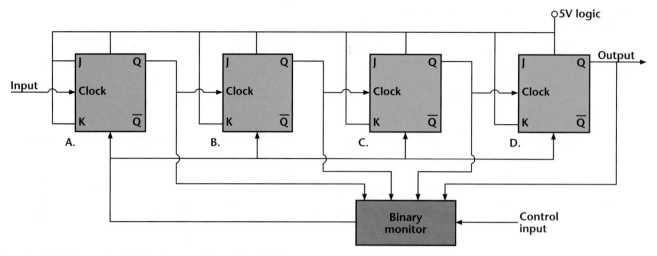

Figure 3-4-7. Schematic of a simple programmable divider.

Combined output decimal value	D-output	C-output	B-output	A-output
0	0	0	0	0
1	0	0	0	1
2	0	0	1	0
3	0	0	1	1
4	0	1	0	0
5	0	1	0	1
6	0	1	1	0
7	0	1	1	1
8	1	0	0	0
9	1	0	0	1
10	1	0	1	0
11	1	0	1	1
12	1	1	0	0
13	1	1	0	1
14	1	1	1	0
15	1	1	1	1

Table 3-4-1. Truth table for a four flip-flop counter. The binary number 1111 is equal to the decimal number 15.

two. Flip-flop circuits connected in this manner are said to be *cascaded*.

Table 3-4-1 depicts a truth table for the divider shown in Figure 3-4-7. The binary monitor can be preset by the control input to clear all the flip-flops when the inputs show any number between 1 and 15, or 1 and 1111 base 2. With flip-flops cleared, the counting starts over. In this way, the divider is programmable. For example, if the control input is used to set the binary monitor to reset when it observes the number eight, then the flip-flops are cleared when the binary monitor observes the number eight, and the circuits then begin counting to eight again.

Stabilized master oscillators for aviation radios must count by much higher numbers and have large integrated circuits containing many more flip-flop circuits.

Comparator

The *comparator* compares the output of the fixed divider with the output of the reference oscillator and provides a variable duty cycle signal output, which is converted into a tuning voltage. The comparator is constructed using interconnected flip-flop circuits and logic gates. If the output of the programmable divider is higher than the reference input, then the duty cycle of the comparator output lowers, as shown in Figure 3-4-8.

If the output of the programmable divider is lower than the reference input, then the duty cycle of the comparator output rises, as shown in Figure 3-4-9.

Low Pass Filter

The *low pass filter* converts the variable duty cycle output of the comparator to DC voltage. The low pass filter contains inductors, capacitors, and are very similar to the low pass filters described in Chapter 1. As the duty cycle of the comparator output rises, so does the DC voltage output of the low pass filter. This DC voltage is known as tuning voltage and is used to control the VCO, as shown in Figure 3-4-10.

Receivers with preselectors may use tuning voltage from the low pass filter for automatic tuning, as shown in Figure 3-4-11.

SMO Example

Figure 3-4-12 shows a diagram of the same SMO used in the above examples with frequencies and descriptions of wave shapes.

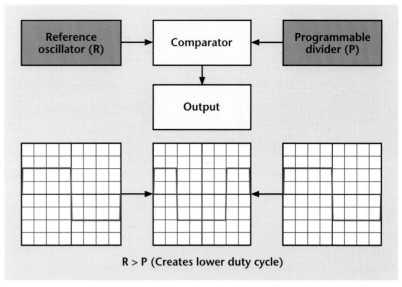

Figure 3-4-8. Diagram depicting a programmable divider output higher in frequency than reference oscillator output.

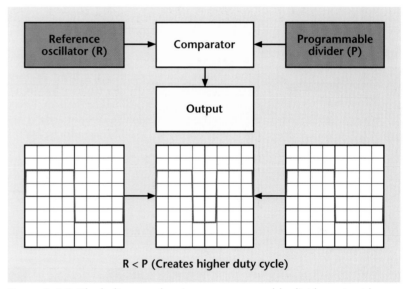

Figure 3-4-9. Block diagram showing a programmable divider output lower in frequency than reference oscillator output.

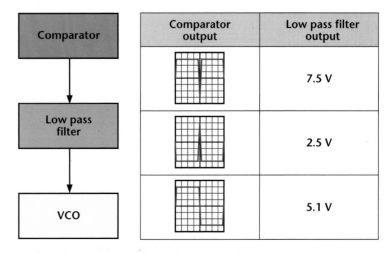

Figure 3-4-10. Low pass filter outputs compared to comparator outputs.

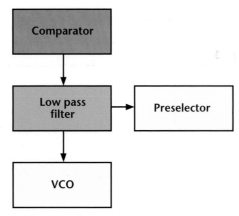

Figure 3-4-11. Block diagram of a low pass filter with two tuning voltage outputs.

Designed for a super-heterodyne receiver with a 10 MHz IF section and low side injection, this SMO provides 108.00 MHz to the mixer for reception of 118.00 MHz. In this case, the VCO provides a 108.00 MHz output to the buffer, which in turn supplies the same signal to both the mixer and the squaring amplifier.

The squaring amplifier converts the signal to a square wave and sends it to the fixed divider. In this case, the fixed divider divides the signal by two, producing a 54.0 MHz (half of 108.00 MHz) to the programmable divider. The channel selector is set to 118.00 MHz, which sets the programmable divider to divide the 54 MHz input by 2,160. The result is a 25 kHz square wave provided to the comparator.

With the reference oscillator also running at 25 kHz, the comparator provides a square wave to the low pass filter that converts the signal to a 3.0 VDC tuning voltage, which will control the VCO.

Large Scale Integration

Figure 3-4-13 shows a block diagram of a stabilized master oscillator using large scale integration. The term *Large scale integration* refers to a single integrated circuit with thousands of junctions, which is able to perform multiple functions. This integrated circuit is referred to as an LSI. In this case, all squaring and dividing are handled in a single large scale integrated circuit.

Charge Pumps

An SMO using large scale integration is likely to use a charge pump system to create the tuning voltage for the VCO. Figure 3-4-14 shows a schematic of a simplified charge pump.

In Figure 3-4-14, charging C1 creates the tuning voltage. During normal operation, the LSI sends positive pulses to Q1, periodically

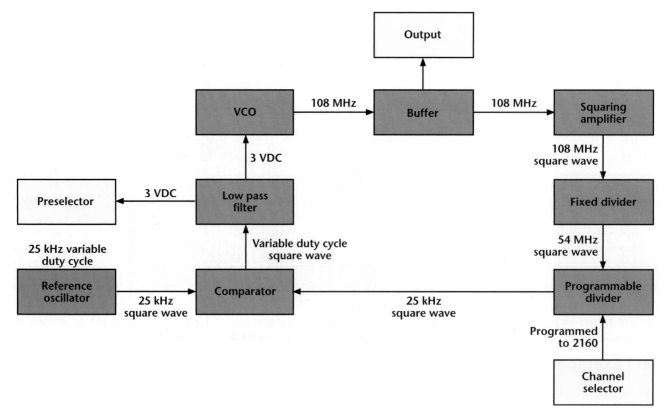

Figure 3-4-12. Block diagram of an SMO.

turning it on and charging C1, which tends to discharge through the VCO; therefore, repeated up pulses are required. If the VCO frequency is too high or if the operator selects a channel lower in frequency, then the LSI will send pump down pulses to Q2, which will discharge C1 more rapidly than it would normally discharge through the VCO. In a normally operating SMO, the pump up and pump down pulses will never occur at the same time.

Section 5

Summary

Aviation navigation and communication may use a variety of receivers, depending on the system design. A direct conversion receivers amplify a single frequency, detect, and then amplify the modulation. Super regenerative receivers use regeneration, which oscillates at an intermediate frequency and detects the audio prior to audio amplification. Super-heterodyne receivers use a local oscillator and a mixer to create an intermediate frequency through the heterodyne process. The IF section amplifies the signal prior to detection and audio amplification. Most receivers have some sort of automatic gain control, in order to allow the system to work with both strong and weak signals.

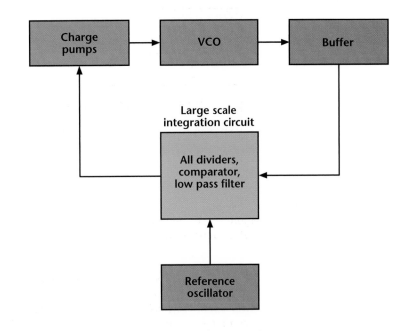

Figure 3-4-13. An SMO using large scale integration.

Most super-heterodyne receivers use a stabilized master oscillator as the local oscillator. The SMO uses a voltage controlled oscillator to create the local oscillator signal and dividers to reduce the frequency to a number that can be compared to a crystal-controlled reference signal. Many SMO circuits in modern equipment are contained within a single LSI.

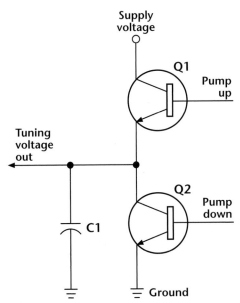

Figure 3-4-14. Schematic of a simplified charge pump circuit.

Figure 3-5-1. Most modern aircraft feature a multitude of avionics receivers. A typical aircraft panel has many different types of units.

Aviation Radio Communication

Aviation Radio Communication (Avionics Communication) was developed to allow pilots to communicate with air traffic controllers. Over the years, the industry has expanded its uses and implemented newer technologies. As a result, a well equipped aircraft today may have systems installed that use various parts of the frequency spectrum from high frequencies to super high frequencies.

This chapter explains the communication systems and their subsystems used on aircraft. Topics such as squelch, transmitter, and modulation systems and how each system is used within the industry are covered. The topics discussed in this chapter are referenced under ATA code 23.

Section 1

History

The history of avionics communication is a subject worthy of its own book. A brief synopsis of this history is covered in this section, with concentration on the developments that affect the world in which modern avionics technicians work.

Early History

Lt. Paul W. Beck accomplished the first air to ground radio communication on January 21, 1911, from a Wright Model B Flyer. Flying at 400 feet above ground level (AGL) he completed a radio communication to a ground station more than 40 miles away. The communication was accomplished using a radio telegraph. Beck

Learning Objectives

REVIEW
- History of aviation radio communication systems

DESCRIBE
- Aviation audio system standards
- Automatic squelch operational theory
- Frequencies, channels and antenna systems used for SATCOM, HF, VHF communication
- ACARS
- SELCAL system
- Flight line testing procedure

APPLY
Draw block diagrams of:
- AM transmitters
- Aviation telephone, SATCOM, HF, and VHF communication systems
- ACARS
- Satellite transponder

Left: Modern air transport depends on reliable radio communication for each and every flight.

Figure 4-1-1. The Narco omnigator was an early panel-mounted NAVCOMM transceiver.

Figure 4-1-2. The King KX-170B is a 720-channel development of the earlier 360-channel KX-170 and KX-170A.

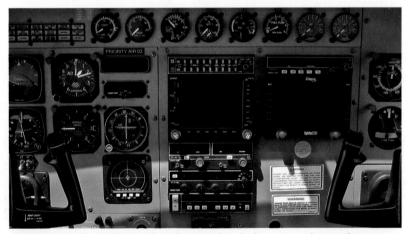

Figure 4-1-3. The radio stack in this panel includes more advanced communication transceivers with digital displays, more available channels and more precise frequency control.

mostly between air mail radio stations, which were forerunners of flight service stations. The first stations, located in Bellefonte, Pennsylvania, and Washington, D.C., began operations in 1919. Since stations were of the radiotelegraph type, several abbreviations were used to speed up the rather slow process of telegraphic communication. Modern abbreviations, such as CAVU (clear, visibility unlimited), ETE (estimated time en route), and WILCO (will comply), originated as telegraphic shorthand.

Throughout the first decades of the twentieth century, radio technology continued to advance. By the end of the 1920s, amplitude modulated transceivers became available for aviation use. These radios not only allowed voice communication between aircraft but also between aircraft and stations on the ground. Scientists also began experimenting with radio communication in the HF spectrum and with crystal stabilization of radio transmitters during this period.

Advancing Technology

As time passed, technology became available to increase the operating frequency of radio transceivers into the VHF spectrum. In addition, technology advancements allowed transceivers to become smaller and lighter. By the 1950s, radios were small enough to be mounted in the instrument panel of general aviation aircraft (Figure 4-1-1). These radios had crystal stabilized transmitters, thus eliminating the need for an operator to constantly monitor and adjust transmit frequency.

During the 1950s, radios that operated on a 90- channel communication band ranging from 118 MHz to 127 MHz were widely available. A complete description of current VHF aviation communication system channeling is described later in this chapter. Each channel was spaced 100 kHz from the next channel. As the number of aircraft grew and as more aircraft became equipped with radios, the industry determined 90 channels weren't enough.

Increasing Channels

During the 1960s, the communication band was expanded to 136 MHz, and the spacing between channels was cut in half to 50 kHz. This made 360 channels available for communication. Before the 1960s ended, the industry realized 360 channels still weren't enough and the band was subdivided yet again.

In 1973 the spacing between channels was cut to 25 kHz, thus giving radios in the united states 720 available channels (Figure 4-1-2). The Europeans had frequencies to 137 MHz

held the 29 pound transmitter in his lap, while another pilot, Phil Parmalee, flew the airplane.

Radio communication equipment in the first part of the twentieth century was heavy and cumbersome to operate, requiring the full attention of the operator. These systems operated on the low frequency band from 71 kHz to 200 kHz. Communication with these systems occurred available for aviation communication use. As a result, 760 channels were available in Europe. In 1990, frequencies up to 137 MHz became available for aviation use in North America.

Late Twentieth Century

During the 1970s, the problem of older 90-channel and 360-channel radios broadcasting on several channels at one time became evident. Units with 90 channels and a channel spacing of 100 kHz were not stable or precise enough for a communication system designed for channels every 25 kHz. For example, a 90-channel radio transmitting on 118.5 MHz could easily interfere on 118.475 MHz and 118.525 MHz. The possibility existed for this 90-channel transmitter to interfere even further into the frequencies from 118.450 MHz to 118.55 MHz. As a result, the transmitting 90- channel radio could make up to five channels unusable for anyone else within range.

In 1983 the United States ratified the 1979 World Administrative Radio Conference (WARC '89) agreement. The WARC is now known as the World Radiocommunications Conference (WRC). This conference is held by the International Telecommunications Union (ITU), which is an agency of the United Nations dedicated to coordinating the use of the radio frequency spectrum. Ratification of this agreement meant the FCC would tighten tolerances for aeronautical mobile transmitters from .005 percent to .003 percent. No 90- or 360-channel aviation communications transmitter could meet this requirement. In addition, even some 720- and 760-channel transmitters could not meet the requirement because of the transmitters' stability. This requirement for increased transmitter stability did not take effect until 1997 (Figure 4-1-3).

During the 1970s satellite communication became available, and frequency terrestrial telephone systems came into wide usage on business aircraft. Details of both types of systems are included in this chapter.

During the 1980s digital communication on the VHF aeronautical band came into wide use. This type of communication system is described in detail later in this chapter.

A New Century

At the end of the twentieth century, 760 channels were no longer enough. In 1999 the Europeans began to phase in a 2,280-channel system. The United States began implementation of the same system in 2007.

Radio silent	Squelched	Squelch on	Squelch closed
Noise or station heard	Not squelched	Squelch off	Squelch open

Table 4-2-1. Squelch terminology.

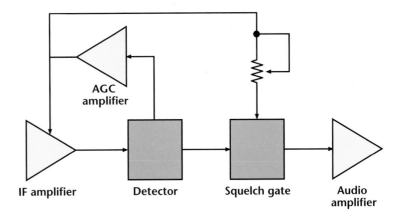

Figure 4-2-1. Block diagram of a simple squelch system.

Technicians need to be aware of this tightening of transmitter tolerances, since some older aircraft may have transceivers installed that are not legal to use. The owners may not be aware of the transmitter stability of the radios installed nor of the laws regarding transmitter stability. Furthermore, technicians also must be aware aircraft may have 720-, 760-, or 2,280-channel communication systems installed.

Section 2

Aviation Radio Systems

Squelch

Squelch is the circuit within a radio receiver that turns off the audio when a signal is not being received. Pilots and those who are not technicians often use the word incorrectly to describe the rushing noise heard in a receiver not tuned to a station. In fact, this noise is *mixer noise* created by random currents in the mixer. Squelch is the circuit designed to remove mixer noise when the radio channel is not being used. Table 4-2-1 shows proper squelch terminology with its respective radio condition.

In a communication receiver, a simple squelch system consists of a pilot-adjustable squelch gate between the detector and the audio section, as shown in Figure 4-2-1. The

Figure 4-2-2. VHF communication radio controls with adjustable squelch.

squelch gate detects the presence of a signal by monitoring the AGC output. If enough signal is received to activate the AGC, then the squelch gate opens and allows audio to pass to the audio amplifier.

The pilot or technician should adjust the squelch control in a simple squelch system, like the one shown in Figure 4-2-2, until the noise disappears. If the pilot or technician continues to turn the control after the noise stops, then the radio may not receive weak signals.

The majority of radio receivers have automatic squelch. The name is somewhat misleading because a technician may adjust the squelch circuitry; however, to the pilot, the squelch appears to be completely automatic. Automatic squelch circuits monitor both AGC voltage and mixer noise. Since received signals reduce mixer noise, the system can be designed to open the gate when the mixer noise is reduced below a certain level. Since

some received signals may contain noise, automatic squelch systems also monitor the AGC voltage. If the received signal is too noisy for the noise monitor, then the AGC voltage will allow the squelch gate to open. Automatic squelch logic is shown in Figure 4-2-3, and a truth table is shown in Table 4-2-2.

Many radio receivers that incorporate automatic squelch have a switch that is labeled either test, squelch, or simply SQ, as shown in Figure 4-2-4. When the switch is pressed, the squelch gate will open, allowing mixer noise to pass to the audio system.

Audio Standards

Aviation radios are designed to meet standards particular to the aviation industry. There are two types of audio output standards: the first is considered low level and has enough power to operate headphones; the second is considered high level and has enough power to operate cabin speakers.

All aircraft radios produce low level audio designed to operate headphones with a 500 Ω impedance. For this reason, home entertainment headphones do not work in an aircraft because home audio equipment operates between 8 and 16 Ω. The low level power is typically between 50 and 100 mW, with the volume control set at maximum and a strong signal at the antenna.

Some radios produce high level audio for a cabin speaker. With a few exceptions, the high level audio is designed to operate cabin speakers with a 3.2 Ω impedance. Typical speaker power levels are 5 W, with the volume control set at maximum and a strong signal at the antenna.

Aviation Microphones

Aviation communication radios are designed to use carbon microphones; therefore, microphones in aircraft must be of the carbon type or imitate a carbon-type microphone if they are electronic. Since many airplanes have a high ambient noise level, a noise cancelling microphone is most often used.

A carbon microphone button contains carbon grains. The radio supplies voltage to the microphone and current flows through the carbon. Figure 4-2-5 shows a simple button with carbon grains attached to an oscilloscope.

When the pilot speaks into the microphone, the carbon grains vibrate causing a change of resistance. The changing resistance results in a changing current, which is detected by the oscil-

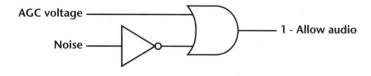

Figure 4-2-3. Automatic squelch logic.

AGC voltage	Noise	Squelch opens to pass audio
0	0	Yes (1)
0	1	No (0)
1	0	Yes (1)
1	1	Yes (1)

Table 4-2-2. Truth table.

Volume/squelch test switch

Figure 4-2-4 VHF communication and navigation radio with a combination volume and squelch test switch shown.
Courtesy of Garmin

loscope. The radio uses the changing current to create modulation when it is transmitting.

Noise cancelling microphones are designed with two openings. One opening is connected through a baffle to the rear of the microphone element, as shown in Figure 4-2-6. The pilot speaks into the other opening. Since noise from opposite directions enters the microphone through both openings, it cancels itself out. The pilot's voice is not cancelled, because it comes into the microphone through only one opening. For a noise cancelling microphone to work properly, it must be held close to the user's mouth so that the user's voice goes through only one opening, thus preventing it from being cancelled or partially cancelled.

Radio Transmitters

A *radio transmitter* is a device that amplifies radio frequencies to a high level so they can be radiated into space through an antenna. All radio communication systems use some form of transmitter.

AM Transmitters

Amplitude modulated (AM) transmitters are common in aviation communication systems. The transmitter shown in Figure 4-2-7 amplifies radio frequency signals from the stabilized master oscillator.

The first stage of the transmitter is a buffer stage, with little or no gain. The buffer isolates the transmitter from the stabilized master oscillator. The transmitter uses three stages of amplification. Some systems use more stages and others less, depending on the design. The

pre-driver, driver, and final amplifiers are Class C and rely on tuned circuits between each stage to maintain a sinusoidal waveform. Gain at the final stage is controlled by a modulator.

The *modulator* is an amplifier that acts as a power supply for the final amplifier. The modulator operates in Class A and receives its signal

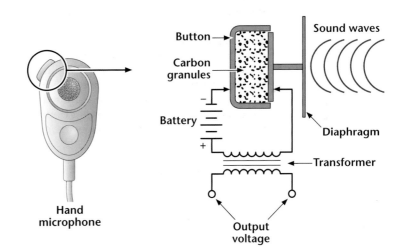

Figure 4-2-5. Simple carbon microphone.

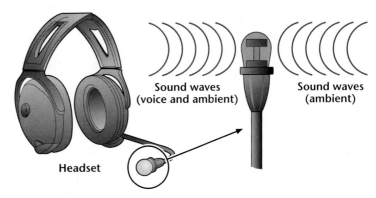

Figure 4-2-6. Noise cancelling microphone.

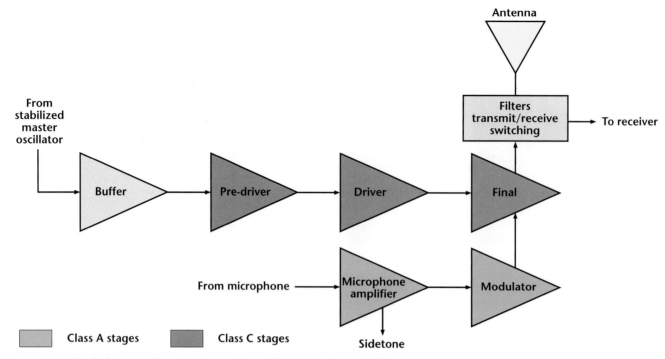

Figure 4-2-7. Block diagram of an AM transmitter with high level modulation.

from a microphone amplifier. The microphone connects to and supplies an audio signal to the microphone amplifier, which produces an output to which the pilot can listen and outputs a signal to the modulator. The output to the pilot is called *sidetone* and is sent to the headphones during transmission.

Radios have filters and switching circuits between the final amplifier and the antenna. During receive, the transmit/receive (TR) switching circuits connect the antenna to the receiver. During transmit, the TR circuits connect the antenna to the transmitter. Filters are included in this section of the radio to prevent interference with other systems.

Figure 4-2-8 shows an AM transmitter using low level modulation. In this case, the first amplifying stage of the transmitter is modulated. As a result, all stages must be Class A amplifiers in order to preserve fidelity.

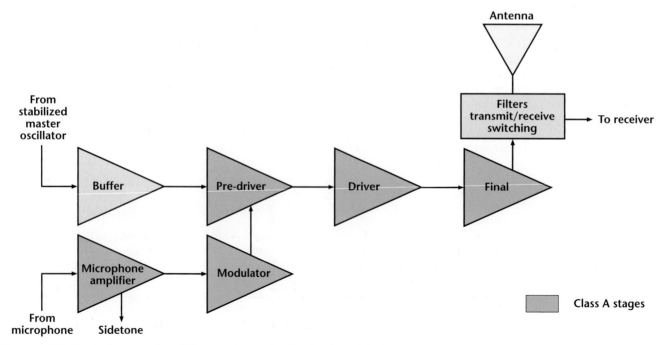

Figure 4-2-8. Block diagram of an AM transmitter using low level modulation.

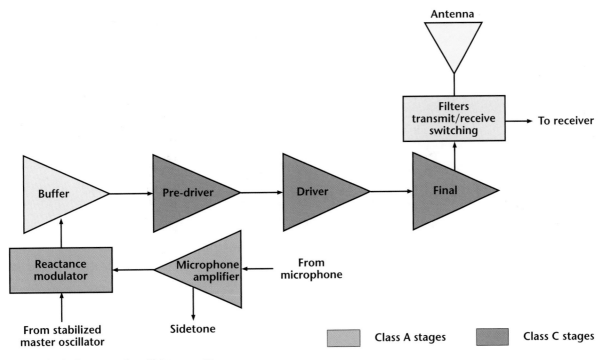

Figure 4-2-9. Block diagram of an FM transmitter.

Many transmitters have a circuit built into the TR switching block to detect excessive standing waves. If standing waves develop due to a transmission line or antenna problem, then the circuit will reduce the power output of the transmitter.

FM Transmitters

Frequency modulated (FM) transmitters have a circuit at the start of the transmitter chain to vary the phase or frequency of the incoming signal, as shown in Figure 4-2-9. In this case, the signal from the microphone is used to vary the phase of the signal from the stabilized master oscillator. This will deviate the phase or frequency that is amplified through the Class C pre-driver and a final driver. Like an AM transmitter, the number of amplification stages vary with design requirements. At the output, the filters and transmit/receive switching work in the same fashion as an AM transmitter.

Section 3
Aeronautical VHF Communications

The topics discussed in this section are referenced under ATA code 23-10.

Frequencies and Channels

Aeronautical VHF communication systems, or VHF COM for short, are named for the part of the frequency spectrum the channels occupy, as shown in Figure 4-3-1. The aviation VHF communication frequencies range from 118.000 MHz to 136.99163 MHz and are divided into 2,280 channels.

The original and main purpose of the VHF communication system is to allow pilots to

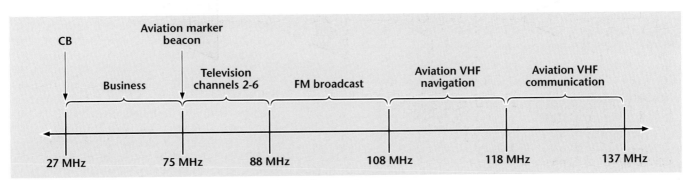

Figure 4-3-1. A section of the VHF band showing aviation frequencies.

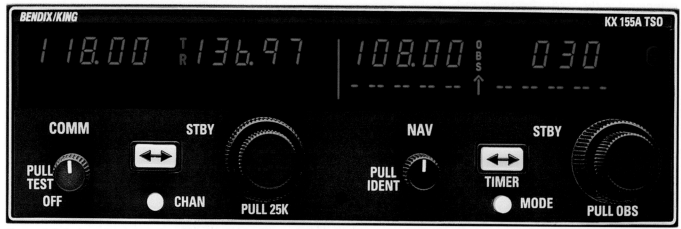

Figure 4-3-2. A navigation and communication radio.

Courtesy of Bendix/King by Honeywell

communicate with air traffic controllers. As described in Chapter 2, radio waves propagate as space waves in the VHF spectrum; therefore, VHF COM is only usable over a relatively short range. To increase the usable range of the system, the FAA installed remote controlled transceivers at strategic locations around the United States. Still, pilots must change frequencies often to communicate with controllers via a transceiver station located on a line of sight with the aircraft.

The original VHF communication system consisted of 90 channels, using frequencies from 118.0 MHz to 126.9 MHz, and most aircraft radios could only transmit on a few channels. In this system, channels were spaced 100 kHz apart. As air traffic increased, so did the breadth of the frequency spectrum used and the number of

available channels. The first change to the system raised the high end of the frequency band to 135.95 MHz and increased the number of available channels to 360. Later, by subdividing the frequency spectrum into channels spaced 25 kHz apart, the number of channels increased to 720.

In the early 1970s the concept of *offset carriers* was introduced. Space on a radio control panel is limited, so manufacturers designed the display to truncate, or drop, the least significant digit of the frequency. As a result, a radio tuned to 118.025 MHz would display 118.02, thus eliminating the final five. Figure 4-3-2 shows a navigation and communication unit with the standby communication frequency displaying 136.97. The actual standby frequency is 136.975 MHz.

In 1990 another megahertz of frequency spectrum was added to the highest frequency, and the number of channels increased to 760. In the '90s, a problem developed: older, less frequency-stable transmitters were interfering with adjacent channels. At this point, all 360-channel transmitters and some 720-channel transmitters became illegal to use for transmission.

The frequency was recently subdivided again so that a channel occurs each 8.33 kHz, as shown in Table 4-3-1. Furthermore, the offset carrier concept was expanded and, on many channels, the display no longer represents the exact frequencies used.

Table 4-3-2 shows the channels and frequencies from 118.00000 MHz to 118.100000 MHz, along with the numbers that could be displayed on the faceplate. Note how both 118.000 and 118.005 are used for the same frequency, 118.00000 MHz. This could give the false impression that more channels are available. The technician needs to remember to set test

Frequency (MHZ)	VHF COM channels (currently available)	VHF COM channels (previously available)
118.000	1st Channel	1st Channel
118.00833	2nd Channel	
118.01666	3rd Channel	
118.025	4th Channel	2nd Channel
118.0333	5th Channel	
118.04166	6th Channel	
118.050	7th Channel	3rd Channel
Etc.	2,273 more channels	757 more channels

Table 4-3-1. VHF communication channel spacing.

equipment to the carrier frequency instead of the displayed frequency.

Many channels are designated for certain types of use. For example, 121.50000 MHz is used for emergency. Many control towers use 119.10000 MHz to communicate with airborne aircraft and use 121.90000 MHz to communicate with aircraft on the ground. Often, flight service stations, which provide a variety of services to pilots, use frequencies between 122.00000 MHz and 122.67500 MHz. Flight schools often use 123.30000 MHz. Aircraft using uncontrolled airports communicate using frequencies between 122.70000 MHz and 123.07500 MHz.

Aviation VHF communication systems are amplitude modulated and, depending on the make and model, transmit between 1 W and 50 W. These systems use either 720, 760, or 2,280 channels between 118 MHz and 136.99163 MHz. Some maintenance data lists the upper limit as 136.992 MHz.

VHF Communication Antennas

VHF communication antennas are of the Marconi type and can be mounted on the top or bottom of the airframe. On larger aircraft, one antenna can be mounted on the top and the other on the bottom. In some cases, the communication antenna may be combined with a satellite antenna for either navigation or entertainment. Antennas on small aircraft, as shown in Figure 4-3-3, are usually constructed of a conductor integrated into fiberglass and are slightly swept backward for improved aerodynamic efficiency.

The antennas on larger aircraft look like fins or blades, as shown in Figure 4-3-4. The antennas also are slightly shorter than those on small aircraft.

Frequency used (MHZ)	Channel displayed	Alternate display
118.00000	118.000	118.005
118.00833	118.010	
118.01666	118.015	
118.02000	Skipped	
118.02500	118.025	118.030
118.03332	118.035	
118.04165	118.040	
118.04500	Skipped	
118.05000	118.050	118.055
118.05831	118.060	
118.06664	118.065	
118.07000	Skipped	
118.07500	118.075	118.080
118.08330	118.085	
118.09163	118.090	
118.09500	Skipped	
118.10000	118.100	118.105

Table 4-3-2. Frequencies used and displayed in the 2280 offset carrier system.

Figure 4-3-3. Two VHF communication antennas mounted on a small Cessna.

Figure 4-3-4. A blade-type VHF COM antenna for high-speed aircraft.

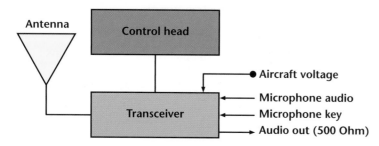

Figure 4-3-5. Generic remote-mounted VHF communication system.

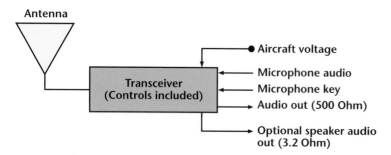

Figure 4-3-6. Block diagram of a panel-mounted communication system.

VHF Communication Configurations

Engineers design VHF communication systems in a variety of ways, depending on the type of aircraft in which it will be used. The block diagram in Figure 4-3-5 shows what many refer to as a generic communication system. At the heart of the system is a *transceiver*. The transceiver is

a radio receiver and transmitter contained in one housing. In this system the transceiver is mounted in an equipment bay with other avionics systems. Since the transceiver is mounted away from the instrument panel, technicians often refer to this type of system as remote mounted. A wiring harness connects the transceiver to a *control head*, which is mounted in the instrument panel. The control head contains channeling switches and displays, along with volume and squelch controls. In some systems the pilot is able to store one or more frequencies in memory. The transceiver has a microphone input and a 500 Ω audio output. Often, the microphone input and the audio output are connected to the audio system in the aircraft.

On small aircraft the transceiver and control head are combined into a single-instrument panel-mounted housing, as the block diagram shows in Figure 4-3-6. In some cases, the transceiver contains a speaker amplifier, and it may be connected to the aircraft speaker.

Many large aircraft use an integrated flight management system, which includes both navigation and communication functions, such as the one pictured in Figure 4-3-7A. As the block diagram in Figure 4-3-7B shows, this system has modules that are connected to a common power supply and data buses. Of the many modules in the system, two or more are VHF communication modules. A system of this type does not have a control head but is controlled through a multifunction control display unit (MCDU).

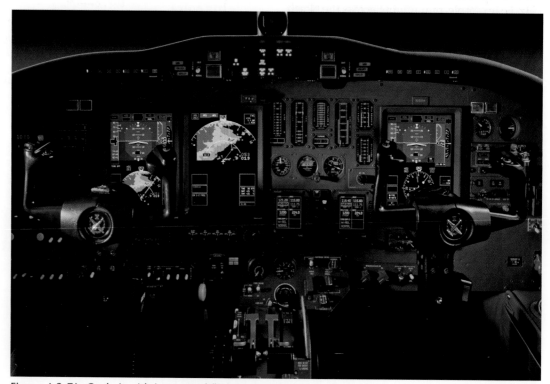

Figure 4-3-7A. Cockpit with integrated flight management system.

In many aircraft the VHF communication system is combined with a navigation system and mounted in the instrument panel (Figure 4-3-8A). The block diagram of this type of system is shown in Figure 4-3-8B.

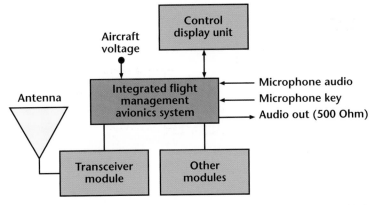

Figure 4-3-7B. Block diagram of a modularized communication system.

Section 4

Aeronautical HF Communications

The topics discussed in this section are referenced under ATA code 23-10.

Aeronautical HF Use

The aeronautical high frequency communication system allows pilots to communicate with controllers or their home base from thousands of miles away. Since the high frequency spectrum favors sky wave propagation, pilots are able to achieve worldwide communication. Most aviation HF communication systems are capable of transmitting and receiving on the entire HF band; therefore, pilots have the responsibility to tune and transmit on specific frequencies designated for aviation use.

Unlike VHF communication systems, the HF system is not channelized. Many HF systems allow frequencies to be selected down to the kHz. For example, pilots flying across the North Atlantic may use 4.675 MHz to make contact with air traffic controllers. Control heads for HF communication systems may be adjustable to 1 kHz precision and include a memory system for storing frequencies that are used often.

Generally, HF communication systems transmit using the single-sideband (SSB) mode of operation. Most systems can be switched to amplitude modulated mode. Single-sideband is the preferred method of transmission because the narrow bandwidth works better for sky wave propagation.

Figure 4-3-8A. The Bendix/King KLX135A is a combination GPS receiver and COMM transceiver. *Courtesy of Bendix/King by Honeywell, Inc.*

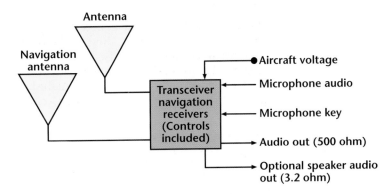

Figure 4-3-8B. Block diagram of a NAVCOMM system.

Antennas and Configurations

Transmitting and receiving efficiently on a variety of frequencies between 3 MHz and 30 MHz presents a problem for system designers.

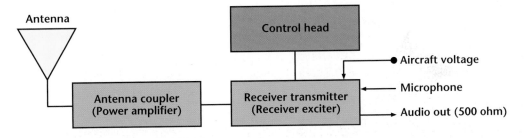

Figure 4-4-1. Remote-mounted HF communication system.

Figure 4-4-2. Three different HF antenna arrangements.

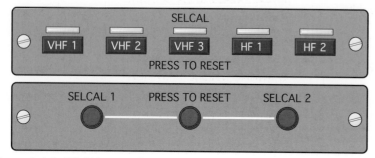

Figure 4-4-3. SELCAL controls.

As described in Chapter 2, the wavelength for 3 MHz is 100 meters, and the wavelength for 30 MHz is 10 meters. A Marconi-type antenna suitable for 3 MHz would be 25 meters long, which is slightly longer than 82 feet. For 30 MHz, the Marconi-type antenna would be over 8 feet long. Antennas of such great length are not suitable for most aircraft. Furthermore, an antenna that is efficient at one end of the band would not be suitable for use at the other end.

If a transmitter is connected to an antenna of inappropriate length, then the antenna impedance will not match the transmission line. This will cause losses because of standing waves. Since antenna options on aircraft are limited, engineers add a unit to HF communication systems called an *antenna coupler*. Most often, the high powered transmitter amplifier is included in this unit, as shown in Figure 4-4-1.

After changing frequencies, the pilot momentarily keys the HF transmitter. The antenna coupler uses the energy from the transmitter to measure the standing waves generated by the antenna length that is not appropriate for the frequency used. The antenna coupler adds capacitance or inductance as necessary to eliminate the standing waves, thus allowing maximum power transfer between the antenna and the HF system.

The transmission line located between the antenna coupler and the antenna exhibits loss; therefore, the antenna coupler must be located as close to the antenna as possible. In some cases, the antenna coupler and the antenna are a single unit, as shown in Figure 4-4-2A.

In Figure 4-4-2B the upper portion shows a long wire antenna connected from the engine cowl to the vertical stabilizer and forward to a point on the fuselage. Figure 4-4-2C shows a wire called a stub connected from the cabin to the wing. In this system, the airframe itself becomes the antenna.

SELCAL

SELCAL is an abbreviation for selective calling. It is a form of squelch operated by modulating tones. SELCAL is referenced under ATA code 23-20. When the receiver receives the appropriate tones, the squelch opens, a light illuminates, and a chime rings. When a selective call is received, the pilot turns on the audio for the system that received the call and presses a button to reset the SELCAL system using controls, such as those shown in Figure 4-4-3.

If the flight crew does not select audio for a receiver using SELCAL, then the chime and light will get their attention. The SELCAL system consists of 16 tones between 312.6 Hz and 1479.1 Hz. Each tone is represented by a letter from A to S. The letters I, N, and O are omitted from the SELCAL alphabet. There are 10,920 possible combinations of SELCAL letter codes. SELCAL-equipped aircraft are assigned a four letter code. When a particular aircraft is to be contacted, the sender transmits the four letter code.

Due to high radio frequency noise levels and weak signal strength, neither simple nor automatic squelch operate effectively on the HF band without a reduction of sensitivity. As a result, SELCAL is often used with HF receivers.

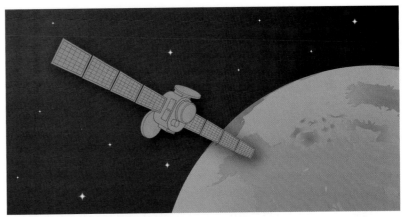

Figure 4-5-1. An orbiting communications satellite.

Section 5

Satellite Communications

The topics discussed in this section are referenced under ATA code 23-10.

Service Providers

Satellite Communication (SATCOM) describe several forms of communication that use space vehicles to relay information between aircraft or from aircraft to a ground station. Figure 4-5-1 shows an example of a communications satellite in orbit. The satellite communication system requires a service provider. The service provider maintains the satellites and also the interface between the space vehicles and various ground-based communication systems. In order to use satellite communication systems, the aircraft owner must subscribe to a satellite service. The satellite service provider charges monthly, and possibly by the minute. Table 4-5-1 provides information about satellite service providers and their systems.

Satellite systems work in *duplex*. Duplex means two different frequencies are used to transmit and receive information. Duplex allows systems to simultaneously transmit and receive. Information is relayed between satellites, as shown in Figure 4-5-2, allowing it to travel back and forth between the aircraft and the ground.

Since the satellite signal is relayed, the flight crew or passengers aboard an aircraft equipped with a satellite communication system can communicate worldwide. Many different types of communications are possible with satellite systems including data, voice, and television. Corporate aircraft use satellite communication to support on board corporate office systems, including internet, telephone, and facsimile.

Satellite communication systems use many different frequencies. The exact frequencies used by any given system depends on the service provider. The service provider uses frequencies for both communication and for satellite control. The satellite communication system transmits over frequencies between satellites as well as frequencies between the service provider and the satellite. The frequency from the aircraft to the satellite is known as an uplink; the frequency from the satellite to the aircraft

Service provider	Number of satellites	Type of orbit	Uplink/downlink frequencies	Mode of operation
Globalstar	44	Low Orbit	Uplink: 2.48439 to 2.49915 GHz Downlink: 1.61073 to 1.62548 GHz	PSK
Inmarsat	11	Geosynchronous	Uplink: 1.6265 to 1.6605 GHz Downlink: 1.525 to 1.559 GHz	PSK
Iridium	66	Low Orbit	Uplink: 29.1 to 29.3 GHz Downlink: 19.4 to 19.6 GHz	PSK

Table 4-5-1. Satellite service providers providing both uplink and downlink service.

Figure 4-5-2. Satellite communication relay.

Frequencies	Band
0.225 - 0.390 GHz	P
0.350 - 0.530 GHz	J
1.53 - 2.7 GHz	L
2.5 - 2.7 GHz	S
3.4 - 6.425 GHz	C
10.95 - 14.5 GHz	Ku
17.7 - 21.2 GHz	Kc
27.5 - 31 GHz	K
36 - 46 GHz	Q
46 - 56 GHz	V
56 - 100 GHz	W

Table 4-5-2. Frequencies used for satellite communication.

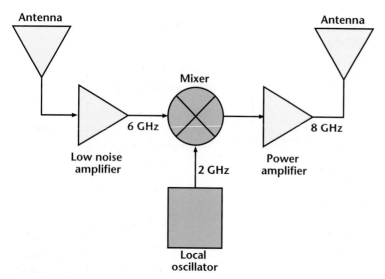

Figure 4-5-3. Block diagram of a simplified satellite transponder.

is known as a downlink. Examples of frequencies in the UHF, SHF, and EHF bands used by satellite providers are provided in Table 4-5-2.

Satellite Communication Segments

Satellite communication systems are divided into segments. The space segment consists of the satellites themselves. The control segment consists of the personnel and equipment required to communicate with and control the satellites. The user segment includes those using the satellites for communication purposes.

The services provided, airborne components, and coverage areas of satellite communication systems, vary by manufacturer. Signals traveling from aircraft or ground stations to the satellite are referred to as uplinks. Signals travelling from the satellites to ground stations or aircraft are referred to as downlinks. Satellites also communicate with each other, and these transmissions are referred to as intersatellite links.

A common method of relaying information from an aircraft or ground station to a space vehicle and back is to use a satellite transponder. Shown in Figure 4-5-3, a satellite transponder consists of a low noise amplifier, mixer, local oscillator, and power amplifier. Decoders and encoders, which are designed to prevent unauthorized transponder use, are not shown in the simplified diagram.

The low noise amplifier receives the uplink and provides the signal to the mixer. The mixer also receives a local oscillator input. The incoming signal is heterodyned to create a new frequency, which is provided to the power amplifier. The power amplifier sends the signal back to earth via the transmitting antenna.

Signals sent to the satellite transponder are multiplexed. *Multiplex* is a method of dividing several simultaneous signals into small pieces, which can be transmitted on a single channel. At the receiving end of the system, the signals are extracted, or demultiplexed, and rebuilt into separate signals, as shown in Figure 4-5-4.

A single satellite contains many transponders, each of which retransmits multiplexed signals. As a result, a single satellite can carry thousands of simultaneous communications.

Satellite Antennas

Engineers are able to design antenna systems that are known as phased array systems. These include an array, or group of antennas, that are connected together with phase shift networks. By controlling the phase of the radio frequency signals received from or transmitted to the array, the engineers are able to control the shape and direction of the radiation pattern or reception/transmission pattern, as shown in Figure 4-5-5. Phased arrays exhibit high gain and directionality. Furthermore, by controlling the phase shift networks, the pattern can be changed without the need to physically move or re-aim the antennas. Phased array antennas are used on many systems including SATCOM, cell phones, and radar.

Globalstar

Globalstar, a low-earth orbit satellite constellation for satellite phone and low-speed communications, operates 44 satellites. Globalstar refers to uplinks as forward links, and downlinks as reverse links. Information flow is approximately 9.6 kB, which is adequate for voice and some forms of data. Using phase shift keying, Globalstar uplinks on frequencies between 2.48439 GHz and 2.49915 GHz. Globalstar downlinks between 1.61073 GHz and 1.62548 GHz.

The satellites provide signal coverage for voice services for most of the northern hemisphere. Globalstar also offers internet and private network connections, position location, and short message service (SMS), which is more commonly known as texting. The system covers most continental areas of the earth for data services.

At minimum, the Globalstar system on board the aircraft consists of a transceiver, antenna, and control panel or handset. The control panel connects between the flight crew audio system and the transceiver. Data terminal devices are available with integrated GPS receivers that provide position information and connections to computers and printers. An external block diagram of a Globalstar system is shown in Figure 4-5-6.

Inmarsat

Inmarsat, British satellite telecommunications company, operates 11 geosynchronous satellites. Information flow occurs at one of two speeds, depending on the antenna system in use. High gain antennas allow speeds up to 432 kbps. Intermediate gain antennas are capable of speeds up to 332 kbps. The coverage areas for Inmarsat communications are referred to as regions. The polar areas are not well covered. Each region has a name and abbreviation:

- Pacific Ocean Region (POR)
- Indian Ocean Region (IOR)

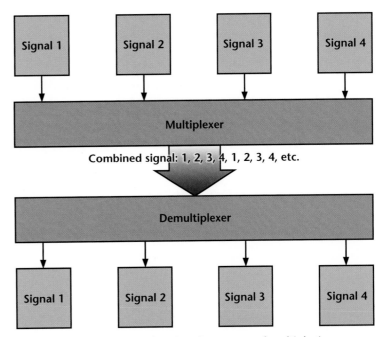

Figure 4-5-4. Block diagram showing the process of multiplexing.

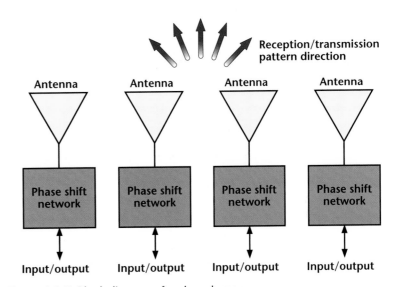

Figure 4-5-5. Block diagram of a phased array.

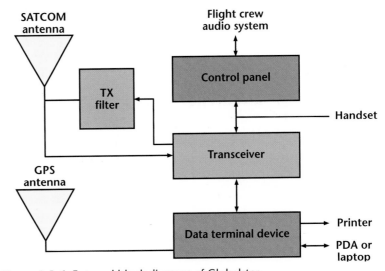

Figure 4-5-6. External block diagram of Globalstar.

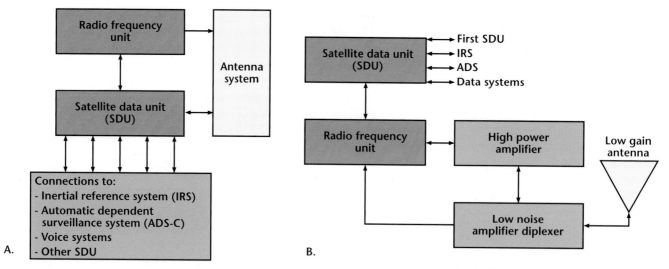

Figure 4-5-7. Simplified Inmarsat block diagram.

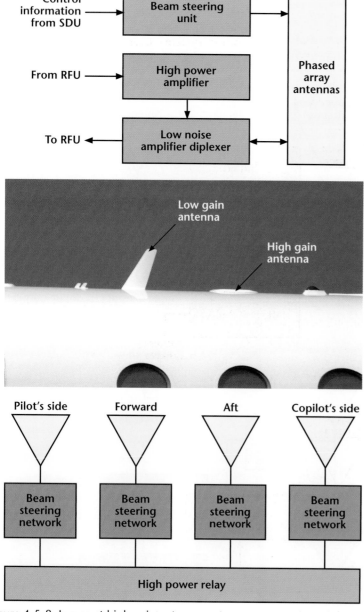

Figure 4-5-8. Inmarsat high gain antenna system.

- Atlantic Ocean Region West (AOR-W)

- Atlantic Ocean Region East (AOR-E)

Each region is larger than the name implies. For example, the AOR-W region covers all of the continental United States, most of Canada, all of Central America, all of South America, the entire Atlantic Ocean, most of Western Europe, and half of the African continent. In addition, the regions overlap. The AOR-E region covers the Atlantic Ocean, all of Africa, most of the Middle East, Europe, South America, Eastern Canada, and most of the Eastern U.S. In addition to the regions, Inmarsat covers certain areas with spot beams. A *spot beam* is concentrated energy directed toward a specific point on the earth using high gain directional antennas. Inmarsat satellites have the ability to focus the spot beams on specific areas to increase communication capacity.

Using phase shift keying, Inmarsat uplink frequencies range between 1.6265 GHz and 1.6605 GHz. Downlinks are between 1.525 GHz and 1.559 GHz.

Inmarsat provides satellite communication services for air transport and business aviation. Business and air transport crews may use Inmarsat for voice, flight planning, engine performance and fault monitoring, and for company business. Passengers can use Inmarsat for telephone, text, email, internet, and entertainment. Moreover, business passengers can video conference, transfer large data files, and connect to their own networks using a secure connection.

As shown in Figure 4-5-7, the Inmarsat system uses two satellite data units (SDU), two radio frequency units, and several other line replaceable units within a sophisticated antenna system, which itself contains several line replaceable units. The SDUs are connected with the inertial reference system (IRS), the automated dependent surveillance system (ADS-C), and

Terrestrial gateways	
Uplinks	29.1 GHz to 29.3 GHz
Downlinks	19.4 GHz to 19.6 GHz
Other frequencies	
Intersatellite links	22.55 GHz to 23.55 GHz
Ground-based users	1.616 GHz to 1.6265 GHz

Table 4-5-3. Inmarsat frequencies.

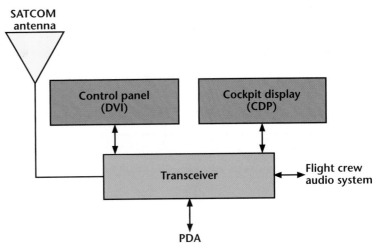

Figure 4-5-9. An external block diagram of an Iridium SATCOM system.

the audio systems. The IRS connection allows Inmarsat to determine aircraft location in order to control the radiation/reception pattern using the phased array.

The Inmarsat antenna system is quite complex. The system includes a beam steering unit to control a group of phased array antennas, a high power amplifier for transmitting, and a low noise amplifier with diplexer to allow transmitted power to travel to the antennas while allowing received energy to couple to the receiver.

As shown in Figure 4-5-8, the antenna system includes a low gain antenna, used for low speed data, and a group of phased array antennas, which support high speed voice and data.

Iridium

Iridium is a United States-based company that operates 66 satellites in low earth orbit—the world's largest commercial constellation. This cross-linked satellite network is used for worldwide voice and data communication from hand-held devices and installed communication systems. Each satellite has a 100-minute orbital period and can handle 1,100 phone calls. Information flow is 2.4 kbps. Iridium covers the world, including the polar regions. Using phase shift keying, Iridium uplink frequencies range from 29.1 GHz to 29.3 GHz , and the downlink frequencies range from 19.4 to 19.6 GHz. Services provided by Iridium include data, SMS, locator beacons, and short burst data (SBD), which is used for tracking, monitoring, or flight following. Uplinks, downlinks, and other frequencies used by Iridium are shown in Table 4-5-3.

An Iridium system may be as simple as a hand-held phone, similar to a cell phone, or as complex as a remote mounted transceiver that is

integrated into the aircraft's avionics system. For example, Aircell—another U.S.-based company that specializes in airborne communication technology for business-class aircraft—provides voice communication systems over the Iridium Satellite Network. Figure 4-5-9 shows one version of an Iridium SATCOM system. Iridium antennas are small in size and omnidirectional.

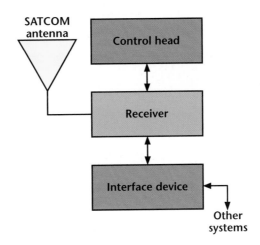

Figure 4-5-10. XM satellite system.

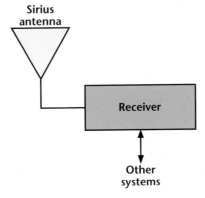

Figure 4-5-11. A remote mounted Sirius system.

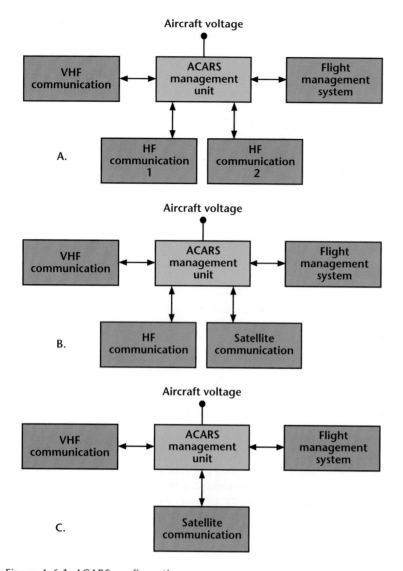

Figure 4-6-1. ACARS configurations.

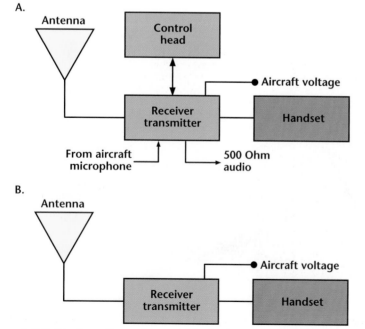

Figure 4-6-2. Configurations of terrestrial telephone systems.

Sirius/XM

Sirius is a downlink only, satellite broadcasting system. Sirius purchased another satellite broadcasting system, XM, in 2008. At this writing, although owned by a single company, two systems are in use. Both provide more than 100 channels of music, news, weather, television, internet, and sports. Both systems use multiplexed phased shift keying to modulate the carrier waves.

The XM system uses two geostationary satellites supplemented by ground based repeater stations located throughout the United States. Receivers can accept signals from the repeater stations and satellites simultaneously. The XM system broadcasts several carrier waves between 2.3325 GHz and 2.345 GHz.

Aircraft receivers capable of displaying XM weather may be hand held, integrated into another system, or stand alone with an interface to other avionics systems, as shown in Figure 4-5-10.

The main Sirius system uses three satellites in elliptical orbits and one geostationary satellite. The orbital period and inclination of the nongeostationary satellites are designed to allow the space vehicles to trace an apparent figure eight pattern for 16 hours during each orbit. Like the XM system, the Sirius system is supplemented with ground based repeaters. The receivers can accept signals from the repeater stations and satellites simultaneously. Sirius broadcasts between 2.32 GHz and 2.335 GHz.

Sirius systems may be part of a larger avionics system or stand alone. A block diagram of a remote-mounted Sirius system is shown in Figure 4-5-11.

Section 6

Communication Systems

The topics discussed in this section are referenced under ATA code 23-20.

Aircraft Communications Addressing and Reporting System

The Aircraft Communication Addressing and Reporting System, known as ACARS, is used to send short digital messages automatically. ACARS can be used to send aircraft condition and phase of flight reports to dispatchers. Phase of flight reports are commonly known as OOOI (pronounced *oohwee),* which stands for out of gate, off ground, on ground, and in gate. Like satellite communication systems, the ACARS system requires a subscription to a service provider. On the aircraft ACARS is connected to a VHF communication system and to HF or satellite communication systems, as shown in Figure 4-6-1.

The flight crew uses the flight management system (FMS) to control the ACARS management unit. The ACARS management unit connects to multiple communication systems and sends or receives messages automatically. If an aircraft has three VHF communication systems and ACARS, then the flight crew typically will leave the No. 3 VHF COM system tuned to an ACARS frequency.

Terrestrial Telephone Systems

A terrestrial telephone system uses a direct radio link between the aircraft and the service provider through ground transceivers. As shown in Figure 4-6-2, the terrestrial telephone system has a remote-mounted transceiver connected to an antenna that is mounted on the bottom of the aircraft. Some systems are designed to integrate with the aircraft audio system and some are not. Some of the systems integrated into the aircraft audio system do not include handsets. Terrestrial telephone systems work in duplex mode. Some systems, such as the Aircell system and some *automatic ground receiver access systems* (AGRAS), are *full duplex,* meaning the system transmits and receives simultaneously. Some AGRAS are *half duplex,* which means they still use two frequencies, but the user must push a PTT switch to transmit.

Terrestrial telephone systems work in a manner similar to cell phones. The AGRAS is an evolution of the mobile telephone system operated by Bell Telephone. AGRAS uses dual tone modulating frequencies (DTMF), commonly known as touch tones, to allow direct dialing from the aircraft through the service provider to the other party.

The Aircell system is an evolution of the cellular telephone system and uses many of the same radio towers. Aircell allows direct dialing in both directions between the service provider and the other party. Frequencies and modes of operation for both AGRAS and Aircell are shown in Table 4-6-1.

Flight Line Testing

The technician must always use the maintenance or installation manual as a guide to flight line test. The most common way to flight

System	Frequencies	Mode of operation
AGRAS	Ground-to-Air: 454.625 MHz - 454.925 MHz Air-to-Ground: 459.625 MHz - 459.925 MHz	FM
Aircell	824 MHz - 894 MHz	FSK

Table 4-6-1. Terrestrial telephone systems.

line test a communication system is to make contact with another transceiver. Many repair facilities have a VHF transceiver set up to monitor a channel in the VHF communications band; therefore, one of the best methods to test VHF communications is to make contact with another technician using the repair shop radio. The technician who receives the transmission can report the strength and modulation quality of the signal. If a shop radio is not available, the technician may be able to contact an air traffic controller, however, controllers should not be contacted if the airport is busy, since traffic control and safety is a controller's primary job. Technicians should also keep in mind that air traffic controllers do not have technical training, so their reports may not be as exact as a fellow technician's report.

To test HF, satellite, and terrestrial telephone systems, the technician may contact another facility and get a radio report. When testing

Figure 4-6-3. The Aircell system provides an aircraft-based telephone system that connects with the ground-based phone network. *Courtesy of Aircell*

satellite and terrestrial telephone systems, a charge will be incurred when the call is made.

If possible, the technician should test both transmission and reception on more than one frequency. Furthermore, the technician must take the utmost care to ensure he or she is not using a channel or frequency that is already in use.

Table 4-6-2 contains a checklist for testing communications systems.

Section 7

Summary

Aviation communication systems started out as heavy radiotelegraph systems, which required an operator. As time passed, technology improved and air traffic increased so the

Figure 4-6-4. The Aircell handset is a compact unit that is mounted in the aircraft cabin for easy access during flight. *Courtesy of Aircell*

frequencies became higher, more channels became available, and transmission tolerances increased.

VHF communication systems are named for the part of the frequency spectrum that the channels occupy. The frequencies used by VHF communication systems are from 118.000 MHz to 136.99163 MHz and are divided into 2,280 channels. The carrier frequency may be offset from the frequency shown on the COM control. VHF communication antennas are of the Marconi-type and may be mounted on the top or bottom of the airframe. Engineers design VHF communication systems in a variety of ways, depending on the type of aircraft in which it will be used. Configurations may be panel mounted, remote mounted, or modularized.

The high frequency communication system allows pilots to communicate with controllers or their home base from thousands of miles away. The HF system operates on frequencies between 3 MHz and 30 MHz. Antennas for HF systems mounted in aircraft are not of sufficient length; therefore, antenna couplers are used to match the impedance of the antenna to the transceiver.

VHF and HF communication systems use squelch, which is the circuit used to turn off the audio when a signal is not being received. Aviation radios are designed to meet standards particular to the aviation industry.

Both VHF and HF communication systems may use SELCAL, which is an abbreviation for selective calling. SELCAL is a form of squelch operated by modulating tones.

Satellite communication describes communication in several forms using space vehicles to relay information either between aircraft or from an aircraft to a ground station. The satellite communication system requires a service provider.

The aircraft communication addressing and reporting system, known as ACARS, is used to send short, digital messages automatically. ACARS uses VHF COM and HF COM or VHF COM and SATCOM.

A terrestrial telephone system uses a direct radio link between the aircraft and the service provider through ground transceivers. Terrestrial telephone systems use antennas mounted on the bottom of the airframe.

The technician must always use the maintenance or installation manual as a guide for flight line testing. The most common way to flight line test a communication system is to make contact with another transceiver.

Test	Result	Pass	Fail	Not applicable
Reciever audio	Loud and clear			
Squelch	Eliminates noise on unused frequencies			
Transmitter	Carrier wave transmitted			
Modulation	Loud and clear			
Sidetone	Users voice heard while transmitting			
Channel control	Above tests pass on high, middle, and low frequencies			
All microphones	Above tests pass using all available microphones and microphone jacks			
Frequency memory	Unit retains last frequency used and frequencies stored in memory			

Table 4-6-2. Communications flight line testing checklist.

5

Aviation Dependent Navigation Systems

It will probably surprise no one to hear the statement that aircraft navigation is of extreme importance. Poor navigation performance, combined with pilot error, were the cause of many accidents in the past. Not being able do find a destination airport could lead to fuel starvation. Controlled flight into elevated terrain during night or weather flight operations was more common than one might think. The accuracy of modern navigation systems is crucial to safety in the aviation industry. Some say the quest for ever more accurate navigation methods is as old as humanity itself. In this modern age, we have a universally accepted coordinate system, plus several methods of very accurate navigation. This chapter examines the VHF, UHF, and even the LF/MF navigation systems. An avionics technician working in the field today must be familiar with them all. The topics discussed in this chapter are referenced under ATA code 34.

Section 1

Navigation Concepts

There are many ways a pilot can navigate. Pilots may navigate visually, also known as visual flight rules, or VFR. Flying VFR is basically using an aeronautical chart to fly from one visual landmark to the next. Of course, visual navigation limits when and where a pilot can fly. Today there are a variety of electronic navigation systems that operate in the VHF and UHF portions of the radio frequency spectrum. These systems allow aircraft to fly in nearly all kinds of weather and virtually anywhere with precision.

Learning Objectives

DESCRIBE
- VHF omnirange system theory
- Localizer system theory
- Distance measuring equipment theory
- Glideslope system theory
- Marker beacon system theory
- Area navigation systems types and theory
- Global navigation satellite system theory
- Automatic direction finder theory
- Instruments used for navigation
- Ramp test equipment

EXPLAIN
- Global coordinate system
- Difference between heading and course

Left: Dependent navigation systems rely on external signals to guide the aircraft safely. This moving map display shows an approach path to a runway.

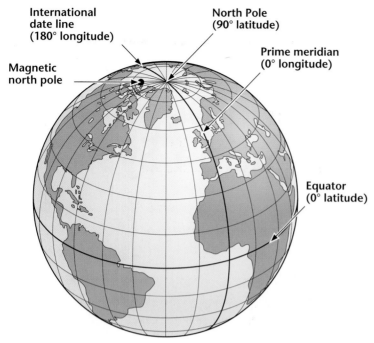

Figure 5-1-1. The global coordinate system.

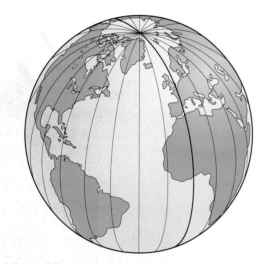

Figure 5-1-2. Meridians used for east and west measurement.

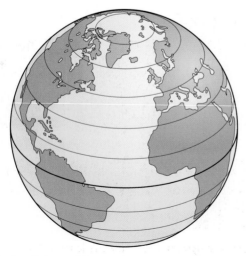

Figure 5-1-3. Parallels used for north and south measurement.

Any form of navigation system requires reference and coordinate points. Many aviation navigation systems are referenced to the *magnetic north pole*, which is not located at the true North Pole around which the earth rotates. Referencing to magnetic north allows a pilot to coordinate the electronic navigation system with the magnetic compass on board the aircraft. The magnetic north pole moves from year to year as the earth's core changes. As a result, electronic systems using magnetic north as a reference must be recalibrated from time to time.

Global navigation systems may reference both magnetic north and the true North Pole. These systems use a *global coordinate system* of latitude, longitude, and altitude. Figure 5-1-1 shows the earth with true and magnetic north marked, along with the equator, prime meridian and the international date line.

Lines of longitude are also known as *meridians*. Meridians circle the earth in a north and south direction (Figure 5-1-2) and converge at the North and South poles. When looking at an aeronautical chart, meridians are marked by lines running vertically. The prime meridian is the *datum*, or reference, for east and west navigation. In other words, the prime meridian is the starting point, or zero degrees, for east and west measurements. The meridian, which passes through the Royal Greenwich Observatory in Greenwich, England, was established as the prime meridian by treaty in 1884.

Meridians are measured in degrees, minutes, and seconds. Many systems are measured in degrees, minutes, and tenths of minutes. The distance between each degree is 60 nautical miles, or 69.047 statute miles. The international date line is on the opposite side of the globe from the prime meridian; therefore it is 180° from the prime meridian.

Lines of latitude are also known as *parallels*. Parallels circle the earth in an east and west direction (Figure 5-1-3). When looking at an aeronautical chart, parallels are marked by lines running horizontally. The equator is the 0° datum for parallels, which are also measured in degrees. Each pole is located at 90° of latitude. Like meridians, parallels are measured in degrees, minutes, and seconds. The distance between each degree at the equator is 60 nautical miles, or 69.047 statute miles. The distance between each degree north or south of the equator decreases until the distance is 0.0 at the poles.

The third coordinate is altitude, which can be referenced to *mean sea level* (MSL) or the ground. MSL is the most common reference used by aircraft and is defined as the average height of the ocean's surface. Aeronautical charts show airport and hazard elevations in altitude MSL.

The height *above ground level* (AGL) is less useful for most aircraft applications, since the altitude above the ground can vary greatly and rapidly as aircraft fly over mountains and valleys. Figure 5-1-4 illustrates the relationship between MSL and AGL.

Any point on or above the earth can be referenced using this coordinate system. Latitude is normally given first, followed by longitude then altitude. For example, the Wright brothers made their first flight at Kill Devil Hills near Kitty Hawk, North Carolina. The coordinates are 36° 00m 51s N, 75° 40m 4.7s W, and 20 ft. MSL.

Heading and Course

Heading is defined as the compass direction in which the aircraft is pointed. This means heading is in reference to magnetic north. Pilots calculate and fly headings that take them to their destination. Air traffic controllers may also assign headings for pilots to fly to aid in navigation, traffic, or terrain avoidance, to name a few reasons. Heading can be shown on a variety of instruments. Figure 5-1-5 shows some of the instruments used

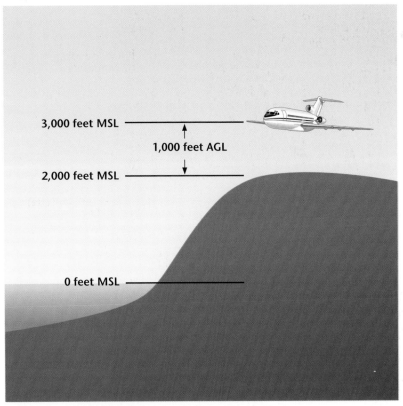

Figure 5-1-4. Altitude MSL and AGL.

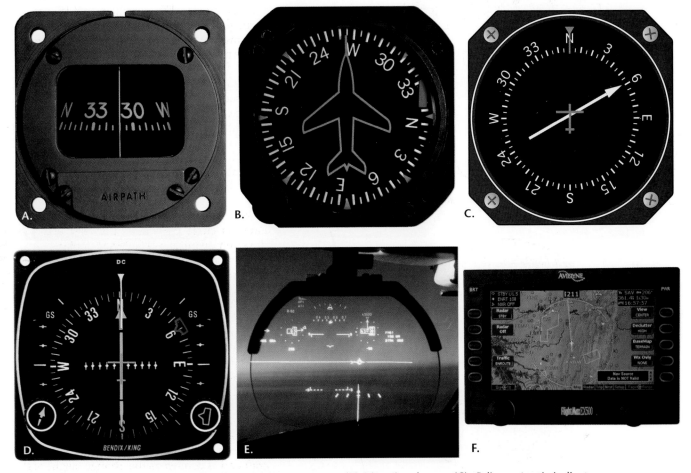

Figure 5-1-5. Instruments that show heading: (A) Wet compass, (B) Directional gyro, (C) rRdio magnetic indicator, (D) Horizontal situation indicator, (E) Heads up display, (F) Electronic navigation display.

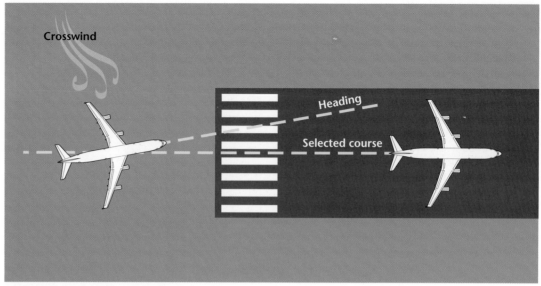

Figure 5-1-6. Heading and course.

to show heading. In most cases, heading is read at the top of the instrument under the *lubber line*. The lubber line is a vertical, fixed line under which the heading will be shown. North is represented by either 360° or 0°, east is 90°, south is 180° and west is 270°. Typically, for headings in between north, south, east,

and west, the least significant digit is eliminated. Thus, 30° is shown as 3°, 210° is shown as 21°, 300° is shown as 30°, and so on.

Course is defined as a path over which the aircraft flies. Courses are most often referenced to magnetic north, but some navigation systems

Figure 5-1-7. Instruments that show course: (A) Course directing indicator, (B) Radio magnetic indicator, (C) Horizontal situation indicator, (D) Heads up display, (E) Electronic navigation display.

Figure 5-2-1. VOR station.

can be set to reference to true north or the North Pole. As shown in Figure 5-1-6, at any given point during a flight, there may be a difference between heading and course. A crosswind tends to push an aircraft off course, for example. The pilot adjusts his or her heading to compensate for the crosswind.

Course can be shown on a variety of instruments. Figure 5-1-7 shows some of the instruments used to show course. Throughout this chapter, references are made to coordinates, heading, and course. Technicians need to understand how to use coordinates and the differences between the various types of references. Like instruments indicating heading, course instruments also eliminate the least significant digit on the display; however, unlike heading instruments, course can be shown in a variety of ways. The various ways of reading course are discussed later in the chapter.

Section 2

VHF Navigation

The topics discussed in this section are referenced under ATA code 34-50. The aviation industry uses the VHF portion of the radio frequency spectrum for three types of navigation systems. Included in the VHF portion are the VHF omnirange, localizer, and marker beacon systems.

VHF Omnirange

VHF Omnirange (VOR) is a navigation system used to guide aircraft flying cross country.

The word *range* has many definitions. Several definitions involve alignment, passing through an area and direction. These definitions may explain why the original aeronautical navigation stations were called range stations. Early navigation systems operated on medium and low frequencies and had no more than four courses.

After the Second World War, electronic navigation was improved by moving the frequencies to the VHF range and by adding an infinite number of courses. Moving the system to VHF removed noise problems associated with the low and medium frequency bands. The addition of courses to the system made the stations much easier to find and navigate by. As a result, the new system was called very high frequency omnidirectional range stations. These stations can also be described as VHF omnirange, omni, or are most commonly known today as VOR stations.

VOR Signals

The VOR system radiates RF on frequencies from 108.00 MHz to 117.95 MHz. This band of frequencies is divided into 200 50 kHz channels with 160 of those available for VOR. All channels from 112.00 MHz to 117.95 MHz can be used for VOR. Below 112.00 MHz, VOR may only use channels with an even number or 0 in the 100 kHz position. For example, 108.00 MHz and 108.05 MHz are VOR channels but 108.10 MHz and 108.15 MHz are not.

The VOR ground station, as shown in Figure 5-2-1, transmits an amplitude modulated signal, which is radiated from an array of antennas. The signal is fed to the antennas in such a way that the radiation pattern is rotated elec-

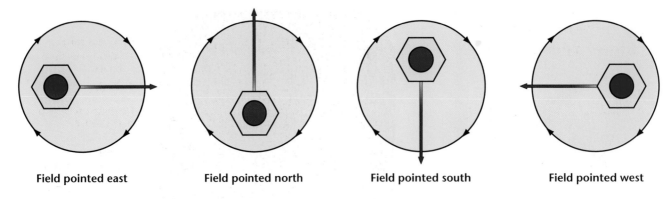

Field pointed east   Field pointed north   Field pointed south   Field pointed west

Figure 5-2-2. VOR signal rotation.

tronically, as illustrated in Figure 5-2-2. The rotation rate is 1,800 r.p.m.

The system on board the aircraft in Figure 5-2-2 receives a signal with a constantly changing strength. When the field is pointed east, the signal is the strongest. When the field is

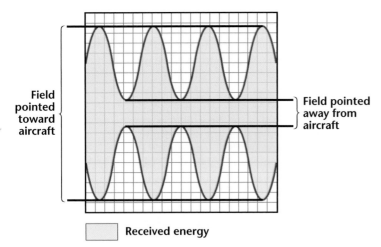

Figure 5-2-3. Received energy from a VOR station.

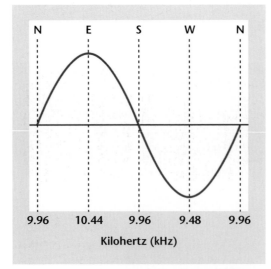

Figure 5-2-4. VOR reference signal frequencies are synchronized with field rotation.

pointed west, the signal is the weakest. Since the field is rotating at 1,800 r.p.m., this signal variation repeats 30 times each second. As shown in Figure 5-2-3, the constantly rotating field presents the appearance of an amplitude modulated envelope.

A navigation receiver on board the aircraft receives this energy and demodulates it, which will result in a 30 Hz sine wave. This 30 Hz sine wave is called the *variable signal*, since it is derived from the varying energy radiated from the VOR station.

The key to navigating using the VOR is for the system on the aircraft to sense where the energy from the transmitter is pointed. In doing so, the system is able to determine the direction of the aircraft in relation to the VOR station. To allow the aircraft system to determine where the field is pointed, the transmitted signal is amplitude modulated with a *reference signal* of varying frequency centered on 9.96 kHz. This frequency deviates from the 9.96 kHz center frequency by 480 Hz. In other words, the reference signal is constantly varying from 9.48 kHz to 10.44 kHz. The rate of variation is 30 Hz. Put yet another way, 9.96 kHz is frequency modulated with 30 Hz. Thus, the 9,960 Hz reference is considered a subcarrier. In the field, this signal is referred to as the 9,960 Hz reference signal, or simply the reference signal. The variation of the reference signal is synchronized with the rotating radio frequency. After reception, the equipment on the aircraft uses the reference signal to determine where the field is strongest and then derive the aircraft position. As Figure 5-2-4 shows, the reference frequency is highest when the field is directed east and lowest when the field is directed west.

VOR Navigation

VOR stations are located throughout the world. All are aligned with magnetic north and, on aeronautical charts, are illustrated by a hexagon with a circle in the middle, as shown if Figure

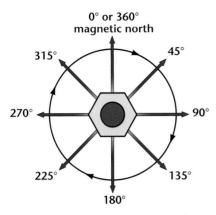

Figure 5-2-5. VOR station showing radials every 45°.

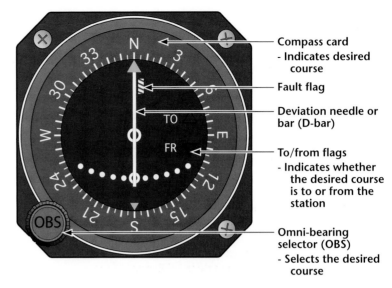

Figure 5-2-6. Course directing indicator.

5-2-5. In the United States, there are three different types of VOR stations with three different *service volumes*. The service volume is the amount of airspace served by a VOR station. *Terminal VOR stations* serve the smallest volume of airspace. Located at airports, terminal VOR stations serve aircraft out to 25 nautical miles and from 1,000 feet AGL up to 12,000 feet AGL. *Low altitude VOR stations* serve aircraft out to 40 nautical miles and from 1,000 feet AGL up to 18,000 feet AGL. Serving the greatest amount of airspace are the *high altitude VOR stations*. The high altitude stations serve aircraft out to 130 nautical miles at altitudes of 45,000 feet AGL.

There are site-related limitations to navigating with VOR. Mountains and buildings can cause signal reflections and distortions, which will create D-bar oscillations, commonly referred to as *scalloping*. Before a VOR station is installed, the site is carefully surveyed to ensure adequate service volume and lack of signal-distorting terrain features. At some locations, the VOR may not work below a certain altitude due to terrain or other obstructions, which is noted on the aeronautical chart.

Radials are imaginary lines on the ground that radiate in all directions from a VOR station. Certain radials are marked on aeronautical charts as airways. The first airway stretched from New York City to Chicago. Today there are low en route airways, which are below 18,000 feet MSL, and high en route airways, which are above 18,000 feet MSL, covering the world. Navigation using a VOR requires familiarization with various VOR indicators on board today's aircraft. Figure 5-2-6 shows a *course directing indicator* (CDI), which allows pilots to select and determine their aircraft's relationship to a course.

The pilot uses the omni bearing selector (OBS) to choose a course. As the pilot rotates the OBS knob, the compass card turns. In most CDIs, the lubber line is located at the top and shows the selected course. In Figure 5-2-7, the selected

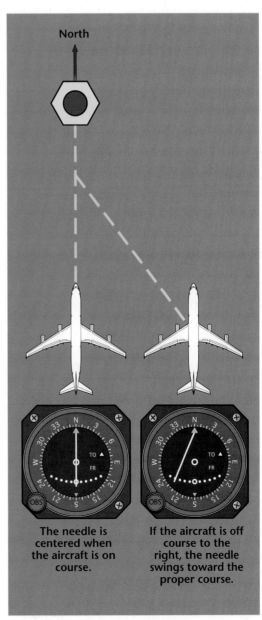

Figure 5-2-7. CDI D-bar operation.

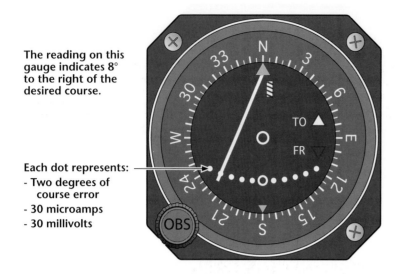

The reading on this gauge indicates 8° to the right of the desired course.

Each dot represents:
- Two degrees of course error
- 30 microamps
- 30 millivolts

Figure 5-2-8. Standard markings and indications on a CDI.

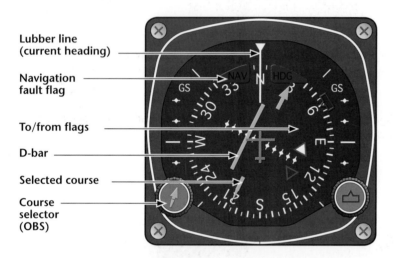

Lubber line (current heading)

Navigation fault flag

To/from flags

D-bar

Selected course

Course selector (OBS)

Figure 5-2-9. Horizontal situation indicator showing navigation and heading faults: a heading of 175°, a selected course of 205°, 3° to the right of course and flying toward the station.

Figure 5-2-10. RMI indicating a heading of 0° and a bearing to the VOR station of 60°.

course is north. The CDI also contains a flag to indicate whether or not the signal being used is valid. If the flag is in view, then the pilot should not trust the indicator or use it to navigate. The CDI also contains a to/from indicator, which, in Figure 5-2-6, is combined with the flag. The to/from indicator tells the pilot whether the desired course leads toward (to) or away (from) the VOR station. The deviation needle, or D-bar, is normally hinged at the top and indicates whether the desired course is to the right or to the left, as shown in Figure 5-2-7.

Most CDIs are constructed to ARINC standards. The meter has a load resistance of 1 kΩ, and each dot represents 30 μA and two degrees of course error, as shown in Figure 5-2-8. Since the load resistance is 1 kΩ, using Ohm's law, it can be found that each dot also represents 30 mV.

VOR information can also be presented on a *horizontal situation indicator* (HSI), also known as a pictorial navigation indicator (PNI). An HSI combines heading information and course deviation information on a single indicator, as shown in Figure 5-2-9.

The method used to present information on an HSI is very popular among pilots. In fact, the method is so popular, electronic flight instruments use variations of the same presentation method.

One of the earliest ways to indicate VOR bearings was a radio magnetic indicator (RMI) as shown in Figure 5-2-10. The *radio magnetic indicator* shows heading on the compass card and shows bearing to the VOR station with the needle. Still popular as a secondary instrument, some RMIs have dual needles and are connected to multiple navigation systems.

It is important to remember the OBS selects the desired course. The VOR system cannot determine the heading of the aircraft. It can only determine the desired course and whether the aircraft is right, left, or directly on the course selected. In a sense, the indicator is making an if/then logical statement to the pilot, as shown in Figure 5-2-11.

The key is the phrase, "If you turn the aircraft." If the pilot does not turn the aircraft or calculate in his or her head—the relationship between the current heading and the desired course—then the CDI does not give a meaningful indication.

The pilot must determine a proper intercept heading and not simply turn left when the indicator swings to the left. In Figure 5-2-12

If the aircraft is turned to the indicated heading of 300° on the compass card, then the course will be on the left and the station to the rear.

If the aircraft is turned to the indicated heading of 60° on the compass card, then the course will be on the right and the station to the front.

Figure 5-2-11. The IF/THEN statement with examples.

the pilot must turn the airplane to a heading of 330° in order to intercept the 0° radial. If the pilot merely turns left, then he or she will fly in circles. At all times during the maneuver, the needle should point toward the left side of the instrument.

Another concept is to divide the world into quadrants based on the VOR station in use, as shown in Figure 5-2-13. In this case, each quadrant represents a particular indication. The quadrants rotate as the OBS is turned. In the bottom half of the figure, the OBS has been set to 300°. This rotates the quadrant counter clockwise.

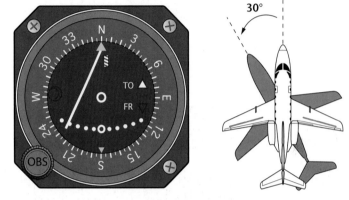

Figure 5-2-12. An intercept course of 330° will lead the airplane to the desired course.

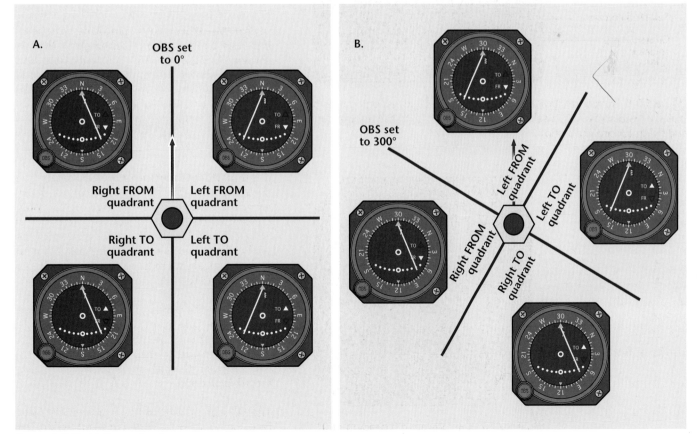

Figure 5-2-13. VOR quadrants.

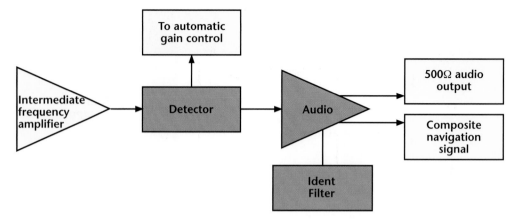

Figure 5-2-14. Detector, audio, and ident filter sections of a NAV receiver.

Figure 5-2-15. Navigation receiver (NAVCOMM).

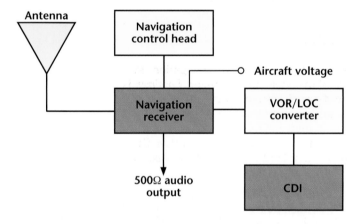

Figure 5-2-16. Generic remote mounted VHF navigation system.

VHF Navigation Receivers

Navigation receivers are almost identical to the communication receivers described in the last chapter. The vast majority are super-heterodyne, using an SMO for a local oscillator. The key differences between a VHF COM receiver and a VHF navigation receiver are NAV receivers do not have squelch; they do have an extra output for the navigation signal and an ident filter, as shown in Figure 5-2-14.

In a VHF NAV receiver, the 500 Ω audio output is adjustable by a knob on the radio controls. The audio section also provides a navigation signal output, known as *composite*, which is at a fixed level, to be converted into a visual indication. The ARINC standard composite level is 0.5 V RMS in VOR mode. VOR stations are identified by a 1,020 Hz Morse code tone amplitude modulating the carrier. Some VOR stations transmit voice. The voice transmissions could be weather or airport information or even air traffic controller communications. The pilot can switch on the ident filter to reduce the 1,020 Hz Morse code, thus making the voice

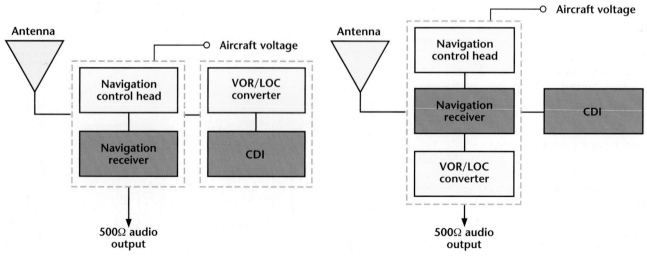

Figure 5-2-17. Panel-mounted VHF navigation systems.

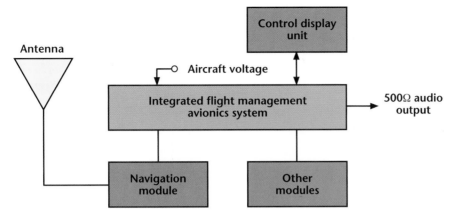

Figure 5-2-18. Modularized VHF navigation system.

transmissions more understandable. Figure 5-2-15 shows a navigation receiver on which the ident filter is controlled by pushing or pulling the volume control knob.

VHF Navigation Configurations

Engineers design VHF navigation systems in a variety of ways, depending on the type of aircraft in which the systems are used. Figure 5-2-16 shows a block diagram of what many refer to as a generic VHF navigation system. At the heart of the system is a receiver. In this system the receiver is mounted in an equipment bay with other avionics systems. Since the receiver is mounted away from the instrument panel, technicians often refer to this type of system as remote mounted. A wiring harness connects the receiver to a control head, which is mounted in the instrument panel. The control head contains channeling switches and displays, along with volume and ident controls. In some systems the pilot is able to store one or more frequencies in memory. The receiver has a 500 Ω audio output and a composite output to a VOR/LOC converter. A *VOR/LOC converter* converts the composite signal into information that can be displayed on a CDI, HSI, RMI, or electronic flight instrumentation system (EFIS). *Localizer*, or LOC, is a system used to guide aircraft to the runway and is described later in this chapter. Often, the audio output is connected to the audio system in the aircraft.

On small aircraft, the receiver, converter, and control head are combined into a single instrument panel mounted housing, as the block diagram shows in Figure 5-2-17. In some cases, the receiver is combined with a VHF communication transceiver, contains a speaker amplifier, and may be connected to the aircraft speaker. In other cases, all parts of the system, including the indicator, are combined into a single, panel-mounted unit.

Many large aircraft use an integrated flight management system that includes both navigation and communication functions. As the block diagram in Figure 5-2-18 shows, this system has modules connected to a common power supply and data buses. Of the many modules in the system, two or more are VHF navigation modules. A system of this type does have a control head. Instead, control of the VHF navigation system is through an MCDU.

Localizer

The vast majority of VHF navigation systems combine VOR and localizer. *Localizer* is a ground-based system used to give aircraft horizontal guidance to a runway. This topic is referenced under ATA code 34-30. Localizer is part of an *instrument landing system* (ILS). The instrument landing system brings several

Figure 5-2-19. Localizer antenna array.

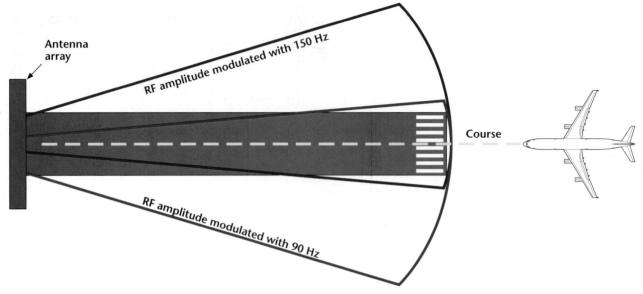

Figure 5-2-20. Localizer signals.

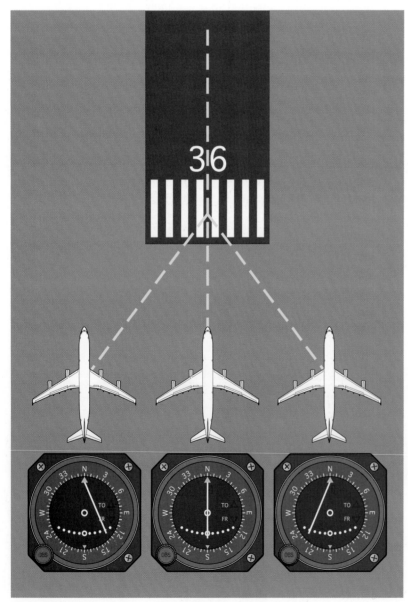

Figure 5-2-21. Navigating with localizer.

different navigation methods together to provide precise guidance as an aircraft approaches an airport. There are different categories of ILS. Starting with Category I, each category of ILS offers higher precision, which allows aircraft to descend lower before making visual contact with the runway. The most precise category is Category III, which is precise enough to allow landings under weather conditions with zero forward visibility.

Localizer uses the same receiver, converter, and indicator as the VOR system shown in Figures 5-2-17, 5-2-18, and 5-2-19, with the exception of the RMI, which cannot display localizer information. On localizer frequencies, the receiver sends an enable signal to the converter, which switches from VOR conversion to localizer conversion.

VHF navigation frequencies below 112.00 MHz with an odd number in the 100 kHz position are reserved for localizer use. There are 40 localizer channels available. For example, 108.10 MHz, 108.15 MHz, 108.30 MHz, and 108.35 MHz are localizer channels, and 108.00 MHz, 108.05 MHz, 108.20 MHz, and 108.25 MHz are for VOR use.

Figure 5-2-19 illustrates the radio shack and an array of antennas used to transmit the localizer signals. These antennas are placed at the opposite end of the runway from the intended landing direction.

The antenna array and transmitters radiate two signals, as shown in Figure 5-2-20. The signal on the right side of the runway is amplitude modulated with a 150 Hz tone. On the left, the signal is amplitude modulated with a 90 Hz tone. The receiver receives these signals simultaneously. The LOC converter measures the signals to determine which modulation is stronger.

If the 150 Hz tone is stronger, then the CDI D-bar moves to the left, indicating the aircraft is to the right of the course. If the 90 Hz tone is stronger, then the CDI D-bar moves to the right, indicating the aircraft is to the left of the course. If the tones are equal, then the D-bar centers, indicating the aircraft is above the extended runway centerline. Examples of indications are shown in Figure 5-2-21.

At certain airports, a *backcourse* approach is available. If the area behind the localizer antenna array is clear of obstructions and signal distortions, the FAA may publish an approach procedure that allows pilots to use the localizer from the opposite direction. This approach is known as a backcourse approach. In the case of a backcourse approach, the sensing needle is backwards, as shown in Figure 5-2-22. For example, a left pointing needle indicates the pilot is off course to the left and must steer to the right.

Since there is only one inbound course per runway, the localizer is designed for one course only. As a result, in localizer mode the OBS or course selector is not operative. Furthermore, there is no *to/from* displayed in localizer mode. Indicators with separate flag and to/from indicators remove the flag when the received signal is valid, but do not display *to* or *from*. Indicators with a combination to/from/fault flag display a *to* indication. In localizer mode, an indicator must never display a *from*. If *from* is displayed in localizer mode, there is a malfunction in the system.

Like the VOR system, localizer signals are adversely affected by tall buildings or mountains. The service volume for localizers is ±10° from the centerline out to 18 nautical miles and ±35° from the centerline out to 10 nautical miles.

Converters

The signal received by the navigation receiver tuned to a VOR station is quite complex. Once the RF is removed, the resulting composite signal contains several frequencies. The VOR composite has 30 Hz, plus the continuously changing 9,960 Hz reference frequency. On an oscilloscope, the signal appears as shown in Figure 5-2-23.

Converters are used to change the composite signal into voltages that can be displayed on an indicator. The basic idea for a converter is illustrated by the block diagram in Figure 5-2-24.

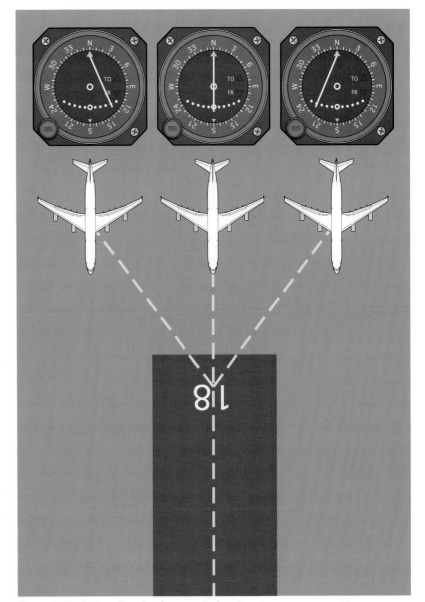

Figure 5-2-22. Localizer backcourse indications.

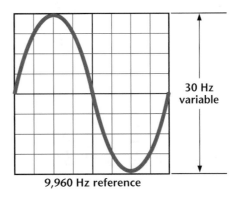

Figure 5-2-23. VOR composite signal.

VHF navigation composite signals always have two components. The converter has a separate channel that filters and amplifies each component. The outputs from these channels are sent to detectors and comparators to determine

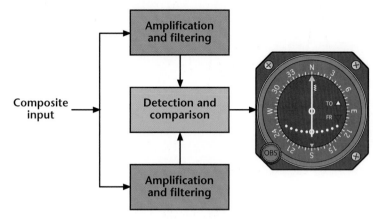

Figure 5-2-24. Basic converter block diagram.

validity or, in the case of VOR, to/from indications.

A generic VOR converter block diagram is shown in Figure 5-2-25. In this case, the variable amp simply filters in and amplifies 30 Hz. The other channel is more complex. The limiter eliminates the 30 Hz signal by limiting amplitude changes to the signal. The output of the limiter is the frequency modulating 9,960 Hz. The discriminator is used to extract the 30 Hz reference signal from the 9,960 Hz subcarrier.

Once the 30 Hz signal is extracted, it is fed to a resolver. The resolver is connected to the OBS knob. As the pilot turns the OBS, the resolver delays the signal, thereby introducing a phase change. The VOR station itself is referenced to magnetic north. The resolver allows the pilot to change the reference to any desired bearing. The resolver may be of the transformer type, or it may be a resistor network. Either way, the result is the same. Once the reference signal is

phase-changed, it is fed to an amplifier, which amplifies the 30 Hz signals.

The flag circuit is simply a detector. It detects the presence of both the reference 30 Hz and the variable 30 Hz. If one or both are present, then the circuit produces a DC voltage up to 300 mV, which is used to pull the fault flag from view.

The L/R circuit is a phase comparator. If the variable and reference signals are 90° apart, then the needle is centered. As signals vary from a 90° phase difference, the L/R circuit produces up to ±150 mV to drive the D-bar right or left. The polarity of the voltage depends on whether or not the variable signal leads or lags the reference signal.

The T/F circuit works almost identically to the L/R circuit; however, a 90° phase change is placed into the variable signal. As a result, maximum voltage is produced when the L/R circuit is producing 0 V. Again, the polarity of the T/F circuit output depends on whether the variable signal leads or lags the reference signal.

There are many approaches to VOR conversion. Some converters place the resolver circuit in the variable channel. Some convert the reference signal to a square wave, which drives a switching circuit. Still others digitize the output for use with digital indicators. Technicians are urged to read the theory of operation section of any VOR converter they intend to maintain.

Localizer uses the same basic two channel concept as the VOR converter; however, as Figure 5-2-26 shows, the localizer composite is quite different from the VOR composite. The localizer signal consists of the algebraic addition of 90 Hz and 150 Hz.

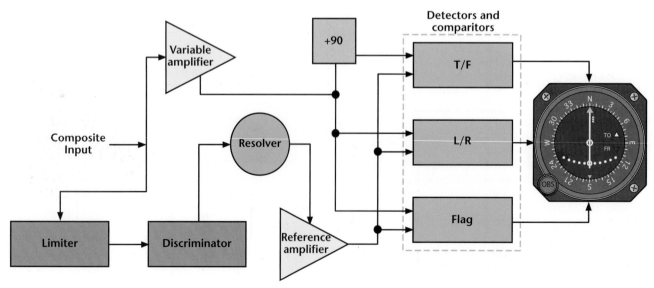

Figure 5-2-25. Block diagram of a generic VOR converter.

A localizer converter uses two filtering amplifiers, as shown in Figure 5-2-27. One amplifier is for 150 Hz, and the other is for 90 Hz. Once filtered and amplified, the signals are sent to the deviation drivers, which convert the signals to DC (±150 mV) in order to drive the D-bar. Outputs from the filtering amplifiers are also fed to the flag driver, which detects the presence of both signals. If both signals are present, then the flag driver will produce up to 300 mV to pull the fault flag out of view.

Like VOR converters, there are a variety of designs for localizer converters. Technicians are urged to read the theory of operation section of any VOR converter they intend to maintain. A common design uses electronic switches. In antique systems, relays are used to change the variable and reference amplifiers

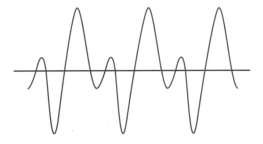

Figure 5-2-26. Localizer composite signal.

over to 90 Hz and 150 Hz and to alter the comparators, so they accurately measure the difference in modulation depth. In this way, the same components can be used for both VOR and LOC. Figure 5-2-28 shows a block diagram

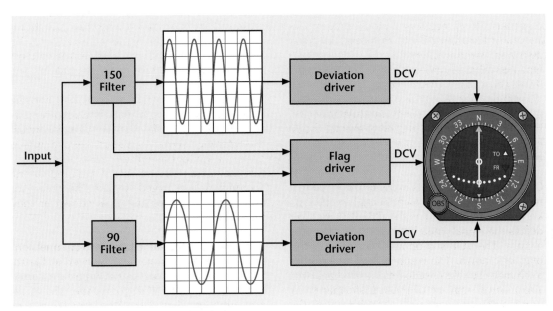

Figure 5-2-27. Localizer converter block diagram.

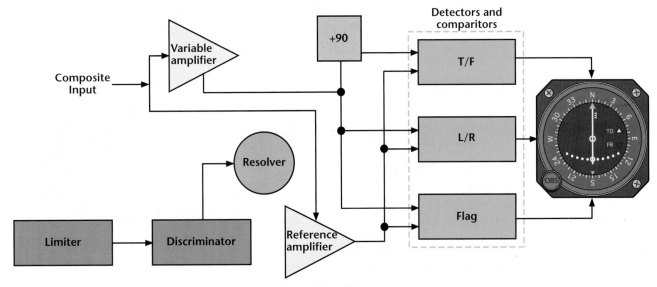

Figure 5-2-28. Block diagram of a VOR converter reconfigured for LOC conversion.

of a VOR converter reconfigured for LOC conversion. Note how the limiter, discriminator, and resolver are bypassed.

VOR and Localizer Antennas

Since VHF navigation systems do not transmit, they often share an antenna. The antenna is a Marconi type, and, in most cases, it is mounted on the vertical stabilizer. On small aircraft with simple VHF navigation systems, the antenna is likely to be constructed of stainless steel rods. On aircraft requiring better reception, the antenna may be a variation of the Marconi type known as a *balanced loop antenna*. On high speed aircraft a balanced loop antenna may look like two horizontal fins. Three types of VHF navigation antennas are shown in Figure 5-2-29.

Since these antennas are balanced and the transmission line leading to the navigation receivers is not, a *balun* is necessary. A balun is a transformer designed to match an unbalanced transmission line with a balanced antenna. Many antenna systems are designed with a built-in balun. Many of the simple stainless rod antennas require the technician to construct a balun in the field. FAA advisory circular 43.13-2B contains instructions on a field-built balun, as shown in Figure 5-2-30.

The advisory circular does not describe how to calculate wavelength (λ). To calculate wavelength use the formula described in Chapter 2 adjusted for the propagation velocity of the cable being used. First, choose a frequency in the middle of the VHF navigation band; 112.975 MHz is exactly in the middle. Next, multiply the speed of light constant by the velocity of propagation of the cable being used. Calculate wavelength for 112.975 MHz using the adjusted constant, then convert to inches. To calculate the balun length:

$$\frac{9.95 \text{ MHz}}{2} = 4.975 \text{ MHz}$$

Determine the middle of the band:

$$108.00 \text{ MHz} + 4.975 \text{ MHz} = 112.975 \text{ MHz}$$

Multiply the speed of light constant by the velocity factor:

$$300 \times 0.66 = 198$$

$$\frac{198}{112.975} = 1.7526$$

Wavelength = 1.7526 m

$$\frac{1.7526}{4} = 0.43815 \text{ m}$$

$^1/_4$ Wavelength = 0.43815 m

Convert to inches:

$$\text{meters} \times 0.0254 = \text{inches}$$

$$0.43815\text{m} \times 0.0254 = 17.25 \text{ in}$$

Since more than one receiver is connected to a single antenna, a device is needed to allow the receivers to share a single transmission line. Whenever two navigation receivers use the same antenna, a *duplexer*, also known as a splitter, similar to the one shown in Figure 5-2-31, is installed.

Flight Line Testing VHF Navigation Systems

Testing the VHF navigation system involves simulating a VOR or localizer ground station with a test generator, then manipulating the signals to test various outputs and indications.

The following is a generalization: technicians should always refer to the maintenance and installation manual when testing VHF navigation systems on the flight line. For flight line testing, the technician must use a signal generator with the output attenuator set for maximum signal output. Since the test may take

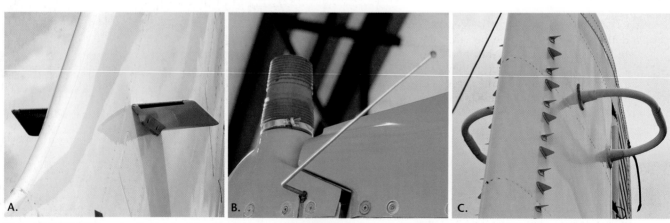

Figure 5-2-29. VHF navigation antennas: (A) Balanced blade, (B) Rabbit ears, (C) Balanced loop.

several minutes, the aircraft should be operated on external power to avoid running down the battery.

1. Application of power. Apply power and turn on the radio. This may involve turning on the aircraft master switch, the avionics master switch and, possibly, the radio itself.

2. Frequency notes. Take note of the frequencies. If they are both at the default setting, which will be noted in the maintenance manual (MM), then the system may have a memory problem. Otherwise, write the frequencies down and, upon conclusion of the test, set the radio back as you found it. The pilot will appreciate the effort.

3. Generator setting. Set the generator and the navigation receiver to the same, unused, radio frequency. Set the generator to produce an identifier 1,020 Hz tone.

4. Audio selection. Select the navigation radio you are testing on the audio panel.

5. Volume and identification filter testing. Turn off the ident filter and listen. Turn up the volume. The tone should be extremely loud with the volume up. Return the volume control to a comfortable listening level and turn the ident filter on and off. If the filter is working properly, then a significant difference in the tone volume should be heard.

6. Verification of reception on multiple frequencies. With the volume set at a comfortable level, adjust the generator and receiver to other navigation channels and verify that audio is received on those as well.

Next, you can move on to testing the VOR accuracy of the system. Accuracy can be checked every 30° at both to and from settings. Specifications for VOR accuracy are at least ±2°, and some systems have accuracy ratings of much less than ±2°.

7. Accuracy testing. Set both the generator and the OBS to the same bearing, and note the position of the D-bar and flags. The fault flag should be out of view, and the to/from indicator should agree with the generator setting. Take note of any errors. Repeat this test every 30°.

8. D-bar sensitivity testing. Verify that the D-bar sensitivity is correct by testing standard deflection, commonly known as course width. Standard deflection for VOR is 10° of error for five dots of D-bar deflection. To measure standard deflection, center the D-bar using the OBS, then

add 10° to the signal generator setting. The D-bar should move five dots. Repeat the test by subtracting 10° from the original generator setting for a centered D-bar. The D-bar should move five dots in the other direction. Make note of any discrepancies.

9. RMI accuracy testing. If the aircraft is equipped with an RMI, while testing the VOR accuracy watch the RMI as well. The

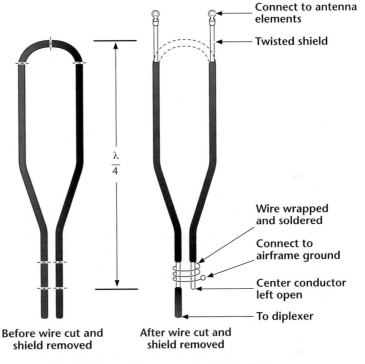

Figure 5-2-30. A balun may be constructed in the field.

Figure 5-2-31. Antenna duplexer or splitter.

VHF navigation flightline check					
Navigation receiver		#1	#2		
	Receiver audio			Aircraft make	
	Indent filter			Aircraft model	
	Proper channel control			Registration number	
	Low			Technician	
	Medium			Date	
	High			Battery condition	
Converter indicator					
VOR accuracy	From 0°				
	To 0°				
	From 30°				
	To 30°				
	From 60°				
	To 60°				
	From 90°				
	To 90°				
	From 120°				
	To 120°				
	From 150°				
	To 150°				
	From 180°				
	To 180°				
	From 210°				
	To 210°				
	From 240°				
	To 240°				
	From 270°				
	To 270°				
	From 300°				
	To 300°				
	Course Width				
	To/From				
Flag	60% Test				
	Invalid signal test				
RMI pointer					
	Accuracy				
Self-test					
	Operational				
Localizer					
	Centering				
	Course width				
Flag	60% Test				
	Invalid signal test				

Table 5-2-1. VHF navigation testing checklist.

RMI should also be accurate and, like most VORs, should be within ±2°.

10. Fault flag testing. There are two techniques for testing the fault flag. A thorough technician uses both methods.

   a. Flag with invalid signal. First, remove the reference modulation. The flag should show. Replace the reference modulation and remove the variable modulation. Again, the flag should show. The second technique verifies the flag will show properly when the signal strength is too weak to support proper D-bar operation.

   b. Flag with weak signal. To start the flag test using the second technique, set the generator and OBS to give five dots of deflection. Next, start reducing the radiated signal level. Eventually there is not enough energy being radiated from the generator to push the D-bar all the way out to the fifth dot. When the D-bar reaches 60 percent of five dots (three dots), the flag should show. Keep in mind the system is very unstable at these low signal levels. You should expect both the D-bar and the flag to be erratic.

Once the VOR test has been completed, test the localizer. Keep in mind, localizer accuracy is not measured in degrees. Furthermore, localizer modulation levels on most test boxes are shown in *difference in depth of modulation* (ddm). If the ddm is zero, then there is no difference between the 90 Hz and 150 Hz modulation levels, and the D-bar should be centered.

1. Accuracy testing. Set the generator to 0 ddm and note the position of the D-bar and flags. The fault flag should be out of view and the to/from indicator should read *to* or not show at all. A typical specification for localizer accuracy is +10 µA. On most indicators the width of the D-bar is about 10 µA; therefore, with the generator set to 0.0 ddm, the D-bar should be centered within a needle width.

2. D-bar sensitivity testing. Verify that the D-bar sensitivity is correct by testing standard deflection. For a ddm setting of 0.093, the D-bar should deflect 90 µA, or three dots. Test deflection in both directions and make note of any errors.

3. Fault flag testing. Like the VOR flag, the LOC flag can be tested two ways.

   a. Flag with invalid signal. First remove the 90 Hz modulation. The flag should show. Replace the 90 Hz modulation and remove the 150 Hz modulation. Again, the flag should show.

   b. Flag with weak signal. The technique for testing flag operation under low signal levels is nearly identical to the VOR flag test described above. This time, 60 percent of 90 µA is used, which is 54 µA, so the flag should appear as the needle falls between the first and second dot.

Some navigation systems have a self-test feature. If the system being tested is so equipped, press the self-test button and verify that the system behaves as described in the MM. Other systems have built-in test equipment, known as BITE. If the system is BITE equipped, the BITE tests should be included in the flight line test. BITE testing may involve the use of a laptop.

Many repair stations use a checklist like that shown in Table 5-2-1 when testing navigation

Figure 5-2-32. Marker transmitter site.

systems. The best way to fill out a checklist is to write down the actual values measured instead of marking items with a check mark or *X*.

Marker Beacon

The marker beacon system is used to mark specific points along the ILS approach path to a runway. The ground-based transmitters broadcast an amplitude modulated signal on 75 MHz. Figure 5-2-32 shows a marker transmitter site. Each marker point along the approach has a different name, modulating tone, and associated color. This topic is referenced under ATA code 34-30.

Farthest from the runway is the outer marker. Typically, the outer marker is located between four and seven miles from the landing end of the runway. The outer marker signal is modulated with a 400 Hz tone, which is turned on and off to emulate Morse code dashes. Approximately 3,500 feet from the landing end of the runway is the middle marker. The middle marker signal is modulated with a 1,300 Hz tone, which is turned on and off to emulate Morse code dots and dashes. Category II and Category III ILS systems use an inner marker. This transmitter is located approximately 1,000 feet along the landing end of the runway, close to where the aircraft is to touch down. The inner marker

Marker	Tone	Location	Color
Outer	400 Hz	4 - 7 miles	Blue
Middle	1,300 Hz	3,500 feet	Amber
Inner	3,000 Hz	1,000 feet from approach end of runway	White

Table 5-2-2 Marker beacon system details.

is modulated with a 3,000 Hz tone, which is turned on and off to emulate a rapid series of Morse code dots. Table 5-2-2 summarizes the location, modulating tone, and associated color of the marker system.

Marker Beacon Receivers

Most marker beacon receivers are of the super-heterodyne type, as shown in Figure 5-2-33; however, some utilize direct conversion receivers.

Typically, the RF section of a marker beacon receiver is a band pass filter with a switchable attenuator, which allows the pilot to reduce sensitivity. Low sensitivity allows the pilot to identify when the aircraft is exactly over the marker location. Since marker beacon receivers receive only one frequency, no stabilized master oscillator is necessary. The local oscillator is of the crystal-controlled type, as described in Chapter 1. The IF is AGC controlled. Most marker systems do not have a pilot adjustable volume control, and the 500 Ω audio is connected directly to the audio system. The audio section also provides a signal to a series of band pass filters. There is a filter for each light that feeds a light driver. The light drivers rectify the filtered audio and create voltage to illuminate the bulbs.

Marker Beacon Configurations

Engineers design marker beacon systems in a variety of ways, depending on the type of aircraft in which it will be used. Figure 5-2-34 shows a block diagram of what many refer to as a generic marker beacon system. At the heart of the system is a receiver. In this system the receiver is mounted in an equipment bay with other avionics systems. Since the receiver is mounted away from the instrument panel, technicians often refer to this type of system

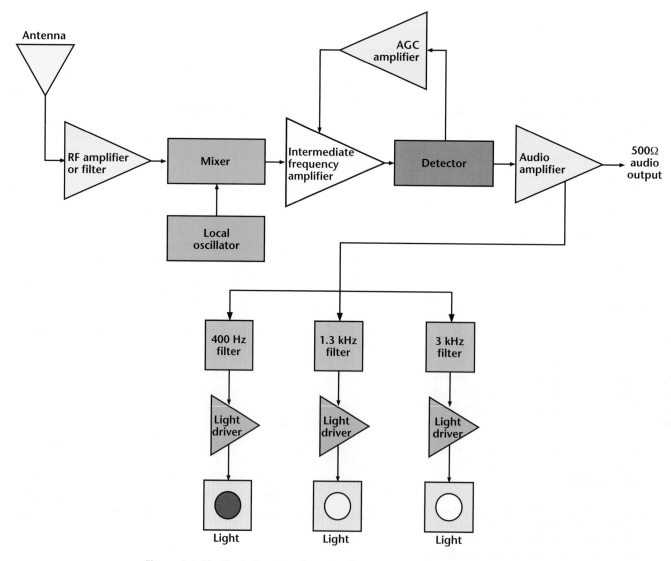

Figure 5-2-33. Block diagram of a super-heterodyne marker beacon receiver.

as remote mounted. A wiring harness connects the receiver to a light panel, which is mounted in the instrument panel. The light panel contains self-test and hi/low sensitivity switches. The receiver has a 500 Ω audio output and may include an auxiliary light output to drive a second set of lights.

The small size and simplicity of marker beacon receivers allow engineers to place a marker beacon system nearly anywhere. In small aircraft they are most often included as part of the audio system, as shown in Figure 5-2-35. Other manufacturers may include the marker receiver with the remote VOR/LOC receiver, converter, or within a glideslope receiver. Always check documentation to verify the location of the marker system components before planning any removal or replacement. An integrated avionics system includes a marker module, as shown in Figure 5-2-36.

Marker Beacon Antennas

Antennas for marker beacon system are of the Marconi type, modified to fit on the bottom of the airframe, as shown in Figure 5-2-37. On low speed aircraft a sled runner antenna may be used. The antenna is referred to as a sled runner because the stainless rod is bent back so it resembles a runner. A boat-style antenna, sometimes called a canoe-style antenna, encases the receiving element in a plastic case. Composite aircraft may have a flush mounted marker antenna integrated into the composite structure. A flush mounted antenna may have no recognizable components visible from the outside. On weather radar equipped aircraft, the antenna may be composed of a piece of coaxial cable stripped back to expose the center conductor and taped to the bottom of the radome.

Flight Line Testing Marker Beacons

To flight line test a marker beacon system, the technician needs to use a signal generator. Furthermore, to protect the aircraft battery, the aircraft should be operated on external power. As with other tests described in this textbook, the manufacturer's takes precedence.

1. Self test. Press the self-test button, often marked PTT, and verify that all three lights illuminate.

2. Lights with signal. The generator antenna must be placed close to the marker beacon antenna, typically within a foot. Set the generator for maximum signal output at 75 MHz. Modulate the carrier wave with

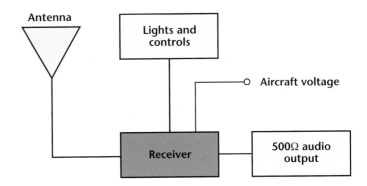

Figure 5-2-34. Generic marker beacon block diagram.

Figure 5-2-35. Marker beacon system included in an audio system.

Courtesy of Garmin

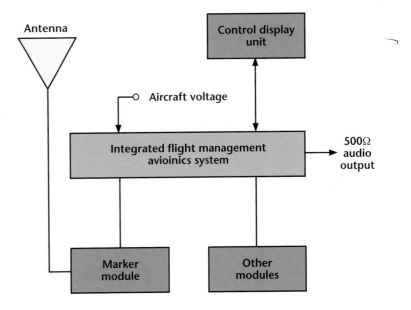

Figure 5-2-36. Marker module in an integrated flight management avionics system.

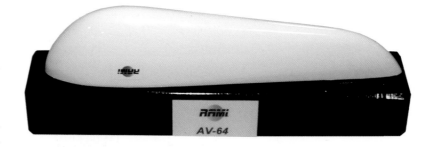

Figure 5-2-37. Marker beacon antenna.

Marker beacon	#1	#2
Receive audio		
Lights with ptt		
Lights with signal		
Hi/low sense		

Table 5-2-3. Flight line testing checklist with marker beacon section circled.

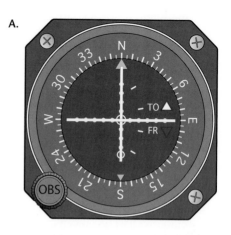
A.

each of the marker audio frequencies: 400 Hz, 1,300 Hz, and 3,000 Hz. Verify that the appropriate light illuminates and has the proper tone.

3. Audio with signal. Select *marker* on the audio system and listen to verify that the tones are heard.

4. Hi and low sensitivity. Reduce the signal level and note at what level the light goes out. Switch sensitivity modes and repeat. The light threshold in high sensitivity mode should be at a lower signal level than the light threshold in low sensitivity mode. A marker testing checklist is shown in Table 5-2-3. Technicians should always refer to the installation and MM when performing marker beacon tests.

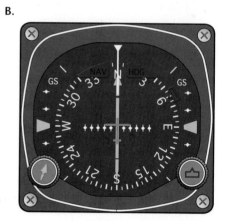
B.

Section 3

Glideslope

The glideslope system is another component of the ILS that provides vertical guidance to the end of the runway. These topics are discussed in this section are referenced under ATA code 34-30. Glideslope works in the UHF band and has 40 frequencies, each of which is assigned, paired, or collocated with a localizer frequency. The glideslope band ranges from 329.15 MHz to 335.0 MHz and has channels located every 150

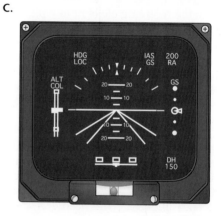
C.

Localizer VHF frequency	Glideslope UHF frequency
108.95 MHz	329.15 MHz
109.30 MHz	332.00 MHz
110.30 MHz	335.00 MHz

Table 5-3-1. Selected localizer and glideslope frequency pairings.

D.

Figure 5-3-1. Glideslope displays.

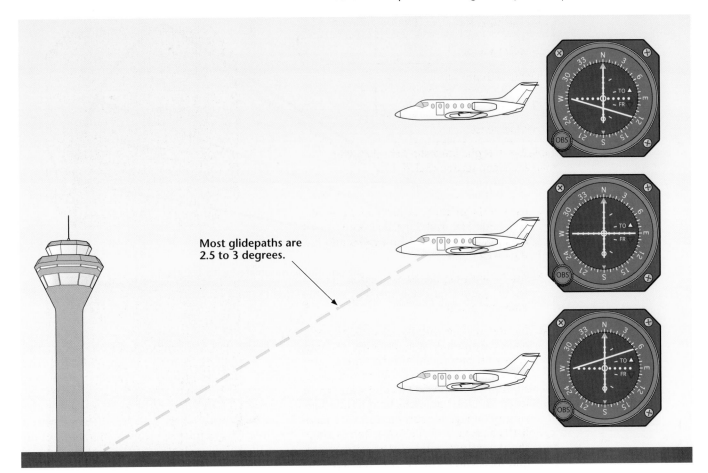

Most glidepaths are 2.5 to 3 degrees.

Figure 5-3-2. Glideslope indications.

kHz. An example of pairing is shown in Table 5-3-1.

Glideslope information can be presented on a dual-needle CDI, HSI, HUD, or EFIS screen, as shown in Figure 5-3-1. An RMI cannot display glideslope information.

The glideslope system guides the pilot along a 2.5° to 3.5° angled path descending toward the runway. If the aircraft is above the path, the needle moves downward. If the aircraft is on the proper glidepath, the needle is centered. Aircraft below the glidepath have the needle swung upward. An invalid or missing signal causes the glideslope fault flag to be displayed. An illustration of the glideslope indications is shown in Figure 5-3-2.

On the ground, the glideslope transmitter is connected to an array of antennas on a small tower alongside the runway, as shown in Figure 5-3-3.

These antennas radiate two signals, as shown in Figure 5-3-4. The signal on the lower side of the glidepath is amplitude modulated with a 150 Hz tone. Above the glidepath the signal is amplitude modulated with a 90 Hz tone. The receiver receives these signals simultaneously.

Figure 5-3-3. Glideslope ground station with antenna tower.

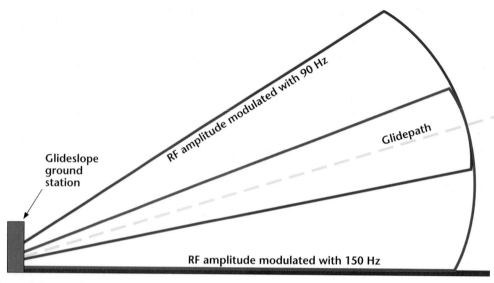

Figure 5-3-4. Radiated glideslope energy.

The glideslope converter within the receiver, measures which modulation is stronger.

Electronically, glideslope systems are quite similar to localizer systems. Many glideslope receivers are almost identical to the VHF navigation receivers described earlier in this chapter. The majority of glideslope receivers are super-heterodyne, using an stabilized master oscillator for a local oscillator, however, some are super-regenerative or super-regenerative/super-heterodyne hybrids. Glideslope receivers have neither an audio output nor their own control head—the key differences between a VHF NAV receiver and a glideslope receiver. In addition, glideslope receivers include a converter that is nearly identical to a localizer converter. An example of a glideslope receiver block diagram is shown in Figure 5-3-5.

The RF section of a glideslope receiver may be a band pass filter or an amplifier. The SMO is programmed by the navigation system control head. The RF or IF is AGC controlled. Glideslope systems do not have any audio output; therefore, the detector feeds directly into the glideslope converter section of the receiver. The converter uses two filtering amplifiers, as shown in Figure 5-3-5. One amplifier is for 150 Hz and the other is for 90 Hz. Once filtered and amplified, the signals are sent to the deviation drivers, which convert the signals to DC ($\pm$150 mV) in order to drive the D-bar. Outputs from the filtering amplifiers are also fed to the flag driver, which detects the presence of both signals. If both signals are present, then the flag driver will produce up to 300 mV to pull the fault flag out of view.

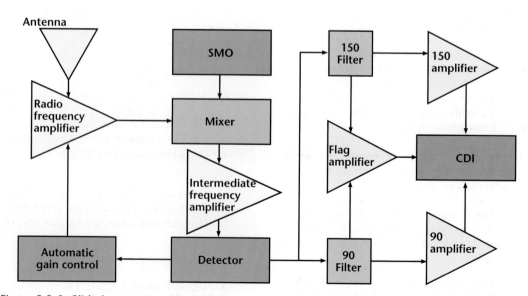

Figure 5-3-5. Glideslope receiver block diagram.

Glideslope Configurations

Like marker systems, glideslope receivers tend to be small and can be found within other systems. Figure 5-3-6 shows the generic remote mounted version of a glideslope system. The glideslope receives channeling information from the navigation control head. The pilot never sees the glideslope frequency displayed.

The glideslope receiver may be in the panel-mounted NAVCOMM or in a remote mounted NAV receiver, a remote mounted VOR/LOC converter, a module in an integrated flight management avionics system, or even in the CDI. A complete navigation block is shown in Figure 5-3-7 and includes both a VHF navigation system and a glideslope system.

Glideslope Antennas

The most common way to connect a glideslope to an antenna is to use a device called a triplexer, which matches the impedance of the glideslope receiver input with the NAV antenna. Triplexers have three outputs, one for the glideslope receiver and two more for the navigation receivers. If an independent antenna is used, it will look very similar to a navigation antenna (Hertzian type), shown in Figure 5-3-8, but will be smaller because of the higher frequency used by the glideslope system.

Flight Line Testing Glideslopes

Keep in mind that, like localizer, glideslope accuracy is not measured in degrees. Furthermore, glideslope modulation levels on most test boxes are shown according to the difference in depth of modulation. If the ddm is zero, then there is no difference between the 90Hz and 150 Hz modulation levels, and the D-bar should be centered. As with other tests on the flight line, this test should be completed with external power applied to the aircraft, and the generator frequency should be set to the glideslope channel associated with localizer frequency shown on the VHF navigation system.

1. Accuracy. With the generator set to 0.0 ddm, note the D-bar position. A typical specification for glideslope accuracy is ±5 μA. On most indicators the width of the D-bar is about 10 μA; therefore, with the generator set to 0.0 ddm, the D-bar should be centered within one-half of the needle width.

2. Standard deflection. Glideslope, like localizer, also has a standard deflection. For a

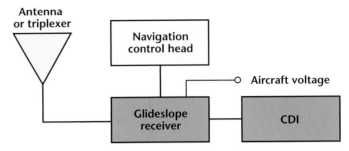

Figure 5-3-6. Generic remote mounted glideslope system block diagram.

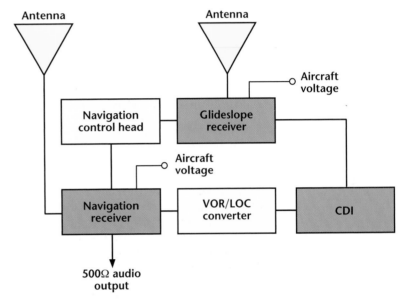

Figure 5-3-7. Block diagram of a complete VHF navigation system with glideslope.

Figure 5-3-8. The glideslope antenna externally mounted on the nose of this aircraft is a Hertzian-type antenna.

.ddm setting of 0.091, the D-bar should deflect 78 μA or about 2.5 dots. Test deflection in both directions, and make note of any errors.

3. Fault flag testing.

a. Flag with invalid signal. Like the LOC, the glideslope flag can be tested in two

Glideslope	#1	#2
Channel control		
Self-test		
Centering		
Course width		
Flag with invalid signal		
Flag with 60% deviation		

Table 5-3-2. Glideslope testing checklist.

ways. First remove the 90 Hz modulation. The flag should show. Replace the 90 Hz modulation and remove the 150 Hz modulation. Again, the flag should show.

b. Flag with weak signal. The technique for testing flag operation under low signal levels is nearly identical to the VOR and localizer flag tests described above. This time, use 60 percent of 78 μA, which is 46.8 μA. The flag should appear as the needle falls between the first and second dot.

Some glideslope systems have a self-test feature. If so equipped, press the self-test button and verify that the system behaves as described in the MM. Other systems have built-in test equipment, known as BITE. If the equipment is BITE equipped, then the BITE tests should be included in the flight line test. BITE testing may involve the use of a laptop.

Many repair stations use a checklist like the one in Table 5-3-2.

Section 4

Distance Measuring Equipment

Distance Measuring Equipment Theory

The navigation systems described so far are passive, in that they receive and process signals transmitted from the ground. *Distance measuring equipment* (DME) is an active system that transmits and receives information from a ground based transceiver known as a DME transponder or TACAN transponder. The top-

ics discussed in this section are referenced under ATA code 34-50.

Tactical navigation (TACAN) was developed by the United States military in the mid-twentieth century. TACAN provides both bearing and distance information to TACAN-equipped aircraft. There are many VOR sites that also have a TACAN ground station at the same location. A ground station with both VOR and TACAN is known as a VORTAC. DME is designed to use the distance feature of TACAN. The technology proved popular, and the FAA equipped DME transponders at VOR and ILS sites so civilian pilots could also use distance information from non-VORTAC sites. The VOR and ILS sites with DME capabilities are known as VOR/DME or ILSDME, respectively.

DME Control and Modes

Like glideslope, the DME operates on the UHF band and can be controlled using the VHF navigation system control head. An example of a DME display is pictured in Figure 5-4-1. DME frequencies do not show on any display available to the pilot. When TACAN and DME were designed, the navigation band had 100 channels; therefore, 100 frequencies were designated for civilian DME use. When the navigation band was subdivided to allow 200 channels, the technology did not exist to subdivide the DME bandwidth. Instead, a new mode of operation was developed to allow the same set of frequencies to be used twice. The original mode was designated X-mode and the new mode was designated Y-mode. The X-mode channels are on frequencies assigned to NAV channels with a 0 in the 50 kHz position. For example, 108.00 MHz, 108.10 MHz, and 108.20 MHz are assigned DME frequencies operating in X-mode. Navigation channels with a 5 in the 50 kHz position have DME frequencies

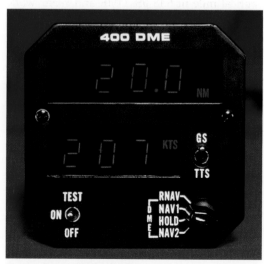

Figure 5-4-1. DME display.

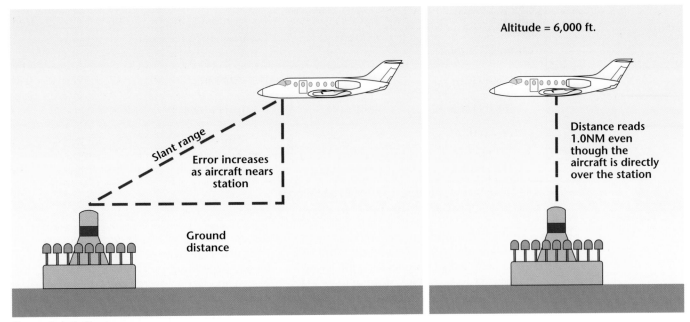

Figure 5-4-2. Slant range error.

assigned using Y-mode. For example, 108.05 MHz, 108.15 MHz, and 108.25 MHz are assigned DME frequencies operating in Y-mode.

Much later, the microwave landing system was developed as a potential replacement to ILS. Advancements in technology allowed two more modes to be developed (W and Z), which supported more precise distance measurements. This text will concentrate on the two modes used for normal X- and Y-mode DME navigation.

The basic principle of DME navigation is similar to radar. The DME transmits energy and measures the time it takes for energy to return. Unlike most radar systems, DME is active. In other words, the system in the aircraft transmits and so does the ground system. Since radio waves travel at the speed of light, physicists have calculated that a radio wave travels one nautical mile in 6.18 μS. DME and radar work on the principle of a radar round trip nautical mile (RRTNM), or 12.36 μS. The main function of a DME is to measure the time it takes for the signal to travel to the transponder, be processed, and come back. Once the measurement is made, the DME does the necessary math and displays the result as nautical miles for the pilot.

Both pilots and technicians should note that DME measures *slant range*. Slant range is the direct distance, not map distance, from the aircraft to the ground station. The closer an aircraft gets to the transponder, the greater the slant range error gets, until the aircraft passes over the station. When the aircraft is directly over the station, the DME reads altitude in nautical miles. Figure 5-4-2 illustrates slant range error.

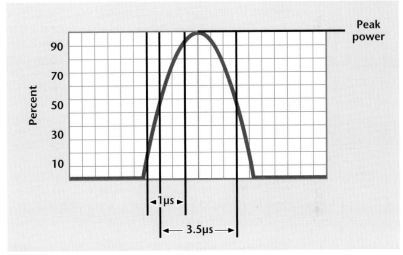

Figure 5-4-3 Single Gaussian-shaped DME pulse.

DME service volume is matched to the service volume of the VOR or ILS with which the system is installed.

DME Pulses

The DME transponder transmits random Gaussian-shaped pairs of pulses on its assigned DME channel on the L-band between 978 MHz and 1,213 MHz. A *Gaussian-shaped pulse* is symmetrical or bell-shaped, as shown in Figure 5-4-3, and conforms to strict timing parameters.

All DME pulses are 3.5 μS wide at the 50 percent point and have rise and fall times of 1 μS. X-mode stations transmit the pulses spaced 12 μS apart. Y-mode stations transmit pulses spaced 30 μS apart. DME transponders receive at a frequency different from the frequency at

VHF NAV channel	DME transmit frequency	Transponder transmit frequency (DME receive)	Mode of operation
108.00 MHz	1,041 MHz	978 MHz	X
108.05 MHz	1,041 MHz	1,104 MHz	Y
113.30 MHz	1,104 MHz	1,167 MHz	X
113.35 MHz	1,104 MHz	1,041 MHz	Y

Table 5-4-1. Sample of DME frequencies and modes.

which they transmit. For any station, the frequencies are always 63 MHz apart. Since two frequencies are used for operation, the system is considered to be duplex. A sample of VHF navigation channels and the associated DME frequencies and modes are shown in Table 5-4-1.

At all times, the DME or TACAN ground station sends random pulses. These random pulses are called *squitter pulses*, or the squitter. At regular intervals the transponder stops sending the squitter and, instead, sends out its maximum capacity of 2,700 pulse pairs per second at a constant rate resembling dots and dashes. The DME in the aircraft uses these pulse pairs to create a 1,350 Hz identification tone.

DME Operation

The distance measuring process in the aircraft starts with the pilot tuning the NAV receiver to a VOR or ILS channel. The navigation control head tunes the DME to the appropriate channel pair. The DME listens for the squitter from the ground station. If the DME receives squitter, then the DME begins transmitting in search mode. Typical search mode transmission rates are approximately 100 pulse pairs per second (PPS) or higher. Although the pulse spacing is constant, the time between pulse pairs varies at random, as shown in Figure 5-4-4.

This random variation is called *jitter*. Jitter allows a DME to recognize transponder replies

directed to it. The DME transponder receives the pulse pairs, delays them for either 50 μS or 56 μS, depending on whether the channel is X- or Y-mode, then retransmits the pulse pairs. The delay time allows the electronic components to operate and allows aircraft to lock on to the station when close by. When the DME receives its pulses back, it will lock on, remove any fault flags and display a distance. At this point, the transmission rate drops to approximately 20 to 25 pulse pairs per second. Once locked, the DME begins to track the changes in timing as the pulses return. The DME calculates the rate at which the distance is changing and begins to display other information, such as speed and estimated time en route (ETE). The order of operation of a DME is always listen, search, lock, and track. DME pulse and spacing details are shown in Table 5-4-2.

There are two other operational mode characteristics of DME. The first is *memory mode*, which is also referred to as coast mode. Memory mode allows the DME to continue to display distance, speed, and estimated time en route numbers for a short period of time after the loss of the signal. Memory mode allows the DME transponder to ident without starting the listen, search, lock, and track process again. Memory mode also prevents a restart when the signal is temporarily lost due to signal blockage during aircraft maneuvers or landing gear operation.

The second operational mode is known as *DME hold*. DME hold locks the DME on the

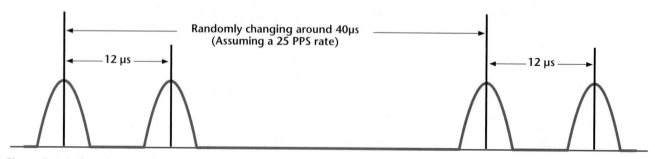

Figure 5-4-4. Jitter in X-mode.

	X-mode	Y-mode
Air-to-ground pulse spacing	12 µS	36 µS
Ground-to-air pulse spacing	12 µS	30 µS
Delay time	50 µS	56 µS

Process order all modes:
(1) Listen, (2) Search, (3) Lock, (4) Track

Table 5-4-2. DME pulse and spacing details.

current frequency. By placing the DME in DME hold mode, the pilot can change channels on the VHF NAV without interrupting distance information. For example, the airport at Williamsport, Pennsylvania, does not have an ILSDME; however, it does have a VORTAC nearby. A pilot approaching Williamsport may be using the VOR frequency of 114.40 MHz. At this point, the DME is transmitting on 1,115 MHz and receiving on 1,178 MHz in X-mode. When the pilot begins his or her final approach, he or she may press the hold button and tune the VHF NAV to the ILS frequency of 110.10 MHz. The DME remains locked on the local VORTAC station and continues to provide the pilot distance information from the Williamsport VORTAC.

DME Transceivers

DME transceivers have a receiver of the superheterodyne type, as shown in Figure 5-4-5.

The transmitter has a *current wave* section and a pulsed section. Current wave is another name for a constant unchanging frequency. Since the transmit and receive frequencies are always 63 MHz apart, the stabilized master oscillator or synthesizer do not have to change frequencies from receive to transmit. The mixer simply operates with high side injection, or low side injection as necessary, to create an IF of 63 MHz. At the heart of the system is the processor. The processor detects and validates incoming pulses and controls the timing of the transmitter and receiver sections. Moreover, the processor measures elapsed time, calculates distance, measures the change rate of the received pulse time, calculates speed, and calculates estimated time en route. Speed is reported on the indicator in knots, which means nautical miles per hour are not accurate when first reported but will become more accurate with time as the DME gathers information. If the aircraft is flying toward the DME station, then the ETE is an estimate of the time passage before reaching the station. If the aircraft is flying away from the station, then the ETE is an estimate of time elapsed since station passage. The DME distance calculations are rather simple:

$$1.286 \text{ µS} \times 100 = 1,286 \text{ µS}$$

$$1,286 \text{ µS} - 50 \text{ µS X-mode delay} = 1,236 \text{ µS}$$

$$\frac{1,236 \text{ µS}}{12.36 \text{ µS rrtnm}} = 100 \text{ nm}$$

rrtnm = radar round trip nautical mile

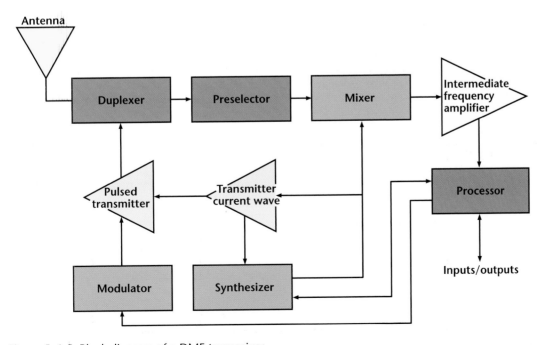

Figure 5-4-5. Block diagram of a DME transceiver.

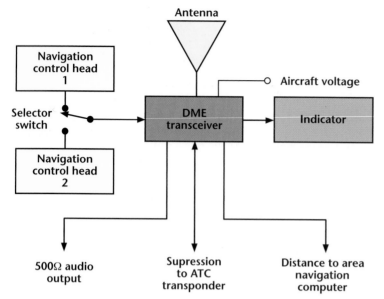

Figure 5-4-6. Generic remote mounted DME system block diagram.

Figure 5-4-7. Panel mounted DME display.

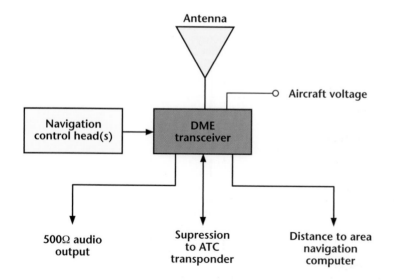

Figure 5-4-8. Block diagram of a panel mounted DME system.

The modulator does not work in the same way as an amplitude modulator. In the case of DME, the modulator works more like a trigger, allowing the pulsed transmitter to fire off the Gaussian-shaped pulses. The duplexer also works as a dual filter to allow transmitted energy out to the antenna and received energy into the pre-selector.

DME Configuration

Engineers design DME systems in a few different ways, depending on the type of aircraft in which the systems will be used. Figure 5-4-6 shows a block diagram of what many refer to as a generic DME system used with two VHF navigation systems. At the heart of the system is a transceiver. In this system, the transceiver is mounted in an equipment bay with other avionics systems. Since the transceiver is mounted away from the instrument panel, technicians often refer to this type of system as remote mounted. A wiring harness connects the transceiver to the VHF navigation control heads through a selector switch that is mounted in the instrument panel. The wiring harness also connects the transceiver to the DME indicator mounted in the instrument panel. The indicator may contain the navigation system selector switch and the hold switch.

The transceiver has a 500 Ω audio output connected to the audio system. The suppression connection prevents interference from occurring between the air traffic control transponder and the DME. The suppression accepts both inputs and outputs. A positive pulse on the suppression bus momentarily stops transmission. The RNAV distance output supplies VOR/DME area navigation computers with distance information.

A popular configuration on small aircraft includes a control head, transceiver, and indicator in one panel-mounted unit, as shown in Figure 5-4-7. A block diagram of this type of unit is shown in Figure 5-4-8. This type of system does not include a hold switch, since the DME has its own control head. If the pilot wants the DME to operate on a frequency that is different from the VHF NAV, then he or she sets the DME to operate from its internal frequency control.

An integrated flight management system contains a DME transceiver module like the one diagramed in Figure 5-4-9.

DME antennas are of the Marconi type and are mounted on the bottom of the aircraft. Typically, they look like a small blade about two inches long, as shown in Figure 5-4-10.

Flight Line Testing DME

The following is a generalization regarding DME flight line testing. The technician must always follow the instructions in the manufacturer's installation and maintenance manual regarding tests. DME testing requires a special signal generator designed to test DME systems. Most of these generators require the test antenna be placed at a specific distance from the DME antenna on the aircraft. In addition, many generators require the technician to set the specific antenna distance and height.

1. Sensitivity. On the flight line, a DME can be tested for sensitivity to verify that it locks on at a low signal level. To perform this test, the signal generator is set to a very low output that the technician may slowly increase until the DME locks. If the technician starts at a high signal level, then he or she will be fighting the DME memory function and will not get an accurate reading. The test for minimum lock-on should be performed on more than one frequency in both X- and Y-modes.

2. Transmitter power. The peak transmitter power can be read from the test box. Again, the test should be repeated on more than one frequency in both X- and Y-modes.

3. Pulse repetition rate (PRR). The PRR is read from the test box. Sometimes the PRR is referred to as pulse repetition frequency, or PRF. The PRR should be checked in both search and track modes. If necessary, the technician can program the test box to produce continuous identification to force the unit into search mode.

4. Audio output and memory operation. Select DME on the audio system and watch the time. The DME will lose lock as soon as the tone is engaged. While waiting for the unit to return to search mode, verify memory operation and audio output. When the DME returns to search mode, verify the search PRR.

5. Accuracy. The distance, speed, and time to station values should agree with the test box within the limits set forth by the MM.

6. Transmit frequency. Frequency is read from the generator and should be within the specifications set forth in the manual.

Table 5-4-3 illustrates a portion of a testing checklist used for DME.

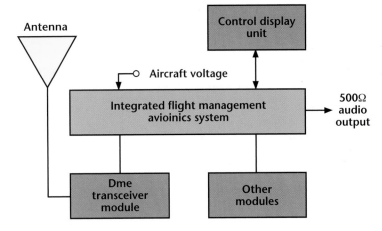

Figure 5-4-9. Block diagram of a DME module in an integrated flight management system.

Figure 5-4-10. DME antenna.

DME	#1	#2
Receive Audio		
Stable Lock On		
Channel Control		
Hold		
Memory		
Sensitivity		
Accuracy		
Distance		
Speed		
TTS		
Frequency		
Power		

Table 5-4-3. DME testing checklist.

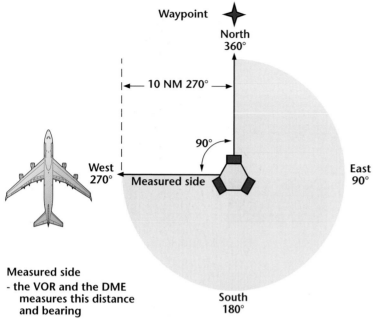

Figure 5-5-1. The measured side of an RNAV triangle.

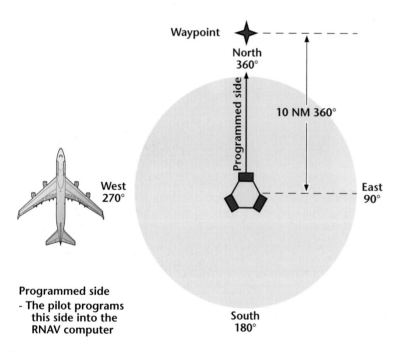

Figure 5-5-2. The programmed side of an RNAV triangle.

Section 5

Area Navigation

All the navigation systems described to this point give information relative to a spot on the earth. For VHF navigation and DME the spot is the location of the VOR, VORTAC, VOR/DME, or ILSDME. Glideslope gives information relative to a spot at the runway touchdown point. Markers literally mark the spot. Area navigation is different. The topics discussed in this section are referenced under ATA code 34-50.

As the name infers, area navigation systems allow aircraft to get information relative to any spot within a specified area. This spot is referred to as a *waypoint*. The name waypoint grows from the original and long name for roads: roadway. We are familiar with the terms roadway, highway, tollway, and freeway. A waypoint—in this case, an airway—is simply a specific point along the way.

VOR/DME Area Navigation

The area served by VOR/DME area navigation systems is the service volume of the VOR/DME or VORTAC station. Aircraft equipped with VOR/DME-based area navigation systems may get bearing and distance information for any location within the area.

VOR/DME area navigation systems are trigonometry computers that work problems and give the answers to the pilot in the form of bearing and distance. They calculate constantly, thus giving the pilot real time information. For example, as Figure 5-5-1 shows, an aircraft is flying 10 nautical miles west of a VORTAC station crossing the 270° radial. Since the aircraft is crossing the 270° radial, the angle between 270° and magnetic north is 90°. The information gathered so far can be thought of as the measured side of an RNAV triangle because the VOR and DME make these measurements.

The next step is for the pilot to decide where he or she would like to go. In other words, the pilot chooses a waypoint, then programs the waypoint bearing and distance into the RNAV computer. For discussion purposes, this can be thought of as the programmed side of an RNAV triangle, as shown in Figure 5-5-2, because the information is programmed into the RNAV unit.

One of the first facts of trigonometry a student learns is that when given the measurements of two sides and one angle of a triangle, the third side and other two angles can be calculated. This is what the RNAV unit does. In the following example, two sides and one angle are given, as shown in Figure 5-5-3.

The triangle used in this example is a right triangle and is quite easy to calculate because we can use the Pythagorean theorem to determine the length of the calculated side. Furthermore, the example is an isosceles triangle, which means the two remaining angles to be calculated are equal. To calculate the remaining side and angles of the triangle:

Use Isosceles Triangle Theorem to find bearing.

$$\frac{90°}{2} = 45°$$

The bearing to the waypoint is 45°

$$45° + 180° = 225°$$

The bearing from the waypoint is 225°

Use Pythagorean Theorem to find distance of calculated side.

$$A^2 + B^2 = C^2$$

A = Measured Side, B = Programmed Side, C = Calculated Side

$$10 \text{ NM}^2 + 10 \text{ NM}^2 = C^2$$

$$(10 \times 10) + (10 \times 10) = C^2$$

$$100 + 100 = 200$$

$$\sqrt{200} = 14.14 \text{ nm}$$

In this example, the RNAV indicates a bearing and distance to the waypoint of 45° and 14.14 nautical miles. This example is useful for verifying calculated bearing, since the calculations result in a whole number bearing of 45°. Of course, the RNAV can do much more complex calculations, and it can calculate the angles and sides of any triangle, all in real time.

For a second example, a triangle that conforms to a Pythagorean triple is used, as shown in Figure 5-5-4. To keep the example simple, ignore the calculations for the angles. This example is useful for verifying distance, since the distance calculation results in a whole number. A right triangle with two sides in the ratio of 3:4 has a the third side continue the ratio to 5. This type of triangle is known as a 3:4:5 triangle. The angles on this triangle do not work out to whole numbers.

In this case, the aircraft is on an approximate radial of 270° from the station, and the bearing to the station is approximately 36.86°. Although this triangle is not useful for verifying the bearing calculation ability of an RNAV, it is useful for checking the distance calculations.

As the previous figures and text show, a VOR/DME RNAV system calculates bearing and distance using trigonometry in real time. As Figure 5-5-5 shows, the system is connected as a substitute for the VOR/LOC converter between the DME and DME indicator. The RNAV uses the NAV composite signal to get bearing information, and it uses DME distance output to get side information. The navigation solution (calculated side) is displayed on the navigation and DME indicators.

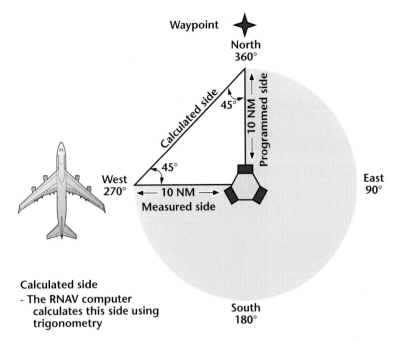

Figure 5-5-3. RNAV calculates the third triangle side and remaining angles.

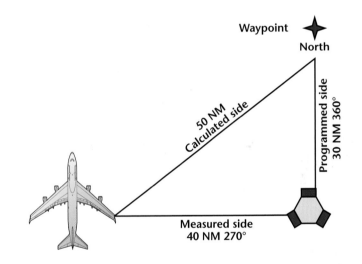

Figure 5-5-4. RNAV 3:4:5 triangle.

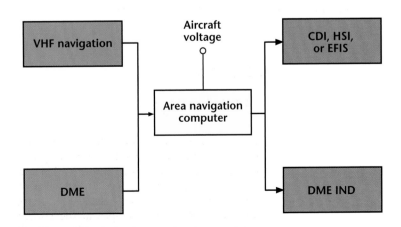

Figure 5-5-5. Block diagram of VOR/DME area navigation system.

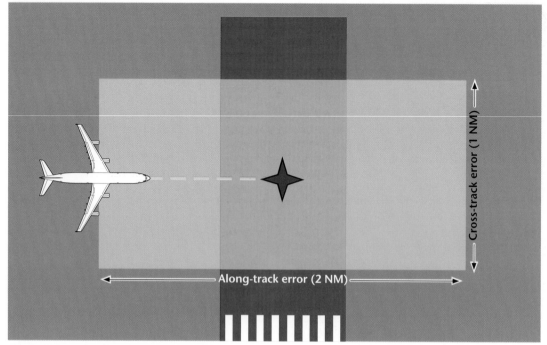

Figure 5-5-6. Along- and cross-track error rectangle.

Flight Line Testing VOR/DME Area Navigation

To certify a VOR/DME RNAV, the aircraft must be flown to a waypoint so that *along-track error* and *cross-track error* can be verified. Along-track error is an inaccuracy along the flight track and shows up as a distance error. Cross-track error is an inaccuracy across the flight track and shows up as a bearing or course deviation error. Together, along- and cross-track errors form a rectangle, as shown in Figure 5-5-6. Once an appropriate waypoint is chosen, the aircraft must be flown to the waypoint, and the pilot can visually verify that the aircraft is within the rectangle when the RNAV says the aircraft has arrived.

Before taking a certification flight, a technician may want to check the RNAV system using the example triangles. Table 5-5-1 gives a quick reference for triangle testing. For troubleshooting purposes, technicians should remember the VHF navigation system and the DME must be operating properly before the RNAV can work. Furthermore, testing the RNAV requires the technician to use both the DME and VHF navigation test equipment.

Flight management systems, and other devices, offer other types of VOR/DME area navigation. One type uses multiple VORs and performs calculations using only angles. Yet another form uses multiple DMEs and performs calculations using only sides. All forms of area navigation have long and cross error specifications.

Global Navigation Satellite System

Global navigation satellite system (GNSS) is a generic term for satellite navigation, which is another form of area navigation. In this case, the area served is the entire earth and skies above. The United States Global Positioning System (GPS) is one form of GNSS. The Russian GLONASS and the European Galileo systems are also examples of GNSS. Figure 5-5-7 shows an example of an onboard GNSS unit. This topic is referenced under ATA code 34-50.

Sides	Measured by VOR and DME (entered into test equipment)	Programmed into RNAV	Calculated by RNAV
For testing bearing and cross track	10 NM 270° From	10 NM 360° From	14.14 NM 45° To 225° From
For testing distance along track	40 NM 270° From	30 NM 360° From	50 NM 36.86° To 53.13° From

Table 5-5-1. VOR, DME and RNAV testing triangles.

Figure 5-5-7. Global navigation satellite system (GNSS) unit.

Time Delay Navigation

Satellite navigation systems operate using the principle of *time delay* (TD) navigation. These systems measure the time it takes for the signal to reach the receiver satellite. Using time delays, the navigation system can plot *lines of position* (LOP). The position of the system can be determined by estimating where the LOPs cross. The crossing points of the LOPs can be converted to the coordinate system of latitude, longitude, and altitude.

To understand GNSS navigation, it's helpful to understand how a point can be determined using TDs and LOPs. Navigating by time delays has been used by navigators since the fifteenth century or before. Longitude can be determined by setting a clock when the sun reaches the highest point in the sky at the prime meridian and noting the time at the location to be determined. In the mid-twentieth century, radio navigation using time delays became available. Since the radio transmitters were located on the earth's surface, the lines of position based on those time delays were parabolic and resulted in a two dimensional position fix. In the late twentieth century, engineers began designing navigation computers with microprocessors, which made position determination automatic and available to pilots. Shortly after the introduction of microprocessors databases became available, which truly revolutionized area navigation. Since GNSS navigation transmitters are space vehicles (SV), the lines of position based

on their broadcasts are very close to a sphere. Figure 5-5-8 shows lines of position based on TDs from two SVs. As the figure shows, the intersection of the two spheres forms a circle. If the GNSS is only able to receive transmissions from two SVs, then the microprocessor will only be able to determine that its position is somewhere on the circle. If the SVs are very distant, then the circle may have a diameter of thousands of miles. As a result, the intersection of two spheroid lines of position is not adequate to determine a location.

If the GNSS is able to receive transmissions from three SVs, then the computer is able to narrow the possibilities to two points. As

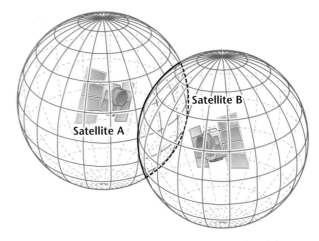

Figure 5-5-8. The intersection of two spheroid lines of position produces a circle.

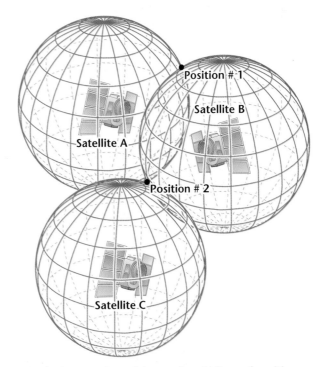

Figure 5-5-9. The intersection of three spheroid lines of position produces two points.

shown in Figure 5-5-9, three spheres intersect in two points. Still, there is ambiguity because the microprocessor is not able to determine which point is correct.

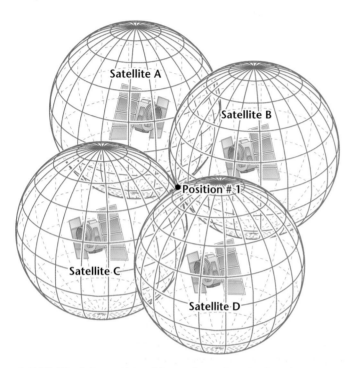

Figure 5-5-10. The intersection of four spheres is a single point.

Figure 5-5-11. Artist's rendering of a GPS satellite. *Courtesy of NASA*

Figure 5-5-12. Perpendicular lines of position with error region marked.

Figure 5-5-13. Angled lines of position with error region marked.

In order to resolve the ambiguity, the reception of a fourth satellite is necessary. The fourth satellite provides the time information necessary to determine which point is correct. As shown in Figure 5-5-10, the intersection of four spheres is a single point in space.

GNSS are able to receive up to 12 SVs, thus refining their estimated position considerably. Since the SVs are moving constantly, calculations for the estimated position must be continually recalculated. Many systems monitor pressure altitude, since altitude gives them a reference to yet another sphere—the earth. Nearly all GNSS feature a moving map display with a database-generated chart showing airspace and terrain features.

GPS

GPS consists of a constellation of 24 satellites in six orbital planes, each orbiting the earth in about 12 hours. In addition, there are spare satellites in orbit, which can be moved into position if one of the 24 space vehicles fails. As a result, the satellites have the same configuration in the sky from any place on earth once every 23 hours and 56 minutes. Several satellites are visible in the radio spectrum at any time and at any place on earth with a clear view of the sky. An example of a GPS satellite is shown in Figure 5-5-11.

There are three segments of GPS. The control segment monitors satellite operation, controls the SVs, and uploads information. The space segment consists of the space vehicles. Pilots are part of the user segment, which uses GPS to navigate.

SVs broadcast on two frequencies. The L1 frequency is 1.57542 GHz and is used by the civilian user segment for position determination. GPS receivers are mostly of the direct conversion variety in order to preserve the phase changes in the carrier wave. The L2 frequency is 1.2276 GHz and is currently in use by the military to measure errors caused by the ionosphere.

The signal on the L1 frequency is a phase-shifted code known as *course acquisition* (C/A) code. The C/A code is phase shifted over a full megahertz of frequency. As a result, to a simple receiver the C/A code appears to be random noise; however, the noise is not random, and a receiver with the proper key can decipher the code. Therefore, the C/A code is also called a pseudorandom noise (PRN) code and repeats 1,023 bits each millisecond. The PRN is unique for each SV and is used for SV identification. Also, the L1 frequency carries a navigation message, which is a 50 Hz signal containing bits of data.

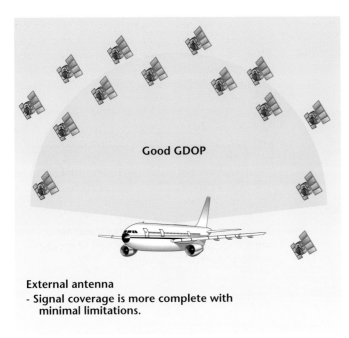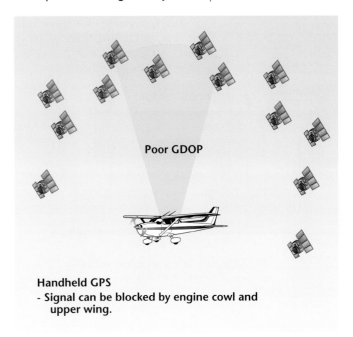

Good GDOP

External antenna
- Signal coverage is more complete with minimal limitations.

Poor GDOP

Handheld GPS
- Signal can be blocked by engine cowl and upper wing.

Figure 5-5-14. Good and poor GDOP.

The navigation message builds the *almanac*. The almanac contains data about errors in the GPS clock, where the SVs are supposed to be, and data about *ephemerides*. An ephemerid is a small distortion in the orbit of an SV that can result in errors in position calculations. To prevent ephemerides from causing errors, *ephemeris data* (information regarding ephemerides) is part of the navigation message. Ephemeris data is updated at two hour intervals and remains valid from four to six hours. A GPS receiver must have a current almanac, including ephemeris data, to navigate properly. Due to the low rate of data transmission of 50 bits/sec, it takes at least 12.5 minutes to download a complete almanac. Typically, GPS receivers continually download the navigation message and have enough current data to begin navigating quickly. If the receiver has been turned off for a long period of time, then it might have to download the complete almanac, which means it will not be ready to navigate for at least 12.5 minutes.

The exact distance between the SV and the receiver is impossible to determine because of the difference in transmit time and receive time. For example, the C/A code may begin at 12:00 exactly but is received by the GPS receiver approximately 67.4 mS later. At orbital speeds, the SV has time to move quite a distance in 67.4 mS; therefore, the range determined by the GPS receiver is known as *pseudorange*, since the range is approximate.

When navigating using lines of position, the best solutions are generated when the lines of position are perpendicular to each other, as shown in Figure 5-5-12.

If the lines of position are not perpendicular, as shown in Figure 5-5-13, then the region of possible area is enlarged and is not a uniform shape and more error is possible.

A GPS receiver is able to calculate its position most precisely when the SVs received are widespread, giving the most perpendicular lines of position. Error based on line of position angles is known as *geometric dilution of precision* (GDOP). Figure 5-5-14 illustrates good and poor GDOP situations.

Other errors in the GPS error budget are shown in Table 5-5-2; these include ionospheric effects, ephemerides, clock errors, multipath (signal reflections), and calculation errors. Altogether, the worst case scenario for GPS accuracy is 100 meters laterally and 156 meters vertically. This accuracy is sufficient for cross country navigation and non-precision approaches.

GPS error budget	
Error sources	**Amount of error**
Ionospheric effects	± 5 meters
Ephemerides	± 2.5 meters
Clock errors	± 2 meters
Multi-path effect	± 1 meter
Tropospheric effect	± 0.5 meters
Calculations errors	± 1 meter

Table 5-5-2. GPS error budget.

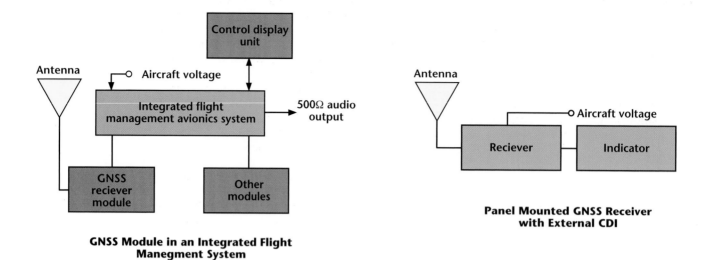

GNSS Module in an Integrated Flight Manegment System

Panel Mounted GNSS Receiver with External CDI

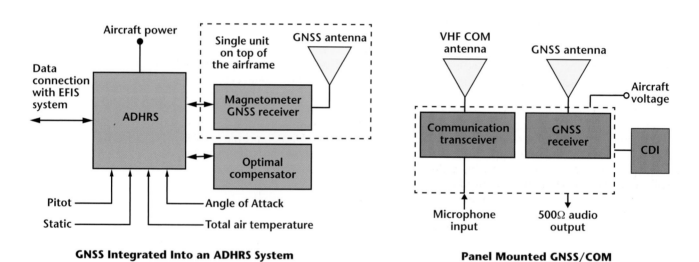

GNSS Integrated Into an ADHRS System

Panel Mounted GNSS/COM

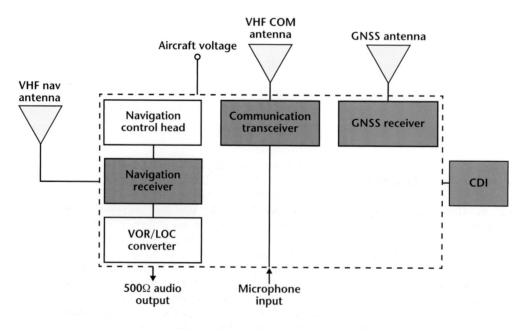

VHF NAVCOM with Integrated GNSS

Figure 5-5-15. GNSS system configurations.

GPS Augmentation

GPS accuracy can be improved by using a *ground based augmentation system* (GBAS). An augmentation system uses a GPS receiver at a precisely surveyed location. The system compares the GPS calculated position with the surveyed position and broadcasts correction information to the GPS receiver on another frequency. In the non-aviation world, the augmentation system is known as differential GPS.

The wide area augmentation system (WAAS) has been in use since 2003 and consists of over 25 reference stations, three uplink stations, and two geosynchronous satellites. The geosynchronous satellites make WAAS available for 99 percent of the continental United States and 95 percent of Alaska. WAAS corrections are broadcast from the geosynchronous satellites on the L1 frequency. One might think interference would be a problem, but the PRN code is spread over a megahertz, so the GPS receiver still is able to receive and decode messages without difficulty.

A typical specification for a WAAS-corrected GPS position is one meter lateral and two meters vertical. At any given time, the GPS is experiencing some GDOP. A typical GDOP error is approximately six meters. Multiply the GDOP by the specification and the product is the *maximum allowable error*. For example, given the one meter lateral accuracy described above multiplied by the six meters of GDOP, the maximum allowable error would be six meters, or 18.68 feet, laterally, and twice that amount vertically.

WAAS allows enough precision for landing approaches nearing or at minimum altitudes for Category I approaches. For more precision, the FAA is implementing the local area augmentation system (LAAS). The LAAS focuses its service within 20 to 30 miles of the airport area and has an accuracy of less than one meter. Correction messages are broadcast via a VHF radio link on the VHF navigation band.

GPS Fault Detection and Warning

Differences exist in the flagging system between GPS and previously described navigation systems. SVs generate a signal called a health flag; however, the time lag between the SV fault and the health flag transmission may be several hours. GPS using GBAS can get fault information over the GBAS. GPS without GBAS use receiver autonomous integrity monitoring (RAIM). RAIM monitors the pseudorange measurements from at least six SVs. If one or more of the measurements disagrees, then an RAIM alarm is issued. The time from a fault detection to a RAIM alarm can be anywhere from 10 to 30 seconds, depending on the phase of flight. Furthermore, at times, six SVs may not be visible, thus rendering RAIM unavailable. Since RAIM may not be available, pilots may be required to do RAIM predictions before departing on an instrument flight. WAAS and LAAS eliminate RAIM requirements by allowing the system to alert the pilot within six to eight seconds of fault detection.

Fault detection and exclusion (FDE) analyzes the RAIM alarm to determine which SV is causing a problem. Once analyzed, FDE automatically excludes the faulty SV from navigation calculations.

Configuration

GNSS systems are configured in a variety of ways. Their small size allows them to be included within other avionic systems, as shown in Figure 5-5-15. Although many GNSS systems are designed to stand alone, they may also be integrated with a communication system, a NAVCOM system, or as part of a modular avionics suite. Some instrumentation systems, such as ADHRS, include a GNSS receiver integrated into the magnetometer housing.

Database

The database is crucial to proper GNSS operation and must be current for the pilot to complete an instrument flight. The database may be contained in a user-replaceable memory card. In other cases, the database must be updated via a data port connected to a PC.

GPS Operation

The startup process for a GPS differs depending on how long the unit was turned off and whether or not the unit was moved while turned off.

In order to navigate, the GPS receiver requires a current almanac. Almanacs are downloaded in the navigation message and are good for three months. If the unit has been off for a long period of time, it goes through a procedure known as a *cold start*. For a cold start the unit begins downloading the almanac and displays the approximate last known location. It prompts the user for the current location if it differs from the last known position. If necessary, it may also prompt the user to enter the current time. Once the almanac, including current ephemeris data, is downloaded, the system locks and displays present position.

Upon shutdown a GPS saves position, time, almanac, and ephemeris data. For a warm start, the unit recalls the data saved at the last shutdown and displays present position quickly. For any start-up the GPS goes through multiple steps before displaying a position. Below is a summarized list of steps:

1. Download the navigation information.

2. Calculate the exact satellite position.

   a. Apply troposphere modeling corrections.

3. Calculate the pseudorange data and then correct for ionosphere and other modeling errors.

4. Repeat these steps for each available satellite.

5. Correct the SV position for earth's rotation.

   a. Correct using GBAS data if available.

6. Calculate the initial receiver position.

7. Convert the data for datum and grid system.

8. Add in the leap seconds and time offset from UTC time and convert it for display.

9. Refine the position based on additional satellites and the correct time to obtain a 3D fix.

Galileo

Galileo is the name of the European GNSS system, which began launches in 2010. The full constellation of Galileo space vehicles will number 30 satellites evenly spaced in three orbital planes. Each satellite will take approximately 14 hours to make a complete orbit. The European GNSS Supervisory Authority expects six to eight satellites to be visible to receivers from most any location on earth.

GLONASS

GLONASS is an abbreviation for the Russian GNSS. Roughly translated, GLONASS is short for Global Navigation Sputnik System. The system consists of 21 satellites in three orbital planes. Each satellite orbits the earth in 11 hours 15 minutes.

Flight Line Testing GNSS Systems

Always review the flight manual supplement, installation manual, and MM before flight line testing a GNSS. Technicians may flight-line test GNSS on the ramp by simply turning them on and allowing them to calculate present position. Most systems have utility screens that show the number of satellites being received and the signal integrity from each one. This test requires a clear view of the sky.

If the aircraft cannot be removed from the hangar or if a clear view of the sky is not available, there are ramp test simulators available to test the receive capability, or full capability, of the GNSS receiver. Caution should be used with any ramp test equipment because of the fact that the GPS may complete a download of almanac data during the test, and testing should not be performed for inordinately long periods of time.

An effective way to prepare for a test of the GNSS is to document the aircraft's present position in latitude, longitude, and altitude. In addition, document the bearing and distance to another airport or other waypoint known to be in the GNSS database.

Once in the aircraft, power up the system and note the software version and currency of the database. When it displays present position, compare the readout with the previously documented coordinates and take note of any error. Then, use the *direct to* button shown in Figure 5-5-16 and program in the previously documented waypoint. Note the reported bearing and distance. Compare the readout with the previously documented information and note any discrepancies.

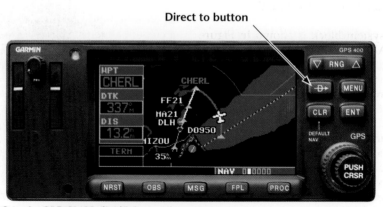

Figure 5-5-16. Garmin GPS GNSS display.

Section 6

Required Navigation Performance

The United States is beginning to shift to define airspace by required navigation performance (RNP). Aircraft will not be cleared into airspace for which they cannot maintain RNP or a certain amount of precision. Dual GPS and/or dual FMS systems may be necessary to meet certain RNP requirements. RNP is based primarily on cross-track error. Aircraft must be able to maintain a certain cross-track error within 95 percent of the time and another amount of error within 99 percent of the time. The RNP required for approaches is RNP-0.3. This means a cross-track error of no more than 0.3 nautical miles 95 percent of the time and a cross-track error of no more than 0.6 nautical miles 99 percent of the time. RNP-4, which is expected to become the universal standard, is illustrated in Figure 5-6-1.

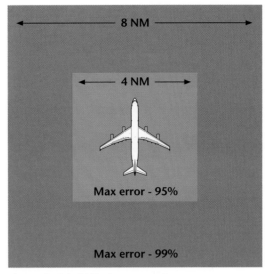

Figure 5-6-1. RNP-4 cross-track error.

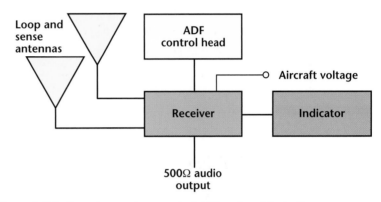

Figure 5-7-1. Generic remote mounted ADF system block diagram.

Section 7

Automatic Direction Finders

Automatic direction finders (ADF) is a system that operates on the low and medium frequency bands and is used to point the direction of a broadcasting station. This pointing is known as a *relative bearing*, since the bearing is relative to the heading of the aircraft and not to magnetic north. The FAA operates non-directional beacons (NDB), which broadcast at frequencies between 200 kHz and 550 kHz. With the proliferation of GPS, NDBs are being shut down. Also, on the 200 kHz to 550 kHz band are outer compass locators, which indicate lower powered broadcasting stations located at outer markers. Most ADF receivers also cover the AM broadcast band.

The generic system block is shown in Figure 5-7-1. Most ADFs in use today combine the control head and receiver in a single unit. Furthermore, the dual antennas are also combined in a single housing. Figure 5-7-2 shows an example of an early ADF loop antenna.

The loop antenna is horizontally polarized and is designed to receive the H-field being broadcast as part of the radio transmission. The loop antenna narrows the direction down to two possible directions. The sense antenna receives the E-field, and the receiver processes the sense

Figure 5-7-2. Early ADF loop antenna.

Figure 5-7-3. ADF system.

VHF navigation systems include VOR, localizer, and marker beacon. VOR is used for cross country navigation, and localizer is used to provide lateral guidance to a runway. The VOR/LOC band of frequencies include 200 channels from 108.00 MHz to 117.95 MHz. The odd tenths of megahertz below 112.00 MHz are reserved for localizer use. VOR and localizer information are displayed on a CDI, RMI, HSI, or EFIS.

The marker beacon operates on 75 MHz and is used to mark specific points along an ILS. Three AM tones—400 Hz, 1,300 Hz, and 3,000 Hz—illuminate blue, amber, and white lights respectively.

UHF navigation systems include glideslope, DME, and GNSS.

Glideslope is used to give the vertical glide-path information leading to a runway. Glideslope operates on 40 channels from 329.15 MHz to 335 MHz. The channels are collocated with localizer frequencies. The glideslope is channeled from the navigation control head and information is displayed on whichever instrument is displaying localizer information.

antenna signal to resolve the ambiguity of the loop antenna information.

ADFs have a beat frequency oscillator (BFO) so stations can be identified while only broadcasting a carrier wave. As described in Chapter 2, the BFO causes a tone to be heard on the radio output when a station is received. ADF accuracy is ±3° nominally. The navigation information is displayed on an ADF indicator, as shown in Figure 5-7-3, or on an RMI.

Testing ADF Systems

As always, the technician should use the installation and maintenance manual as a guide for ADF testing. ADF systems cannot be tested in the hangar and should be tested with the engine running. Running the engine while testing allows the technician to detect any unwanted noise to which ADF systems are prone. To test an ADF, a technician should have prior knowledge of the location and bearing of local stations on several frequencies. This topic is referenced under ATA code 34-50.

Once the engine is running and the ADF is turned on, select stations on several frequencies and verify that the needle points in the correct direction and moves at the proper speed.

An ADF system is shown in Figure 5-7-3.

DME measures distance and transmits pulses from the aircraft to a ground-based DME or TACAN transponder. The DME frequency band is 978 MHz to 1213 MHz. DME is a duplex system that uses each of the available channels in the bandwidth twice by changing modes. X-mode works on 100 kHz channels and Y-mode works on 50 kHz channels. DME frequencies are collocated with VOR and LOC frequencies. The navigation control head controls channeling information on the DME, and distance information is displayed on a DME indicator.

GNSS includes GPS, GLONASS, and GALILEO. All use a constellation of satellites, measure time delays, and plot lines of position. Four satellites are necessary for an accurate position fix. The civilian GPS system uses the L1 frequency of 1.57542 GHz, which broadcasts phase-shifted data to build an almanac that contains ephemeris data and satellite position information. Most GNSS display information on a moving map.

Figure 5-8-1. Ramp tester.

Section 8

Summary

The coordinate system in use around the world uses latitude, longitude, and altitude. Latitude is marked by parallels north or south of the equator. Longitude is marked by meridians east and west of the prime meridian. Altitude is either mean sea level (MSL) or above ground level (AGL).

GNSS and VOR/DME RNAV are different versions of area navigation systems. The VOR/DME RNAV is limited to the area served by a VORTAC or VOR/DME and uses trigonometry to provide navigation solutions. VOR/DME RNAV information is presented on the DME indicator and on whichever indicator is being used to display VOR information.

The ADF operates on the low and medium frequency bands from 200 kHz to 1650 kHZ and gives relative bearing to an NDB or outer compass locator. ADF information is presented on either an ADF indicator or an RMI.

Ramp Test Equipment

Test equipment is available to test nearly all of the systems discussed in this chapter on the flight line or in the hangar. Known as ramp testers, these generators have an internal battery and an antenna that may be connected to the output connector. An example of a ramp tester is pictured in Figure 5-8-1. To test a system in the aircraft, test equipment is required to simulate the signals the airborne system receives while in flight. Figure 5-8-2 shows a generic and basic internal block diagram of a signal generator.

The modulator block of the generator creates the signals necessary for the system to be tested. For example, if the technician is testing a marker beacon system, then the modulator will produce 400 Hz, 1.3 KHz, or 3 KHz and will amplitude modulate the RF section. The system has controls to adjust or remove portions of, or the entire, modulating signal. This allows the technician to verify flag operation for invalid signal inputs.

The RF section produces the radio frequency necessary to broadcast the signal to the system being tested. Using the marker example, this frequency would be 75 MHz. If necessary for special troubleshooting tests, the technician may externally modulate the RF generator and monitor modulation signals with inputs and outputs connected to the RF block.

An attenuator is connected between the RF generator and the output connector. For most flight line tests, this attenuator should be set for the maximum signal output or the minimum attenuation. Most attenuators are calibrated in negative dBm (-dBm).

For most systems at maximum signal output (minimum attenuation), there is enough signal radiated to reach the aircraft antenna system

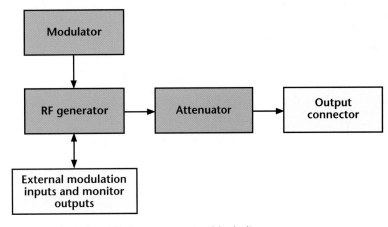

Figure 5-8-2. A simplified test generator block diagram.

and allow normal system operation. For marker beacon systems, the ramp test antenna must be very close to the aircraft marker antenna.

Technicians should be mindful of the affect of signal reflections and blockages. Once the radio energy leaves the signal generator's antenna, the technician has no control. For this reason, it is not possible to make the precise measurements necessary to certify a radio receiver.

Typically, test generators are designed to work on a range of frequencies. As a result, ramp testers are available to test VHF navigation, marker, glideslope, and communications systems. Although these signal generators can produce a modulated signal on VHF communication frequencies, they may not be capable of receiving a communication transmission.

Since DME operates on a much higher portion of the frequency spectrum, and has pulsed modulation, a separate generator must be used. These ramp testers will transmit and receive DME and ATC transponder signals. Some of these DME and ATC transponder generators may also test TCAS. Ramp testers designed for DME testing will have specific antenna distance requirements and possibly calibration settings for the space between the ramp test antenna and the aircraft antenna.

6

Autonomous Navigation Systems

When airplanes were first flown, pilots conducted all navigation without the aid of instruments. Instead, pilots only had what they could see from the aircraft for reference: the visible horizon by which to compare the orientation of the aircraft relative to the earth and landmarks by which to navigate. Over time, engineers have developed systems that can autonomously provide attitude information and navigate with a high degree of accuracy.

One of the first instruments designed to help pilots control aircraft was the airspeed indicator. Early airspeed indicators were anemometer type. Later instruments were developed that measured the difference between dynamic air pressure (the pressure created by aircraft movement) and static air pressure (the ambient air pressure).

The first instrument designed to help pilots navigate was the wet compass. This instrument is totally autonomous, meaning it requires no outside power. It is still used in aircraft to this day.

Over time more instruments were designed to assist with both navigation and aircraft control. Gyroscopes, specifically displacement gyros, were used to report direction of flight and the aircraft's attitude in space. A displacement gyro is a gyroscope that measures and reports angular displacement.

Elmer Sperry, known as the father of modern navigation technology, developed the first directional gyro, which was able to give the pilot heading information and was not subject to the same errors as a magnetic compass. Displacement gyro technology was first used around 1910 and 1911. Since that time, the sophistication and precision of autonomous attitude and navigation systems has progressed greatly.

Learning Objectives

DESCRIBE
- Gyroscopic flight instruments history, theory and operation

- Wet compass operation, alignment, and components

- Electronic compass systems purpose, types, and theory

- Purpose of flight management systems

Purpose, components and theory of:

- Attitude heading reference systems

- Air data systems

- Inertial reference systems

- Inertial navigation systems

EXPLAIN
- Deduced reckoning

- How autonomous navigation systems are installed/aligned and integrated with other aircraft systems

- How air data, heading, and inertial reference systems are combined

Left: Long-range aircraft, like this Airbus A380, use advanced autonomous inertial navigation systems for over-water flights.

Figure 6-1-1A. Aviation wet compass.

Today accelerometers, magnetometers, and microprocessors are quickly replacing gyro-based technology. Still, aircraft using old, new, or a combination of technologies are in use. This chapter describes both old and new systems and instruments used to autonomously determine aircraft attitude and to navigate. The topics discussed in this chapter are referenced under ATA code 34.

Section 1

Deduced Reckoning

Modern autonomous navigation systems use instruments and microprocessors to perform deduced reckoning. Also known as dead reckoning or ded reckoning, deduced reckoning is a form of navigation that involves the deter-

mination of a current or future position by performing calculations based on speed and direction of travel.

Most of us use deduced reckoning nearly every time we take or plan a trip in an automobile. If we plan to visit a friend who lives 65 miles distant near a highway with a 65 m.p.h. speed limit, then we can deduce it will take us approximately one hour to make the trip. In a similar manner, if we start out driving 65 m.p.h. eastbound along a highway, then after an hour we can deduce we are 65 miles east of our starting point.

The more information we can gather, then the more accurately we can make these deductions. If we knew the exact rate of acceleration, how much time we spend at stop signs or traffic lights, and our exact direction of travel, then we could make very accurate deductions.

In an aircraft, an autonomous navigation system must calculate direction in three dimensions: rates of acceleration, deceleration, and speed.

The Compass

An early navigation instrument that survives in aircraft to this day is the compass. The compass is an autonomous device, meaning it requires no radio signal to operate. It simply aligns its internal magnets with the earth's magnetic field and indicates direction. Shown in Figure 6-1-1A, the compass is simple and requires no power or signal, but it is susceptible to many errors. This topic is referenced under ATA code 34-20.

Climbing, descending, accelerating, decelerating, or turning will affect the compass indication. Furthermore, magnetic fields or objects near the compass can adversely affect accuracy.

Figure 6-1-1B. Compass showing a heading of 30°.

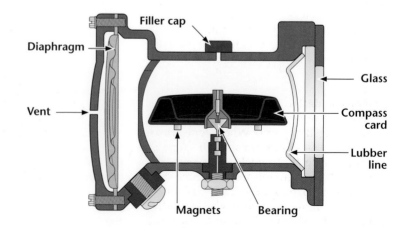

Figure 6-1-2. Construction of an aviation wet compass.

The aviation industry uses a wet compass. This means the compass magnets are attached to a compass card, also known as an azimuth card that is suspended in fluid. In an aviation wet compass, the compass or azimuth card is a cylinder marked in degrees. Behind the glass on the face of the instrument, a vertical bar called a *lubber line* is used to show the heading. As shown in Figure 6-1-1B, in order to read the heading a zero must be added to the markings on the compass card. For example, if the aircraft is heading 30 degrees, then the compass will show 3 under the lubber line.

Figure 6-1-2 shows the inner workings of an aviation wet compass.

The aviation wet compass consists of a sealed housing filled with kerosene. Inside the housing is a pedestal holding a jeweled bearing. The compass magnets are attached on the bottom of the compass card, which rests on a pivot on top of the bearing. The compass card also has a hollow section called a float, which helps keep the compass card upright in the proper position. The instrument is constructed with a rubber diaphragm at the rear to compensate for pressure changes, thus keeping large bubbles from forming inside the case. Below the compass card is an adjustable device called a *compensator*. A technician can adjust the compensator to reduce or eliminate errors caused by metal objects near the instrument panel. These errors are called *compass deviation*. Most airports have a compass rose painted on the ground where technicians may take the airplane and adjust the compass for deviation.

Magnetometers

A *magnetometer* is a solid state device used to sense the direction or strength of a magnetic field. For aircraft navigation purposes, engineers design magnetometers that focus on the direction of the magnetic field rather than the strength of the magnetic field. This is in contrast to magnetometers used by the Transportation Security Administration to detect the presence of hidden weaponry on a potential airline passenger.

Magnetometer design involves using up to three transducers mounted within an integrated circuit and arranged as part of Wheatstone bridge circuits. Figure 6-1-3 shows a simplified circuit diagram showing the transducer as part of a Wheatstone bridge circuit and the three axes the magnetometer measures. Each transducer is affected by movement through the earth's magnetic field, which will cause a resistance change within the transducer that affects the current flow within the bridge circuit.

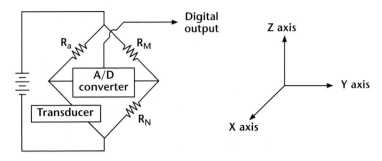

Figure 6-1-3. Magnetometer within a Wheatstone bridge circuit and measurement axes.

Magnetometer design is small enough to allow the device to be mounted on a small circuit card, with additional components installed to convert the current changes into digital signal outputs for use on a data bus.

Gyroscopic Principles

Some of the instruments used for autonomous navigation rely on gyroscopes, which are governed by a set of gyroscopic principles. A gyroscope is a rotating mass. One major principle or characteristic of a gyroscope is rigidity in space. Without any external force a rotating mass remains rigid in space. As a result, gyroscopes are useful in a variety of aircraft instruments.

Gyroscopes in aircraft instruments are built in the form of a spinning wheel or disk, usually called a *rotor*, that spin at rotation speeds of 10,000 r.p.m. or more. The rotor may be electrically or pneumatically driven. It is mounted in a gimbal, which is a device that supports the rotor while permitting it to move freely in any direction, as illustrated in Figure 6-1-4.

In some instruments the gimbals are constructed in such a way as to allow the rotor to rotate freely in all directions through 360° of

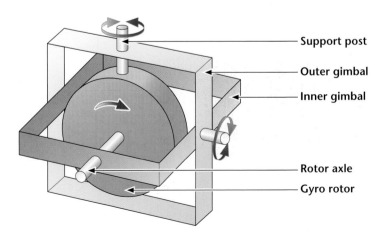

Figure 6-1-4. Gyro rotor mounted in two gimbal assemblies.

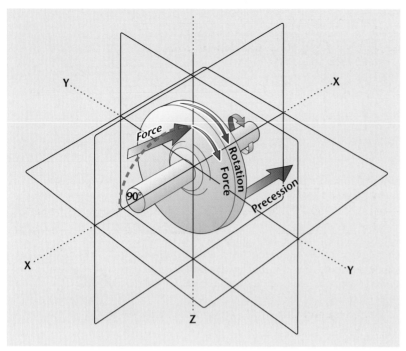

Figure 6-1-5. Precessive force.

movement. Other instruments are not so freely gimbaled. Extreme aircraft angles in either pitch or roll will cause the gimbal assembly to reach its limit. When the limit of movement is reached, the instrument indications become erratic as the rotor housing moves wildly from one limit to another attempting to reach its desired position. This erratic motion is known as *tumbling* or spilling.

Gyroscopic precession, or drift, is the change in direction of the axis of rotation due to forces applied to the gyroscope. In a gyroscopic instrument, gyroscopic precession creates errors. *Precessive force* is the characteristic of a gyroscope to react in a direction 90° to the direction of rotation from the point where the force was applied, as shown in Figure 6-1-5.

Although the bearings in the gimbal assembly and on the rotor axle are designed for a minimum of friction, a small amount of rotation resistance is still present. As a result, the bearings wear and a small amount of error, or drift, occurs as the gyro rotor reacts to friction induced precessive forces. When in operation, the rotation of the rotor distributes forces on the bearings so that damage due to sudden movements is minimized. When the rotor is not rotating, any sudden movement is not distributed on the bearings and more damage is likely. In order to keep bearing wear and damage to a minimum, technicians must handle gyroscopic instruments like eggs.

Instruments that rely on gyroscopes must account for precessive forces. These instruments must be corrected periodically, either manually by the pilot or automatically by an electronic or pneumatic system.

The rotor within a gyroscopic instrument may be electrically or pneumatically driven. An electrically driven rotor is constructed in the form of a motor with stator windings integrated into the rotor housing, as shown in Figure 6-1-6.

Gyro instruments with electrically driven rotors may be designed for AC or DC operation. The most common AC instruments are designed to operate at 26 VAC 400 Hz.

Pneumatically driven gyro rotors may be connected to either a pressure system or a vacuum system. For this reason, the connections on the back of the instrument are labeled air inlet and air outlet, as shown in Figure 6-1-7. Modern instruments require a pressure differential of approximately 5 inches of mercury and an adequate flow rate. Flow rate requirements vary between types and models of instruments but, typically, are between 1 and 5 cu. ft/min.

No matter what the drive system, these gyroscopic instruments are designed to measure and communicate position information to the pilot or to another system. For this reason, gyroscopic instruments are sometimes referred to as *displacement gyros*. A displacement gyro is defined as a gyroscope that measures and sends angular displacement data.

Directional Gyro

Shown in Figure 6-1-8, the *directional gyro,* or DG, is a gyroscopic instrument designed to provide the pilot with stable heading information. This topic is referenced under ATA code 34-20.

The stability of the DG gives it an advantage over the wet compass. Acceleration, decelera-

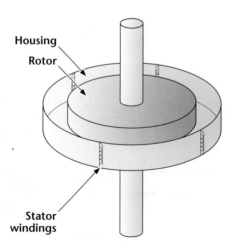

Figure 6-1-6. Electrically driven gyro rotor.

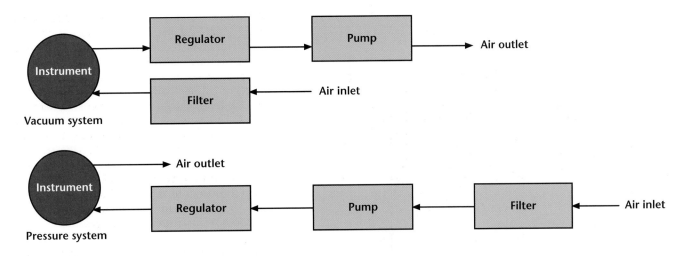

Figure 6-1-7. Different methods of driving a gyro pneumatically.

tion, turns, climbs, descents, and magnetic deviation forces have little or no effect on a directional gyro. Over time, the forces listed above, along with frictional forces will cause the directional gyro to *precess*, which creates a heading error. To precess is to move, or drift, in response to precessive forces.

Prior to taking off, the pilot pushes in the adjustment knob, shown in Figure 6-1-8 in the lower left hand corner, and turns it to match the heading shown on the DG with the heading shown on the compass. As a flight progresses, the pilot compares the heading indicated by the directional gyro with the compass indication and adjusts the DG to maintain accuracy. The pilot will need to repeat this adjustment approximately every 20 minutes.

Directional gyro construction. The directional gyro contains a gyroscope with its shaft mounted in gimbals and horizontally oriented,

as illustrated in Figure 6-1-9A and pictured in Figure 6-1-9B.

The gyro rotor may be operated electrically or pneumatically, and it is mounted within two gimbals. In a properly operating DG, the rotor spins at speeds in excess of 10,000 r.p.m. The gyro rotor is supported by small and relatively delicate bearings. When the rotor spins, the bearings also spin. As a result, sudden jarring forces are distributed across the bearing surfaces. When the rotor is stationary, so too are the bearings, which makes them more susceptible to damage. Technicians must execute extreme care when installing or removing a DG, since bearing damage will occur with the slightest bump.

The gimbal assembly in most directional gyros has limits. If the pilot were to orient the aircraft

Figure 6-1-8. Directional gyro.

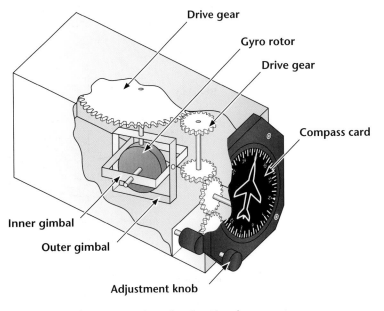

Figure 6-1-9A. The construction of a directional gyro.

Figure 6-1-9B. Internal mechanism of a directional gyro.

Figure 6-1-10. An electrically driven attitude gyro presented as an artificial horizon.

beyond 60° of pitch or roll, then the limits may be reached and the mechanism would lose its ability to hold the card steady. This loss of ability is known as a tumble or a spill.

The gimbals are connected via drive gears to the compass card, also known as an azimuth card. The compass card is a circular plate marked in degrees, as shown in Figure 6-1-9A. In order to read the heading, a zero must be added to the markings on the compass card. For example, if the aircraft's heading is 60°, then the directional gyro will indicate six.

In most small aircraft, the directional gyro is one unit that is mounted in the instrument panel. In larger aircraft, and in some small aircraft, the directional gyro is mounted remotely and drives a compass card in a panel-mounted instrument. Typically, remote-mounted gyros are part of a slaved compass system.

Attitude Indicating Gyros

Attitude indicating gyroscopic instruments, or *attitude gyros*, are used to display the angle of the aircraft about the lateral and longitudinal axes. In other words, these instruments indicate roll and pitch information. In the aviation industry attitude indicating gyros are known by several names, and they may be pneumatically or electrically driven. They are often referred to as vertical gyros when the shaft of the rotor is mounted vertically. Another name for the instrument, artificial horizon, is derived from the method of information presentation. This name, along with attitude indicator, are the two most common names for these instruments, but technicians may also encounter

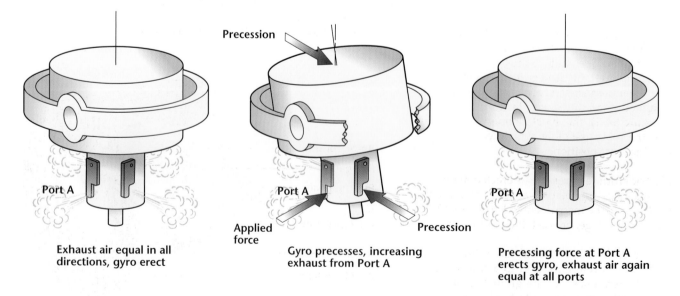

Figure 6-1-11. Pendulums and air holes used to erect the rotor housing.

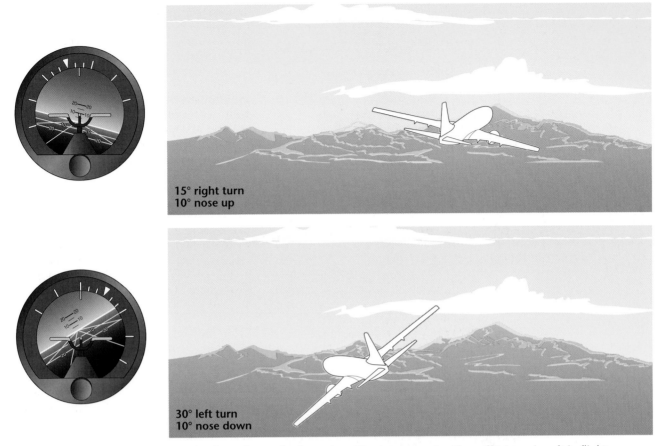

15° right turn
10° nose up

30° left turn
10° nose down

Figure 6-1-12A. Variations in pitch and roll are shown, both on the attitude gyro and as they affect an aircraft in flight.

references to attitude gyro, gyro horizon, or horizon gyro, which are other terms used for attitude indicating gyroscopic instruments. In this text the term attitude gyro will be used. An attitude gyro presented as an artificial horizon is shown in Figure 6-1-10. This topic is referenced under ATA code 34-20.

Construction. The gimbals within an attitude gyro are constructed to allow rotor assembly movement in all directions. In order to indicate properly, the instrument must start out with the rotor shaft in the vertical, or erect, position. Pneumatic instruments have a system of weighted pendulums, similar to those shown in Figure 6-1-11, that block or open air jets built into the rotor assembly, which force the gyro into the erect position.

Electric attitude gyros can be erected manually, known as *caging*, before takeoff. For example, the knob on the instrument in Figure 6-1-10 can be pulled to cage, or erect, the rotor housing.

The rotor housing gimbal assembly is connected via a reference arm to a card called a horizon reference. As the gimbal rotates, the movement is transferred to the horizon reference. When erect, the horizon indicates level and the horizon line aligns with the symbolic

aircraft. Markings on the face of the instrument and on the horizon reference indicate to the pilot the amount of movement in degrees around the lateral or longitudinal axes. For example, the top attitude gyro in Figure 6-1-12A is displaying roll of 15° and pitch at 10° up; the illustration to the right depicts the corresponding angle of the aircraft flying at that heading. Likewise, the bottom attitude gyro and illustration show the instrument

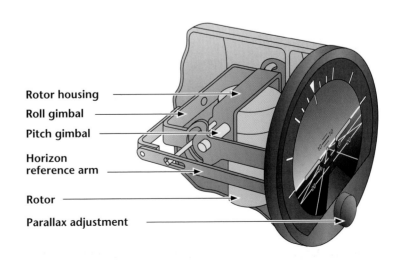

Rotor housing

Roll gimbal

Pitch gimbal

Horizon reference arm

Rotor

Parallax adjustment

Figure 6-1-12B. Internal mechanism of an attitude gyro.

Figure 6-1-13A. Flux detector.

indications and the aircraft angle with a 30° roll left and a 10° pitch down. A knob in the lower center of the attitude gyro (Figure 6-1-12A) adjusts the symbolic aircraft up or down to compensate for parallax caused by different seating positions or pilots of different heights. Figure 6-1-12B shows the internal mechanism of an attitude gyro.

Like a directional gyro, the attitude gyro is susceptible to precession. The erection mechanism in pneumatic instruments exerts a corrective force while the aircraft is in level flight; however, if the pilot remains in turn for an unusually long period of time, then the centrifugal force may cause the artificial horizon to re-erect and show level flight. Electric instruments may need to be recaged periodically.

Slaved Compass Systems

The *slaved compass system* is a set of electronic devices that indicate heading that has been corrected for errors. This topic is referenced under ATA code 34-20. Like a simple compass,

the slaved compass system determines direction by measuring the earth's magnetic field. Unlike a simple compass, the slaved compass system uses a gyro, a sensor, and electronics to correct for error. The heading information can be presented on a variety of instruments, the most common of which provides a simple, comprehensive visual display of the aircraft's heading and position in relation to a desired course. Alternate names for the slaved compass system include;

- Compass system,
- Heading system, and
- Slaved heading system.

There are five main components of the slaved compass system: the flux detector, gyro, coupler, slaving control, and an indicator.

Flux Detector

The *flux detector* is a device used in slaved compass systems that detects the aircraft's orientation in relation to the earth's magnetic flux lines. Other names for the flux detector include:

- Flux valve
- Flux gate
- Magnetic azimuth transmitter
- Magnetic Slaving transmitter
- Magnetic flux sensor

By whatever name the unit is known, it is designed as a toroidal three-phase transformer with an easily saturated, laminated core. A flux detector is pictured in Figure 6-1-13A and a schematic for a typical flux detector is shown in Figure 6-1-13B.

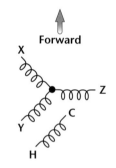

Figure 6-1-13B. A schematic of a flux detector.

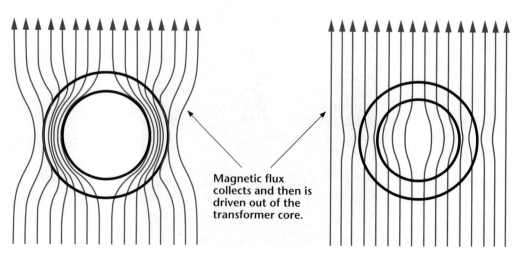

Magnetic flux collects and then is driven out of the transformer core.

Figure 6-1-14. Magnetic flux movement in flux detector transformer core.

The transformer must be oriented toward the nose of the aircraft. The earth's magnetic force collects in the core of the transformer, as shown in Figure 6-1-14. The H and C windings are used to excite the transformer, driving it into saturation and, thus, forcing out the flux from the earth's magnetic field. As the flux lines are forced out, they induce a small voltage and current signal that can be amplified and used to determine aircraft orientation.

Figure 6-1-15 shows the relationship between the excitation signal applied to the flux detector, saturation levels, and output signals. The signal induced by the earth's magnetic field is very small and only appears at the points where the excitation and saturation levels are crossing zero.

The compass system uses these very small voltage spikes to determine heading.

The flux detector must be mounted as far as possible from ferrous metals that could affect accuracy. In general, flux detectors are mounted in wing tips or in the tips of horizontal stabilizers.

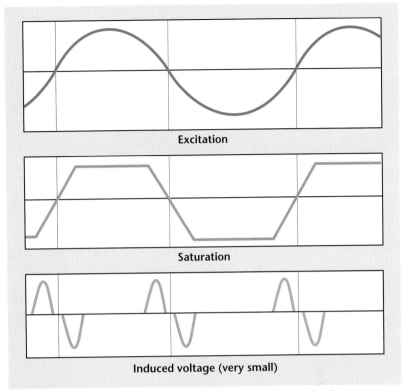

Figure 6-1-15. Excitation, core saturation level, and induced voltage.

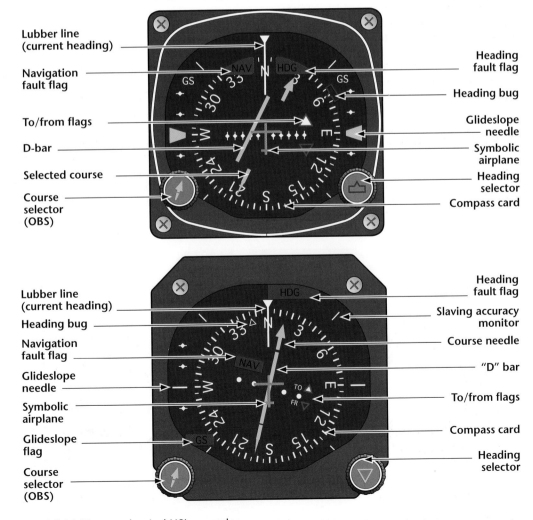

Figure 6-1-16. Two mechanical HSI examples.

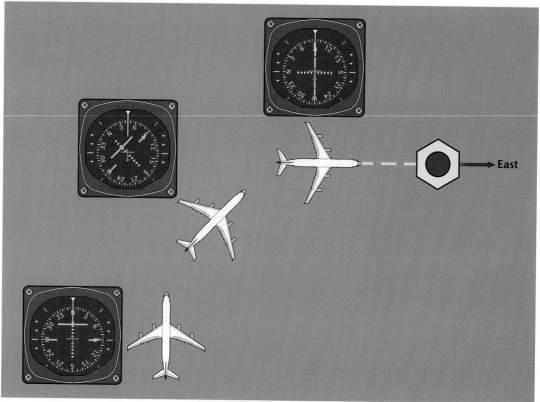

Figure 6-1-17. HSI indications when intercepting a course.

Horizontal Situation Indicator

The *horizontal situation indicator* (HSI) may also be known as a pictorial navigation indicator (PNI), and it is an instrument that shows the pilot heading, course, glideslope information and, in some cases, more information. This topic is referenced under ATA code 34-20. Originally engineers designed the HSI as a mechanical instrument; however, pilots appreciated the presentation method so much, electronic instruments use the same presentation

type. Some electronic instruments are known as electronic horizontal situation indicators, or EHSI. As shown in Figure 6-1-16, the HSI includes a compass card, which makes it similar to a DG, and it has several elements used to present the pilot with navigation information.

These elements include fault flags and deviation and to/from indicators. In addition, the course selector also works as an omnibearing selector for the VOR system. The course indicator, deviation bar, and to/from indicator rotate with the

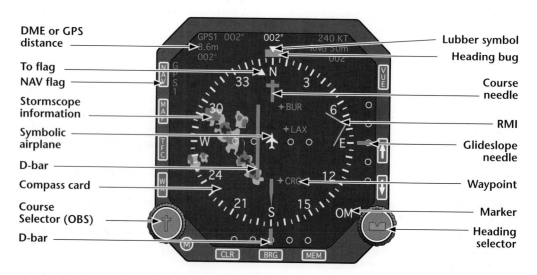

Figure 6-1-18. Electronic HSI.

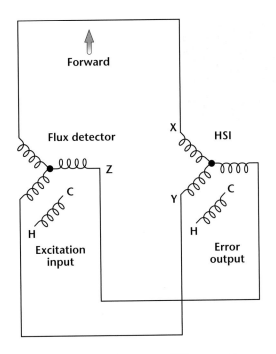

Figure 6-1-19. Flux detector to HSI connection.

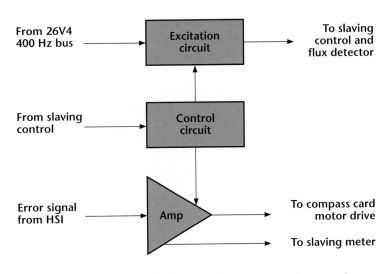

Figure 6-1-20. Simplified block diagram of a compass system coupler.

compass card, thus giving the pilot an overall sky view of his or her horizontal situation. An example of how navigation information is displayed during flight is shown in Figure 6-1-17. In the lower left corner of the illustration, the aircraft is on a heading of 0°, or north. In the upper right, the course is shown passing through a VOR station. The pilot has selected a course of 90°, or east. The elements on the display show the course is ahead of the aircraft, and the course is toward, or to, the station. The pilot turns right to a heading of 45° to intercept the course. As the aircraft approaches the course, the deviation bar gets closer to the center of the instrument. Finally, when the aircraft is on course and heading east, the deviation bar lines up with the course needle, which is now straight up and down.

An EHSI has the capability of showing much more information, as the illustration in Figure 6-1-18 shows. In this case, a moving map, waypoints, marker beacon, distance information, and much more is shown.

Inside a mechanical HSI, a synchronous motor is connected to the flux detector, as shown in Figure 6-1-19.

The unique electromagnetic current, phase, and voltage signature produced in the flux detector is repeated in the HSI motor windings. Unlike other synchronous motors, excitation cannot be used to align the rotor (H and C) properly, since the signals produced by the earth's magnetic field are at a very low level. Instead, the rotor winding is used to produce an error output.

Compass System Coupler and Control

Compass systems include a *coupler*, which is a device designed to send an excitation signal to the flux detector, receive an error signal from the HSI and then process the signal to drive the compass card. This topic is referenced under ATA code 34-20. In some systems, the coupler may be known as a slaving amplifier. The compass system coupler is monitored and controlled using a slaving control, or compass compensator. The slaving control allows the pilot to monitor system accuracy via a slaving meter, deactivate slaving, and, in some cases, manually rotate the compass card in the HSI. Moreover, the slaving control may have adjustments that can compensate for flux detector accuracy errors caused by magnetic disturbances within the airframe.

As shown in Figure 6-1-20, the coupler has two main functions. The first is to provide excitation to the slaving control and the flux detector. The second is to amplify and process the error output from the HSI, so a motor can rotate the compass card.

In some systems, the excitation circuit processes the 26 V 400 Hz bus voltage for passage on to the slaving control and flux detector. Other systems create an excitation voltage independent of any aircraft bus.

The amplifier receives the error signal from the synchronous motor within the HSI, as shown in Figure 6-1-21, then amplifies it, as necessary, to drive a motor with a mechanical connection to the synchronous motor rotor and the compass card.

Figure 6-1-22 shows a generic external block diagram of an entire compass system. In this

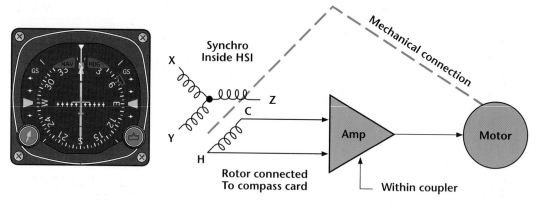

Figure 6-1-21. Compass card drive process.

case, as in most cases, the gyro is allowed to run freely and precess at will. Allowing the compass to precess reduces wear on the gyro rotor bearings. Furthermore, it takes less energy to correct a compass card than to force a gyro assembly to a new position.

There may be variation between systems from different manufacturers. In some systems the gyro may be included in the HSI. In other systems the coupler and gyro may be in a single assembly. There can be several variations, but no matter what the physical layout, all compass systems accomplish these processes.

In this case, the coupler amplifies the error signal from the HSI to create a compass card correction signal of enough amplitude to drive a motor. Furthermore, the coupler creates excitation for both the flux detector and the slaving control.

The flux detector is remote mounted and provides a three-phase signal to the HSI. The slaving control acts as a control head for the system and, as shown in Figure 6-1-22, provides

compensation for magnetic deviations within the airframe.

The HSI is connected to the navigation system, so dependant navigation information can be displayed.

Accelerometers

Accelerometers are devices that measure acceleration forces. There are many different types of accelerometers, some of which are small enough to work within a cell phone, which is why smart phones are able to re-orient the display based on the orientation of the phone. An accelerometer like the one pictured in Figure 6-1-23 is commonly used on some types of aircraft.

There are two types of acceleration measured by accelerometers, static and dynamic. *Static acceleration*, as its name implies, is unchanging, such as the constant force of gravity. *Dynamic acceleration* is a change in the increase or decrease in velocity caused by movement.

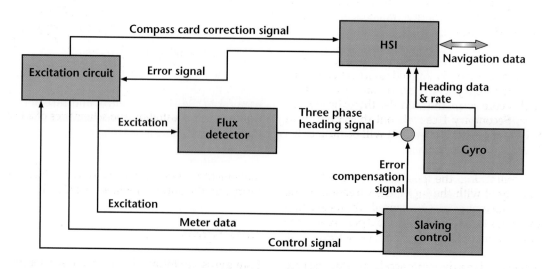

Figure 6-1-22. Generic external block diagram of a compass system.

Figure 6-1-23. Accelerometer.

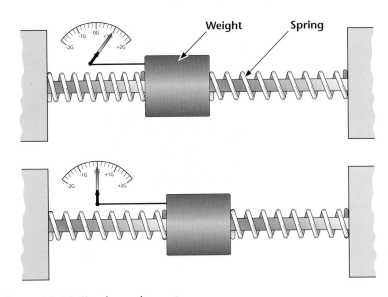

Figure 6-1-24. Simple accelerometers.

Accelerometers can be used to sense aircraft movement, and with the help of microprocessors, can be used to determine aircraft attitude.

Simple Accelerometers

The simplest types of accelerometers may use a weight attached at each end with springs, as shown in Figure 6-1-24. The weight may move the arm of a potentiometer or the needle of an instrument. Autonomous navigation systems use more sensitive accelerometers like those described below.

Linear voltage differential transducer. The *linear voltage differential transducer* (LVDT) is a transformer device with a core that can move in a linear direction, as shown in Figure 6-1-25. An LVDT has a single primary winding and two secondary windings. One of the secondary windings is wound so energy transfers in the same phase as the excitation. The other winding is wound so energy transfers 180° out of phase with the excitation.

As the core moves from side to side, energy from the primary is coupled to either Secondary 1 or Secondary 2, as shown in Figure 6-1-26. If the core is in the middle, then the output from Secondary 1 cancels out the signal from Secondary 2, and the output will be null, or 0.0 VAC.

By comparing the phase of the LVDT output signal with the input, the direction of the core movement can be sensed. By measuring the amplitude of the LVDT output signal, the amount of core movement can be sensed.

When used in a dynamic accelerometer, the core is supported with springs at each end. Aircraft

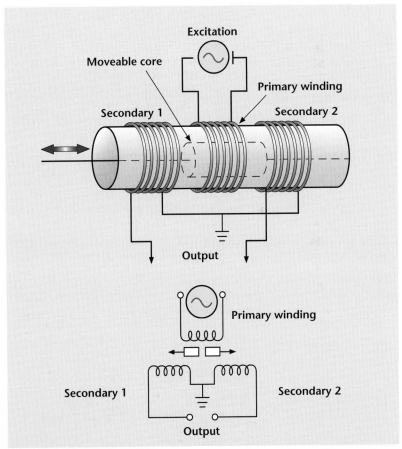

Figure 6-1-25. Illustration and schematics of a linear voltage differential transducer.

movement causes the core to move within the form, and the output changes accordingly.

Rate Gyros

Rate gyros are forms of gyroscopic accelerometers and have been used in aircraft for many

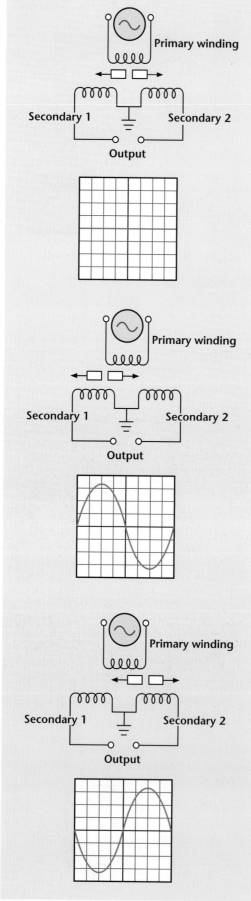

Figure 6-1-26. Schematics showing examples of LVDT outputs.

decades. Pilots know rate gyros as turn and slip indicators, turn and bank indicators, or turn coordinators. Some simple autopilot systems will use either the turn and bank indicator or a rate gyro mounted within the autopilot system. This topic is referenced under ATA code 34-20.

Turn and bank indicator. A *turn and bank indicator*, also called a turn and slip indicator, is constructed with the gyro rotor mounted horizontally, as shown in Figure 6-1-27. The face of the instrument includes an inclinometer to indicate slips and skids, which are unwanted sideways movements of the aircraft, a pointer to indicate turn direction, and standard rate turn markings, known as doghouses, to indicate *two-minute turns*. A two-minute turn is a turn at a rate of 360° in two minutes. Large or fast aircraft may use indicators marked as half standard rate, or four-minute turns, which display turns of 360° in four minutes. An example of a turn and bank indicator is pictured in Figure 6-1-28.

Movement around the vertical axis is known as yaw movement. When the aircraft exhibits yaw movement, precessive forces tilt the gimbal, which in turn moves the needle in the direction of the turn. Movement around the longitudinal axis of the aircraft is known as bank, or roll, movements. Since the gyro shaft is aligned with the lateral axis of the aircraft, the turn and bank indicator does not react to banking movements around the longitudinal axis. The amount of gyro tilt caused by yaw motion is related to acceleration around the vertical axis of the aircraft.

Turn coordinator. Turn coordinators are constructed in a similar way to turn and bank indicators. An example of a turn coordinator is pictured in Figure 6-1-29. The main difference between the two instruments is the manner in which the gyro gimbal is designed. As shown in Figure 6-1-30, turn coordinators have a gimbal tilted at approximately 35°.

Since the plane of the gimbal is tilted, the rotor is able to tilt in reaction to both banking and yawing motions. Turn coordinators include an inclinometer to indicate slipping or skidding motion. Most turn coordinators use a symbolic airplane symbol and markings to indicate standard two-minute rates of turn. The amount of gyro tilt caused by yaw motion is related to acceleration around both the vertical and longitudinal axes of the aircraft.

Solid-State Accelerometers

Piezoelectric accelerometers. *Piezoelectric accelerometers* are solid-state devices that use the piezoelectric effect shown by quartz

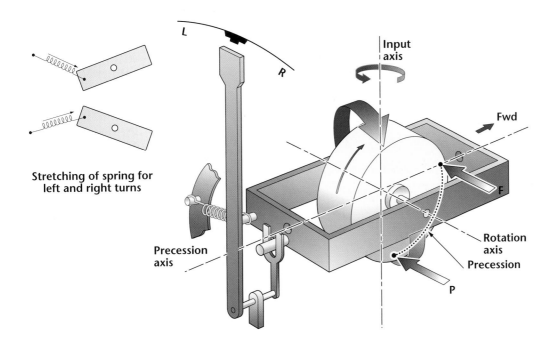

Figure 6-1-27. Internal mechanism of a turn and bank indicator.

Figure 6-1-28. Turn and slip indicator.

Figure 6-1-29. Turn coordinator or turn and bank indicator.

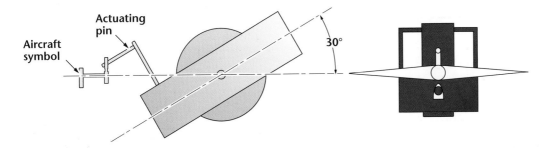

Figure 6-1-30. Internal mechanism of a turn coordinator.

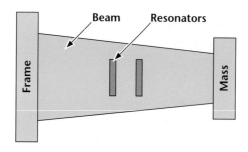

Figure 6-1-31. Inside of a SAW-type MEMS.

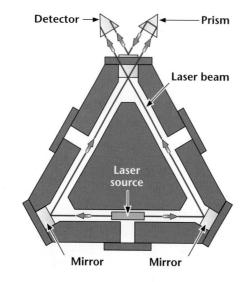

Figure 6-1-32. Laser ring gyro.

crystals. An accelerometer uses microscopic crystal structures that create small voltages when stressed.

Capacitive accelerometers. A *capacitive accelerometer* is designed with a tiny, nearly microscopic capacitor with movable plates. Like the

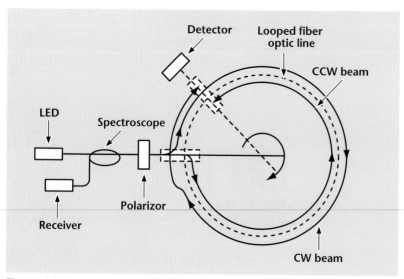

Figure 6-1-33. Fiber optic gyro construction.

piezoelectric accelerometer, capacitive accelerometers are solid state devices. G-forces move the capacitor plates a small amount, thus changing the capacitance, which, in turn, changes capacitive reactance. This change can be detected and used to measure acceleration.

Micro-electro-mechanical systems. A common type of accelerometer used in autonomous navigation systems are a type of solid-state or silicon inertial sensors known as *micro-electro-mechanical systems,* or MEMS. One type of MEMS uses an extremely small moving mass. In theory, these work like the accelerometers described at the beginning of this section by measuring the displacement of a moving mass. In the case of MEMS, the moving mass and related components are very small.

A second type of MEMS is of the surface acoustic wave variety, or SAW. In this case, resonating elements are placed on a beam suspended between a frame and a mass, as shown in Figure 6-1-31. In the case of a SAW-type MEMS, a change in tension on the beam shown in Figure 6-1-31, causes a change in frequency of the resonators. As a result, acceleration is measured as a change in frequency.

Laser Gyroscopes

Although these devices are called gyroscopes, in reality, they are very precise accelerometers. When multiple units are connected to microprocessors as described below, they can serve the same purpose as a traditional gyroscope. This topic is referenced under ATA code 34-20.

Laser ring gyroscope. A *laser ring gyroscope* is a solid-state device that senses phase changes due to movement or acceleration of counter-rotating laser beams. These devices may also be known as ring laser gyros. The basic component of a laser ring is shown in Figure 6-1-32.

Within the laser ring gyro, laser beams travel in both directions around a path controlled by mirrors and a prism. Many laser ring gyros use a triangular path, however some use a rectangular path. When the device rotates one of the laser beams has a longer path to travel. As a result, the light frequencies lower and a phase difference between the beams is sensed by the detector. The information from the detector is processed by a microprocessor that calculates the turn rate. Since each ring serves only one axis, three ring gyros are required for attitude information in three axes.

An advantage of laser ring gyros is the lack of precession. Since there are no moving parts, there are no bearings and, as a result, no friction. A frictionless system does not precess. Other advantages include high tolerance to vibration, relatively small size, and high precision. Although a laser ring gyro system is expensive, the cost of maintenance is very low. Disadvantages of laser ring gyros include their high initial cost and their tendency to go into a condition called lock in.

During very slow turn rates, the phase difference between the laser beams is also very small. In this case, the two beams couple together and "lock in," thus indicating no acceleration. Complex laser ring gyro systems include a system to *dither* the assembly. Dithering is a mechanical movement of the laser ring gyro assembly. In dithered systems the movement must be accounted for by a microprocessor that processes the signal to remove the movement caused by the dithering motion.

Laser ring gyros can give very precise information to a microprocessor, which can convert the data into attitude or direction indications. Since they are not affected by precessive forces or friction, laser ring gyros have become a popular replacement for attitude and directional gyros.

Fiber-optic gyro. The fiber-optic gyroscope, sometimes referred to as a FOG, works using the same principles as the laser ring gyro but differs in construction, as shown in Figure 6-1-33. Like the laser ring gyro, the fiber-optic gyro measures the phase difference between laser beams traveling in opposite directions.

The fiber-optic loop may have over 1 km of fiber looped into the coil. Fiber-optic gyros have the same advantages and disadvantages as laser ring gyros.

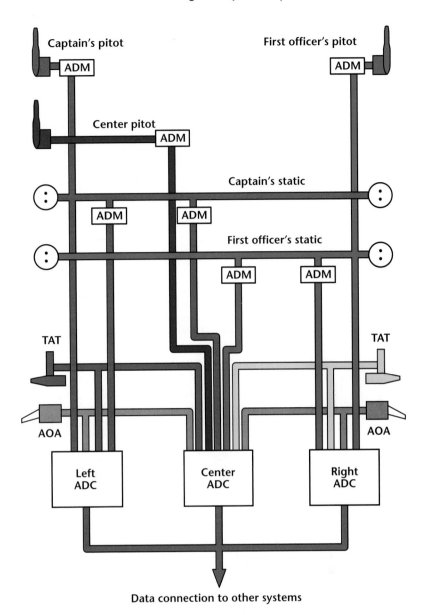

Figure 6-2-1. Schematic of an air data system.

Section 2

Air Data Systems

An *air data system* measures several parameters regarding the ambient air around an aircraft and the state of flight relative to the ambient air. In large aircraft the air data system includes the pitot system, static system, angle of attack measurement, and outside, or total, air temperature. Many air data systems are integrated closely with an inertial reference system. The inertial reference system is described in more detail in succeeding paragraphs. Figure 6-2-1 shows a schematic representation of an air data system. This topic is referenced under ATA code 34-10.

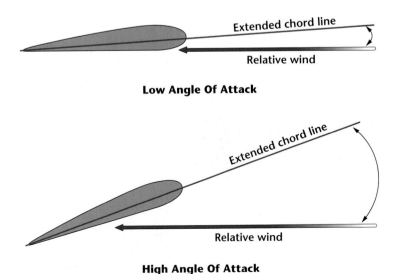

Figure 6-2-2. Low and high angles of attack.

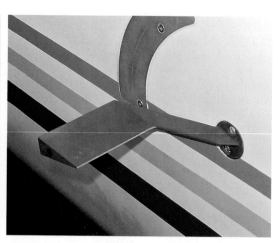

Figure 6-2-3. Angle of attack sensors.

The air data system in Figure 6-2-1 uses four pitot tubes. The captain's, first officer's, and center pitot tubes each connect to an *air data module* (ADM), which converts the air pressure to digital signals. The standby pitot tube is connected directly to a standby air speed indicator (ASI). The static system is also triple redundant, with captain's, first officer's, and alternate ports on each side of the aircraft. The captain's and first officer's static systems each include two ADMs. The alternate static system is connected directly to the cabin differential pressure indicator and both standby instruments. Probes on each side of the aircraft measure *angle of attack* (AOA), which is the angle between the chord line of the wing and the direction of *relative wind*. Relative wind is the movement of air caused by the movement of an aircraft.

Examples of high and low angles of attack are shown in Figure 6-2-2. Angle of attack sensors, or probes, are shown in Figure 6-2-3, and an angle of attack display is pictured in Figure 6-2-4.

Outside air temperature is measured by a *total air temperature* probe on each side of the aircraft, and this data is also fed to the air data system. Total air temperature is the ambient temperature taken at the probe and compensated for pressure caused by aircraft movement.

Airspeed Information

Sophisticated systems such as an air data system and the systems described in succeeding pages are able to show airspeed in different ways.

Indicated Airspeed

Indicated airspeed (IAS) is the speed read directly on a simple airspeed indicator, which measures the pressure difference between the pitot system and the static system. This ratio is displayed as airspeed. In some small or old aircraft the airspeed is shown in miles per hour. In newer or large aircraft the airspeed is shown in knots or nautical miles per hour. As altitude increases, the indicated airspeed decreases.

Calibrated Airspeed

Calibrated airspeed (CAS) is the speed measured by the difference in air pressure between the pitot system and the static system that has been adjusted to correct for system errors. In a simple system, calibrated airspeed is close to the speed shown on the airspeed indicator. As altitude increases, the calibrated airspeed decreases.

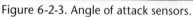

Figure 6-2-4. Angle of attack display.

Figure 6-3-1. Examples of attitude and heading reference systems (AHRS).

True Airspeed

True airspeed is calibrated airspeed corrected for ambient air density. As altitude increases, air density decreases, and the difference between TAS and CAS or IAS increases.

Mach number. *Mach number* is a ratio of true airspeed to the speed of sound. Mach 1.0 indicates aircraft speed is the same as sound speed. Mach numbers less than one indicate aircraft speed is subsonic; Mach numbers greater than one indicate the aircraft is going faster than the speed of sound, or supersonic. Speeds close to Mach 1.0 are referred to as transonic speeds. Hypersonic speeds are those above Mach 5. Since the speed of sound changes with air density and temperature, Mach must be calculated using air density, temperature, and true airspeed.

Section 3

Attitude and Heading Reference Systems

Attitude and heading reference systems are rapidly replacing mechanical gyroscopes and mechanical instruments, such as airspeed, altitude, and vertical speed indicators. Mechanical instruments use either an *aneroid*, which is a sealed expandable container or *bellows*, which is an expandable chamber connected to either the pitot or static system. The aneroid or bellows are connected mechanically to a moveable indicator needle on the face of the instrument. The topics discussed in this section are referenced under ATA code 34-20.

Attitude Heading Reference System

An *attitude heading reference system* (AHRS) uses precise accelerometers and computers to determine the aircraft attitude. Furthermore, it uses magnetometers to determine heading. AHRS are relatively small. In most cases, the AHRS is mounted remotely, and the attitude and direction information is presented on the electronic flight instrumentation system displays. Two examples of AHRS are shown in Figure 6-3-1.

AHRS must be mounted in such a way to be aligned with the axes of the aircraft, level, and as close to the centerline as possible. If mounted improperly, the AHRS gives false indications of attitude.

As shown in Figure 6-3-2, the AHRS system is connected to the aircraft power bus and to the EFIS. A flux valve or magnetometer is used to determine magnetic heading. Typically, flux valves are mounted in wing tips or in the tips of horizontal stabilizers. Some systems include

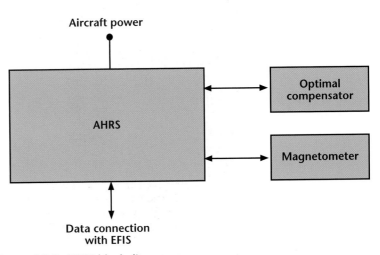

Figure 6-3-2. AHRS block diagram.

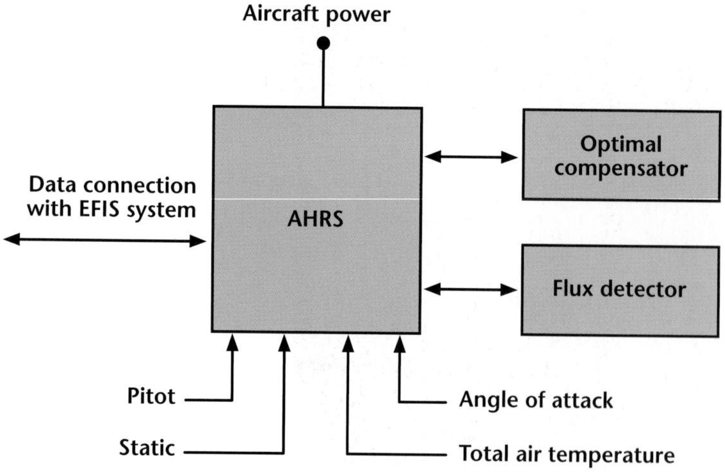

Figure 6-3-3. Block diagram of a single ADHRS system.

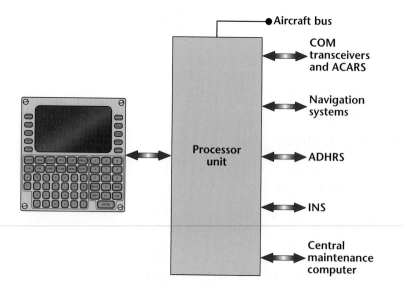

Figure 6-4-1. Control display unit (CDU).

Figure 6-4-2. Flight management system block diagram.

a compass system compensator mounted in the instrument panel. Pilots with panel mounted compensators can monitor slaving accuracy and, if necessary, disable automatic heading adjustments.

Air Data Heading Reference System

Like an AHRS, the *air data heading reference system* (ADHRS) uses precise accelerometers, computers, and elements of a slaved compass system to determine aircraft attitude and heading. In addition, ADHRS supplies air data. As shown in Figure 6-3-3, in large aircraft the ADHRS includes the pitot system, static system, angle of attack measurement, and outside, or total, air temperature. ADHRS in small aircraft may not include angle of attack and may have a simple outside air temperature sensor.

A full featured ADHRS system used on transport category and large business jets provides the flight crew with the following data:

- Attitude information
  - Roll
  - Pitch
  - Yaw
- Heading information
- Airspeed information
  - Calibrated airspeed
  - True airspeed
  - Mach number
- Altitude
  - Altitude trend
- Temperature
  - Static air temperature
  - Total air temperature

Typical transport category aircraft have multiple ADHRS; typical small aircraft have only one ADHRS and use traditional pitot static instruments for redundancy.

Section 4

Flight Management Systems

A *flight management system* (FMS) is a computer system with a database that can communicate with and control virtually all the avionic systems in the aircraft. Most flight management systems include a control display unit (CDU), also referred to as a multifunction control display unit (MCDU), as shown in Figure 6-4-1, and a flight management processor unit mounted remotely from the instrument panel. The topics discussed in this section are referenced under ATA code 34-60.

The CDU contains an LCD or CRT display with multifunction buttons along either side. Below the display are mode buttons and an alpha numeric keyboard. Pilots can communicate with all connected avionic systems using the display and keys on the CDU.

The flight management processor unit contains a database with standard instrument departure procedures (SID), standard instrument arrival procedures (STAR), airway, jetway, VORTAC locations and frequencies, VOR/DME locations with frequencies, instrument flight intersections, gate locations, runway locations, and airport approach procedures, including waypoints. A flight management system can retain several flight plans in memory for the flight crew to recall at will.

Airways and jetways are highways in the sky, which lead between navigation stations. Airways are designed for low altitude flight, and jetways are designed for high altitude flight.

The FMS is integrated with other avionic systems and may include various adaptors and interface units for compatibility purposes. A typical block diagram of an FMS is shown in Figure 6-4-2. Often an aircraft is equipped with multiple flight management systems: large airliners may have three.

Prior to takeoff, the flight crew is able to use the FMS to enter communication frequencies and flight plans into the communication and navigation systems. During operation an FMS monitors all navigation systems and sensors. Using the navigation data from all sources, the FMS presents the pilot with the most accurate navigation data in real time. As the flight progresses, the FMS uses the flight plan data to automatically change VOR and DME frequencies, taking the responsibility away from the flight crew. Moreover, the flight crew uses the FMS and its CDU to communicate with and control the inertial navigation system.

Since the FMS receives air data, information regarding head winds, drift angles, etc., can be displayed on the CDU screen. In addition, the flight crew may enter fuel and weight information into the FMS. As a result, the CDU is able to calculate and display fuel use and reserves in real time.

Figure 6-5-1. Inertial reference unit (IRU).

Section 5

Inertial Navigation and Inertial Reference Systems

Elements of the systems described earlier in this chapter can be combined in a way to produce an extremely accurate deduced reckoning system. An *inertial reference system* (IRS) uses a combination of gyroscopes and accelerometers to determine the attitude of the aircraft. An IRS also has navigational capabilities. The topics discussed in this section are referenced under ATA code 34-40.

An inertial navigation system (INS) navigates by measuring acceleration, speed, and direction traveled from a known starting point. To accomplish this, an INS uses a navigation computer that receives information from extremely accurate gyroscopes, accelerometers, compass systems, and air data systems.

Inertial Reference System

Inertial Reference Unit

At the heart of an IRS is a platform consisting of three laser gyros and three accelerometers. Older systems used gimbaled mechanical gyros on the platform. Modern systems are accurate enough to eliminate any need for flux detectors to determine true north. The gyro platform is contained within an LRU, called an inertial reference unit (IRU) that is mounted in the aircraft's equipment bay. Figure 6-5-1 shows a IRU.

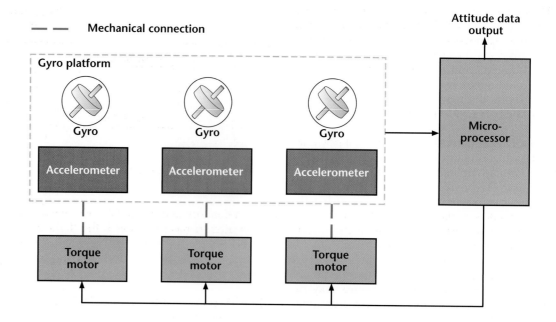

Figure 6-5-2. Simplified stable platform IRU block diagram.

Stable Platform

There are two types of platforms for IRUs. The first is known as a stable platform. A simplified block diagram of a stable platform IRU is shown in Figure 6-5-2.

The stable platform, which may be referred to as a tilt table, is gimbaled and uses gyros and motors to maintain platform stability and alignment with magnetic north and *local vertical*. Local vertical is a direction indicated by an imaginary line drawn from the earth's center to the center of the aircraft. A simple way to get a close approxima-

tion of local vertical is with a *plumb bob*. A plumb bob is a weight at the end of a string, which is used in the construction industry to determine vertical.

The stable platform, or table, tilts in relation to the airframe in order to remain level with the earth. The gyros, especially laser gyros, on the stable platform are sensitive enough to react to earth rotation. The system uses the motors to torque or move the platform back to a level state. Without the torque motors, the platform will tilt at approximately 15° per hour, which is the rate at which the earth rotates.

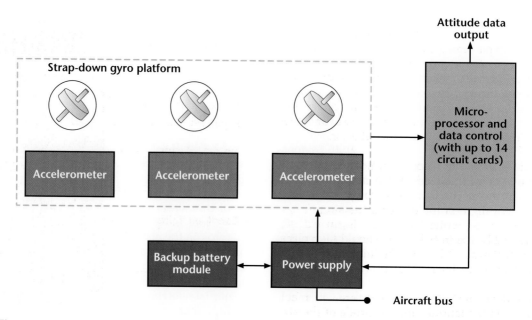

Figure 6-5-3. Simplified strapdown IRU block diagram.

The IRU microprocessor receives data from the gyros and the accelerometers. Furthermore, the microprocessor monitors attitude errors and activates the appropriate torque motor to move the platform back into alignment.

Strapdown Platform

The second type of gyro platform is known as a strapdown platform. A simplified block diagram of an IRU with a strapdown platform is shown in Figure 6-5-3.

The strapdown platform is fastened directly to the airframe. An IRS utilizing a strapdown platform may be referred to as a strapdown system, or strapdown IRS. Technicians should note strapdown systems are not necessarily rigidly mounted. These platforms may be installed using vibration reducing grommets or shock mounts.

The microprocessor in a strapdown IRU computes errors caused by the earth's rotation and other disturbances and corrects the data before sending the attitude data out to other systems.

IRS Architecture

Typically, an IRS provides attitude information to the EFIS, FMS, INS, IFCS, stabilized weather radar, antiskid system, and the flight data recorder. Although an IRS may be integrated with other systems, some are designed to operate independently. Figure 6-5-4 shows a block diagram of a stand-alone IRS.

The IRS control is mounted on the flight deck, typically in the overhead panel and controls multiple IRUs. The IRU is mounted with other LRUs in the equipment bay. The main power for the system is supplied to the IRU. Typically, on transport category aircraft three inertial reference systems are installed. The IRU provides pitch attitude, roll attitude, flight path vector, ground speed, and positional data to other systems in the aircraft. Furthermore, the IRU receives positional data from the FMS or GNSS to initialize or correct positional errors.

Before an IRS can report attitude information, it must be initialized, which may take up to ten minutes, and it must be completed before the first flight of the day or if the aircraft has been moved while the system is turned off. Preferably, the initialization should take place on level ground. During the initialization process, the aircraft cannot be moved.

Initialization starts with a flight crew member entering the latitude and longitude of the aircraft. Most systems hold the last known posi-

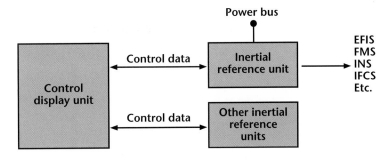

Figure 6-5-4. External IRS block diagram.

tion in memory and display it upon power up. If the aircraft has not moved, the flight crew can accept the position and the initialization can proceed. Figure 6-5-5 shows a control display unit for an IRS.

The IRS control display unit (IRSCDU) may also be known as a mode selector. The unit contains a multifunction display that can display ground track, ground speed, present position, wind speed, or heading, depending on the position of the display selector knob. The information may be displayed from the left, center, or right IRS, depending on the system selector setting. Each IRS has its own align light, condition lights, and mode selector. The keyboard between the multifunction display and the align light is used by the flight crew to enter position data into the system.

In the Boeing 757 system pictured in Figure 6-5-5, the align light is illuminated steadily while the system is in align mode and for 30 seconds as the system goes through the shutdown sequence. If the align light is flashing, then an error in data entry has occurred, the

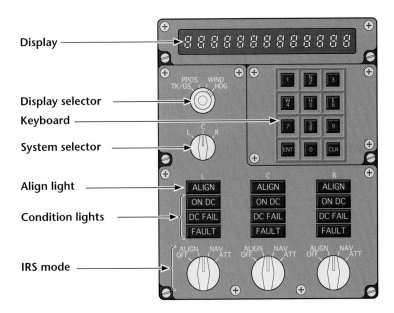

Figure 6-5-5. IRS control display unit.

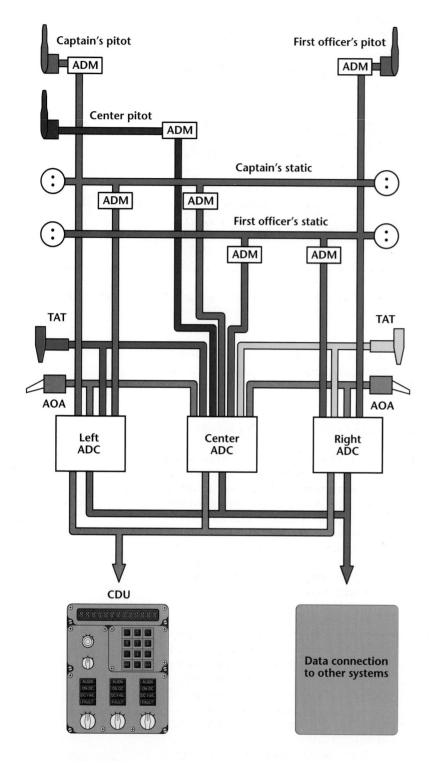

Figure 6-5-6A. Triple redundant ADIRU system and a single LRU.

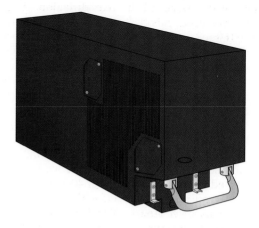

Figure 6-5-6B. Triple redundant ADIRU system and a single LRU.

Mode selectors for each IRS are located below the condition lights. In the off position, the alignment is lost. Placing the mode selector in the align position initiates the alignment when the aircraft is parked or initiates a quick alignment if the system is in navigation mode. Once the system has aligned, placing the mode selector in NAV mode initiates navigation. In attitude mode, the IRS no longer navigates and only outputs attitude (pitch and roll) information. Once placed in attitude mode, the system needs to be aligned again before being used for navigation.

During the initialization process, the IRS measures the earth's gravitational force, the speed of the earth's rotation, and the relative direction of the earth's rotation, which is the reason the aircraft cannot be moved during this process. The gravitation force measurement allows the IRS to determine local vertical, which is the direction at exactly a 90° angle to the earth's rotational axis intersecting the position of the aircraft. The speed and direction of rotation relative to the aircraft, along with local vertical and position, allows IRS to determine true north.

Once initialized, the IRS precisely measures acceleration in any of the three axes—vertical, lateral, and longitudinal. The processor within the IRU can use data regarding acceleration rate, direction, and time to determine the aircraft's attitude and position. Thus, the IRS uses a very precise form of deduced reckoning.

IRS Calculations

The IRS solves the velocity equation in near real time: velocity is equal to acceleration x time. For example, once the IRS is initialized, a Boeing 777-300 is pushed away from the gate. The IRU platform may measure an acceleration

airplane has moved or the previous position is significantly different than the position entered. If the align light is extinguished, then the unit is not in align mode.

The condition lights indicate when the unit is operating on DC only (ON DC), when the DC supply has failed (DC FAIL), or when an internal fault has been detected (FAULT).

rate of 0.6 ft/sec^2 in the rear direction. After two seconds at this rate, the aircraft is moving at 6 ft/sec (2 x 3=6), or a little over 3 kts. Since the IRS senses heading information, it knows the direction the aircraft is moving and can track position. These systems typically update at a rate between 50 Hz for gimbaled systems and 2 kHz for strapdown systems.

The tug continues to push the aircraft back from the gate and the speed stabilizes at 3 kts, or 6 ft/sec, for 40 1/3 seconds. Distance is equal to speed x time; therefore, after 40.333 seconds, the aircraft moves 242 feet, which is approximately its own length. The IRS adjusts and updates its position accordingly up to 2,000 times per second.

The IRS solves rotational velocity problems in a similar manner in all three axes in real time. For example, during takeoff rotation, the laser gyro in the Boeing 777 IRU measures a pitch up rate of 2° per second for 6 seconds. This rate results in a 12° nose up attitude displayed on the EFIS and sent to whichever system requires the data. Since the system measures acceleration in real time, the data and presentation changes as the aircraft attitude changes.

ADIRU

An IRS can be combined with an air data system. The result is known as an air data inertial reference unit, or ADIRU. This system may also be known as an air data inertial reference system, or ADIRS. Like IRS and ADS, ADIRUs are mounted in triplicate within transport category aircraft. A diagram of a triple ADIRU system, along with an ADIRU LRU is shown in Figure 6-5-6.

Like the air data system, the ADIRU requires ADMs to convert air pressure to a digital signal. Also like the air data system, the ADIRU measures total air temperature and angle of attack, using TAT and AOA probes respectively. Like the IRS, the systems are controlled with a control display unit and communicate with other systems using a data bus.

As shown in Figure 6-5-7, an ADIRU LRU contains an air data reference (ADR) unit, which receives airspeed, barometric altitude data, temperature, and AOA information from the air data modules and external sensors. The IRU produces attitude, vector, ground speed, and positional data. The microprocessor and IRINC databus in and out circuits exchange data with the FMS control display units, flight control unit, and ADIRU control panel.

Although the IRS and ADIRU systems navigate and can show navigational information on the

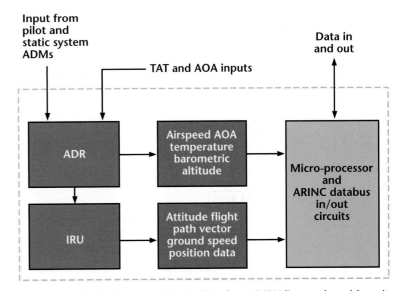

Figure 6-5-7 Block diagram of the inside of an ADIRU line replaceable unit.

CDU, once initialized, the bulk of navigational processes are carried out by the FMS. The FMS coordinates IRS position, dependant navigation systems position, and flight plans.

Inertial Navigation System

The terms *inertial reference system* and *inertial navigation system* (INS) are often used as synonyms. A technician should think of an IRS as an attitude and direction indicating system, which has navigation capability. In contrast, an INS is a navigation system with attitude and direction indicating capability. The systems are nearly identical in architecture. The main difference is in the philosophy of design. This topic is referenced under ATA code 34-20.

An INS is designed to stand alone, meaning it is capable of operating independently from any external (dependent) navigation aids, and it will start at a known position and then measure acceleration in three dimensions while continuously calculating the new location. Like an IRS, a modern INS is not susceptible to precession due to inertia and friction; however, it is subject to drift as a result of small measurement errors in acceleration and velocity known as *integration drift*. Integration drift is the accumulation over time of small errors in the calculation and measurement of acceleration and velocity. The most accurate, commercially available systems drift up to 1.8 kilometers per day. Typically, these systems are used on ships, submarines, and some spacecraft. Most aviation systems will drift up to 1.5 kilometers per hour.

INS is most likely to be used in military applications where maximum stealth is necessary because of tactical requirements. In such cases, external antennas may not be possible,

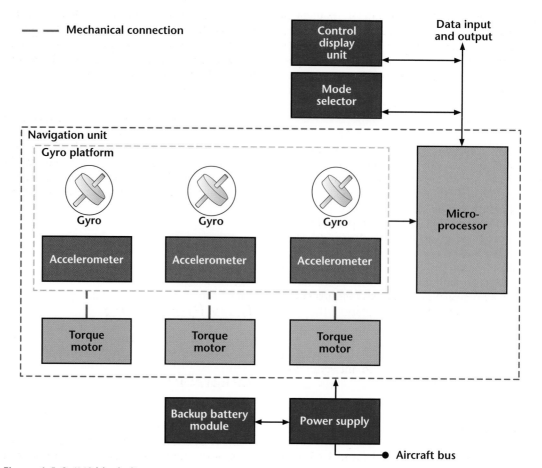

— — Mechanical connection

Figure 6-5-8. INS block diagram.

nor would any transmissions for TACAN or DME.

Figure 6-5-8 shows a simplified block diagram of an INS.

The heart of the INS is the navigation unit, which contains the stabilized platform, torque motors, a microprocessor, and a power supply. The platform may be referred to as the inertial platform or a tilt table. In some inertial navigation systems, the battery backup may be a separate LRU. The control display unit is similar to that of a flight management system with data entered via an alpha numeric keypad.

IRS and INS Errors

Types of INS errors include, accelerometer bias error, accelerometer scale-factor error, accelerometer alignment error, gyro alignment error, gyro alignment errors, and noise error.

Bias and scale-factor errors result simply because of the fact that no accelerometer or gyro can be constructed to be perfect. As a result, small errors that show up in velocity and position will always be present.

Accelerometer and gyro alignment errors are the result of improper or imprecise alignments or long-term degradation due to temperature or other factors that cannot be compensated for by software.

Noise error is also known as gyro angle random walk error. Electronic components are susceptible to random variations known as flicker. In devices that operate at higher frequencies, the flicker is covered up by white noise, such as that heard in the audio of a receiver operating with the squelch off. Noise error affects both solid state gyros and accelerometers.

IRS and INS errors can be detected by a drift check. Both systems compare the autonomous navigation system calculated position with the position measured using dependant navigation systems. If the difference between these values is great enough, a fault message appears on the CDU. The crew can view the error in nautical miles and make a determination whether to consider the IRS or INS to have failed.

IRS and INS Error Correction

Although an IRS and INS are not susceptible to precession due to inertia and friction, they are subject to drift as a result of small measurement errors in acceleration, attitude, and velocity caused by the errors listed above. Both systems may compensate for drift by comparing calculated position with a dependent navigation system, such as GNSS or DME, by error modeling and by a computer process known as *Kalman filtering*.

Kalman filtering is a software program that takes measurements over time, estimates true values of these measurements, then predicts a future value. The program then estimates the uncertainty of the predicted value and computes a weighted average of the predicted and measured values. The result of this filtering software is values, or in the case of an IRS, position estimates, which are more accurate statistically than the raw data. Figure 6-5-9 shows a process block diagram for corrections using Kalman filtering.

Error modeling involves engineers determining what the position errors are most likely to be, then designing software to anticipate and correct for those errors.

Types of IRS and INS Alignments

As described above, both IRS and INS align initially with the assistance of the flight crew entering the starting position.

GPS-aided alignment. The most common form of alignment involves a tie in to the GNSS to verify starting position or to correct for errors during flight. In systems using GNSS for dependent navigation, the verification and correction is known as GPS-aided; however, the process is the same in aircraft equipped with other GNSS. In addition, the IRS or INS may use data from the DME or VOR for correction. This type of alignment does not require the aircraft to remain stationary; however, the process may take several minutes to reduce error to an acceptable level.

Optical alignment. Optical alignments require a small mounted telescope, known as a theodolite, which is rotatable in horizontal and vertical planes. This type of alignment works only with gimbaled systems, since the theodolite must be mounted on a stable platform. Moreover, this type of alignment is most likely to be used with an INS. Using the theodolite, the system uses a line-to-ground based object in a known direction as a reference. At high altitudes or in space, a star may be tracked.

Gyrocompass alignment. Gyrocompass alignment works only if the aircraft is stationary. A gyrocompass alignment involves using the sensed direction of acceleration, both gravity and earth rotation, to determine the local vertical, north, and latitude. Longitude must be determined using other means. Since gyrocompass alignment does not determine longitude, it is not as accurate as optical or GPS-aided methods.

Transfer alignment. If the aircraft has more than one INS in operation, then the INS needing alignment can be synchronized with the INS that is already aligned. To confirm the alignment, the flight crew may be required to perform special maneuvers to verify accuracy.

Section 6
Installation and Integration Considerations

Integration

With the exception of the wet compass and gyro instruments mounted in small aircraft without autopilots, all of the systems discussed previously must integrate or communicate with other systems on board the aircraft.

Flight control (autoflight or autopilot), flight management, EFIS, terrain awareness, collision avoidance, automated dependent surveillance, and transponder systems must communicate with the systems discussed on previous pages. Moreover, AHRS, ADHRS, IRS, ANS, and ADIRU receive information from the pitot and static systems. ANS and IRS require input

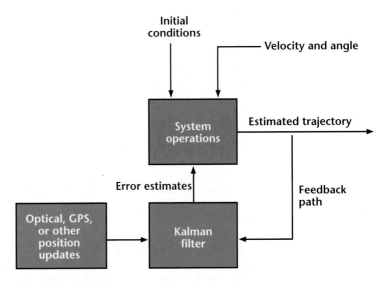

Figure 6-5-9. Block diagram showing the use of Kalman filtering to improve system accuracy.

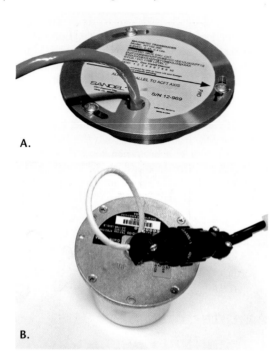

Figure 6-6-1. (A) AHARS magnetometer, (B) Garmin magnetometer.

from the GPS and possible other navigation systems. No system can be considered airworthy unless it communicates successfully with the other systems to which it's connected.

Installation

With the exception of a few simple systems discussed in previous sections, such as the wet compass or gyroscopic flight instruments, most others require that a supplemental type certificate (STC) be granted prior to retrofitting the system. The process of obtaining an STC proves the aircraft continues to meet type certification criteria with the new system installed. Systems requiring an STC must be installed in exact concordance with the approved installation manual. No deviations are allowed.

In general, the STC documentation and the installer must take mechanical, electrical, and magnetic field information into consideration.

Pre-Installation

Before installation of any of the above systems, pre-installation questions must be answered as described in Chapter 8. In general, the technician should ensure the current installation manual is available. Any devices that interface with the system to be installed should be working properly, including data buses. The technician must conduct an electrical load analysis. Furthermore, any system software for operations and troubleshooting must be up-to-date.

Mechanical Considerations

In general, mounting locations for the instruments and devices previously described are not near large magnetic fields. This means the system must be mounted as far as possible from ferrous metal objects, especially those that move, such as hydraulic or electric actuators and control cables. The system must also be mounted as far as possible from DC and AC power cables.

Magnetometers are particularly sensitive to ferrous objects. Small washers, nuts, screws, cotter pins, and other hardware constructed of iron, steel, nickel, or cobalt have a negative effect on their function. Hardware near magnetometers, flux detectors, or magnetic compasses should be constructed of brass, titanium, or nonferrous stainless steel.

Proper mounting minimizes vibration and should be on a shelf designed to be level when the aircraft is in level flight. Units, such as AHRS, magnetometers, flux detectors, IMUs, and IRUs, must align with the aircraft's longitudinal axis. The center of gravity of the unit being installed must be taken into consideration. Some must be mounted near the aircraft's center of gravity, while others work better when mounted forward or aft of the aircraft's center of gravity.

These systems may have an axis indication of X, Y, and Z on the case. A typical mounting method defines the X axis as being equal to the aircraft's longitudinal axis, the Y axis parallel to the aircraft's lateral axis, and the Z axis aligned with the aircraft's vertical axis. The X, Y, and Z axes of the unit being installed must align with the longitudinal, lateral, and vertical axes of the aircraft. When mounted properly, the system measures X and Y at zero and Z at one when it is not moving. Improper mounting causes the system to incorrectly measure acceleration and local vertical. Figure 6-6-2 shows an AHRS unit with X, Y, and Z markings.

The area in which the system is to be installed may require *degaussing*. Degaussing is a process to remove magnetism. A technician uses a degaussing device, which is a large coil through which 60 Hz AC from a wall socket is passed. Holding or waving the degaussing coil near magnetized objects causes them to lose their magnetism. Control cables and some elements within the airframe may have become magnetized and need to be degaussed.

Initial Alignment and Testing

Once installed, the system needs an initial alignment and testing. Installation manuals include procedures for leveling the aircraft and aligning the system for attitude.

Wet Compass and Slaved Compass Systems

Aligning a wet compass or a slaved compass system involves something known as a compass swing. A compass swing is a procedure used to adjust the compass or compensator to reduce error.

A compass swing should be performed when the accuracy of the compass or compass system is in question, after certain modifications have been performed, after a lightning strike, or after a repair to the compass or compass system.

Compass swings can be performed on a compass rose or using a calibrated master compass. If the technician plans to use a calibrated master compass, then an area free of magnetic disturbances, such as underground cables or steel pipes, should be used. Using either method, nonmagnetic tools must be used and aircraft equipment that may have an effect on the system must be stowed in its normal location.

Common installation errors that affect the wet compass' accuracy include using machine screws or nuts rather than brass hardware to mount a compass or instruments; or mounting a compass or instruments near a magnetized control yoke, structural tubing, or improperly routed electrical wiring. Any of these errors may cause unreasonable compass error. The compass swing must be performed with the engine or engines running and the avionics turned on.

To perform a compass swing on a piston engine aircraft, move the aircraft to the north (0°) radial on the compass rose. Use a hairline sight compass (a reverse reading compass with a gun sight arrangement mounted on top) to place the aircraft in the general vicinity. With the aircraft facing north and the person in the cockpit running the engine(s) at 1,000 r.p.m., a technician standing approximately 30 feet in front of the aircraft and facing south "shoots," or aligns, the master compass with the aircraft center line.

On conventional gear aircraft, the mechanic has to position the magnetic compass in the straight and level position or mount the tail of the aircraft on a moveable dolly to simulate a straight and level cruise configuration. Remember the hairline sight compass is only intended to be used as a general piece of test equipment. Using hand signals, the mechanic signals the person in the cockpit to make additional adjustments to align the aircraft

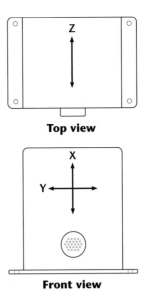

Figure 6-6-2. AHRS unit with axis markings.

with the master compass. Once aligned on the heading, the person in the cockpit runs the engine(s) to approximately 1,700 r.p.m. to duplicate the aircraft's magnetic field and then reads the compass.

If the aircraft compass is not in alignment with the magnetic north of the master compass, the error is connected by making small adjustments to the north-south brass adjustment screw with a nonmetallic screw driver (made out of brass stock or stainless steel welding rod). Adjust the N-S compensator screw until the compass reads north (0°). Turn the aircraft until it is aligned with the east-west, pointing east. Adjust the E-W compensator screw until it reads 90°. Continue by turning the aircraft south 180° and adjust the N-S screw to remove one-half of the south's heading error. This throws the north off, but the total north-south should be divided equally between the two headings. Turn the aircraft until it is heading west 270°, and adjust the E-W screw on the compensator to remove one-half of the west error. This should divide equally the total E-W error.

With the aircraft heading west, start the calibration card and record the magnetic heading of 270° and the compass reading first with the avionics/electrical systems on and then off. Turn the aircraft to align with each of the lines on the compass rose and record the compass reading every 30°. There should not be more than a ±10° difference between any of the compass headings and the magnetic heading of the aircraft.

If the aircraft has an electrical system, two complete compass checks should be performed—one with minimum electrical equipment operating and the other with all electrical

FOR	000	030	060	090	120	150
STEER						
RDO ON	001	032	062	095	123	155
RDO OFF	002	031	064	094	125	157

FOR	180	210	240	270	300	330
STEER						
RDO ON	176	210	243	271	296	325
RDO OFF	174	210	240	273	298	327

Figure 6-6-3. A compass error card.

Figure 6-6-4. Magnetometers are typically mounted in a wingtip to separate them from any aircraft induced magnetic fields.

accessories (e.g. radios, navigation, radar, and lights) turned on. If the compass readings are not identical, the technician should make two separate compass correction cards, one with all the equipment on and one with the equipment off, as shown in Figure 6-6-3.

If the compass or slaved compass system cannot be adjusted to meet the requirements or specifications, either the compass must be replaced or the slaved compass system must be repaired.

Magnetometer Alignments

In a perfect situation, a magnetometer measures only the earth's magnetic field to determine heading. The magnetometer shown in Figure 6-6-4, is mounted in the wingtip. In reality, magnetic fields near the magnetometer add or distort the magnetometer measurements. These distortions are categorized in two ways: soft iron and hard iron. Figure 6-6-5 shows three graphs. In the upper left hand portion of the figure, magnetic field data is shown, which is undistorted.

Nearby materials that produce a constant and additive affect to the earth's magnetic field are called *hard-iron distortion*. For example, the magnet within the cabin speaker can cause hard iron distortion to a magnetometer mounted on the upper fuselage above the flight deck. The graph in the lower left of Figure 6-6-5 shows the effect of hard iron distortion. A typical hard iron effect offsets the data in one direction.

Soft-iron distortion is created by material that distorts the magnetic field, even though the material does not create a magnetic field itself. As shown in the upper right of Figure 6-6-5, soft iron distortion turns the circle into an ellipse.

Systems with magnetometers have complex software that uses mathematical models and Kalman filtering to remove distortions from the data. The system accounts for these distortions by making a series of measurements. The system uses the measurements to model the hard iron and soft iron environment.

Like compass swings, alignments for soft and hard iron distortions must be accomplished with engines running and the avionics turned on. The system being aligned accepts a command to start the measurement and alignment process. Once started, the system uses all succeeding measurements to model the magnetic environment. The technician should make at least one complete turn on a level portion of the ramp. Multiple turns continue to improve the modeling and corrections. Typically, more than three turns does not significantly improve the magnetic field model. Once complete, the technician enters another command to stop and save the alignment algorithm.

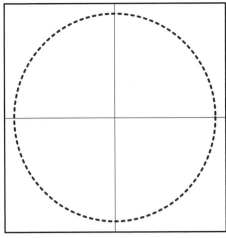

Distortion Free Data

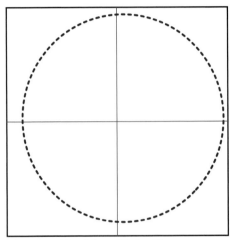

Hard Iron Distortion

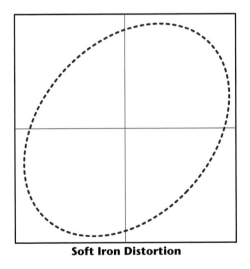

Soft Iron Distortion

Figure 6-6-5. Magnetometer field measurement distortion.

Attitude Alignments

For any attitude measuring system, proper attitude measurements rely on proper installation of the instrument or system. Mechanical gyros or gyro platforms must be installed on a level surface. AHRS, IRS, and INS systems self-align upon power up. As described earlier, complex systems may require up to 10 minutes to complete the initial alignments, during which the system measures the earth's rotation and G forces to determine local vertical.

Post Installation Testing

Once any of the electronic referencing systems, such as AHRS, IRS, or INS, has been installed, the technician must verify proper operation. Verification includes testing the systems with which the reference system interfaces. The aircraft must be tested for proper autopilot and flight director operation, FMS operation, EFIS and any other system that receives data from the reference system.

Section 7

Summary

Although early aircraft relied solely on the pilot's ability to see outside the aircraft, soon after the airplane's invention, instruments were developed for attitude measuring and navigation. Autonomous systems do not rely on signals from outside the aircraft for operation. Modern autonomous navigation systems use instruments and microprocessors to perform deduced reckoning.

An early navigation instrument, which survives in aircraft to this day, is the compass. The compass is a completely autonomous device. It does not require any radio signal to operate, nor does it require a power supply. The compass simply aligns its internal magnets with the earth's magnetic field and indicates direction. An example of a compass installed in a King Air 90 is pictured in Figure 6-7-1.

A magnetometer is a solid-state device used to sense the direction or strength of a magnetic field. For aircraft navigation purposes, engineers design magnetometers that focus on the direction of the magnetic field, rather than the strength of the magnetic field. Magnetometer design is small enough to allow the device to be mounted on a small circuit card with additional components designed to convert the current changes into digital signal outputs for use on a data bus.

Gyroscopes in aircraft instruments are built in the form of a spinning wheel or disk, usually called a rotor, that spins at rotation speeds of

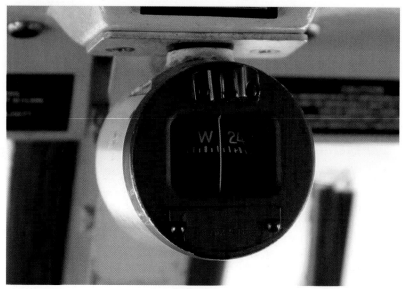

Figure 6-7-1. Compass in an aircraft.

10,000 r.p.m. or more. The rotor may be electrically or pneumatically driven. The rotor is mounted in a gimbal, which is a device that supports the rotor while permitting it to move freely in any direction. The directional gyro, or DG, is a gyroscopic instrument designed to provide the pilot with stable heading information. The stability of the DG gives it an advantage over the wet compass. The instrument panel pictured in Figure 6-7-2 includes several gyroscopic instruments.

The slaved compass system is an improvement on the DG and consists of a set of electronic devices that indicate heading corrected for errors. Like a simple compass, the slaved compass system determines direction by measuring the earth's magnetic field. Unlike a simple compass, the slaved compass system uses a

gyro, a sensor, and electronics to provide stability and correct for error.

The horizontal situation indicator may also be known as a pictorial navigation indicator, and it is an instrument that shows the pilot heading, course, glideslope information and, in some cases, more information.

Attitude indicating gyroscopic instruments, or attitude gyros, are used to display the angle of the aircraft about the lateral and longitudinal axes. In other words, these instruments indicate roll and pitch information. These instruments may be pneumatically or electrically driven, and the shaft of the rotor is mounted vertically. As a result, these instruments are often referred to as vertical gyros.

Modern autonomous navigation and instrument systems rely heavily on accelerometers. There are two types of acceleration measured by accelerometers, static and dynamic. Static acceleration, as its name implies, is unchanging, like the constant force of gravity. Dynamic acceleration is a change in the increase or decrease in velocity caused by movement. A common type of accelerometer used in autonomous navigation systems are types of solid-state or silicon inertial sensors known as micro-electro-mechanical systems, or MEMS.

An air data system measures several parameters regarding the ambient air around an aircraft and the state of flight relative to the ambient air. In large aircraft, the air data system includes the pitot system, static system, angle of attack measurement, and outside, or total, air temperature. An air data computer is pictured in Figure 6-7-3.

An attitude heading reference system uses precise accelerometers and computers to determine the aircraft attitude. Furthermore, it uses magnetometers to determine heading. A Garmin AHRS is pictured in Figure 6-7-4. An air data heading reference system uses precise accelerometers, computers, and elements of a slaved compass system to determine aircraft attitude and heading. In addition, ADHRS supplies air data.

A flight management system is a computer system with a database that can communicate with and control virtually all the avionic systems in the aircraft. The Beechcraft King Air 350 pictured in Figure 6-7-5 includes a flight management system

An inertial reference system uses a combination of gyroscopes and accelerometers to determine the attitude of the aircraft. An IRS has navigational capabilities. An IRS can be combined with an air data system; the result

Figure 6-7-2. Gyroscopic instruments on an instrument panel.

is known as an air data inertial reference unit, or ADIRU. This system may also be known as an air data inertial reference system, or ADIRS. The terms *inertial reference system* and *inertial navigation system* are used often as synonyms. A technician should think of an IRS as an attitude and direction indicating system that has navigation capability. In contrast, an INS is a navigation system with attitude and direction indicating capability.

Types of INS errors include accelerometer bias error, accelerometer scale-factor error, accelerometer alignment error, gyro alignment error, and noise error. Although an IRS and INS are not susceptible to precession due to inertia and friction, they are subject to drift as a result of small measurement errors in acceleration, attitude, and velocity.

With the exception of the wet compass and gyro instruments mounted in small aircraft without autopilots, all of the systems discussed must integrate or communicate with other systems onboard the aircraft. The sophisticated systems described in this chapter require that a supplemental type certificate be issues before retrofitting the system. In general, mounting locations for the instruments and devices described are away from large magnetic fields.

Once installed, systems need an initial alignment and testing. Installation manuals will

Figure 6-7-3. Air data computer.

Figure 6-7-4. Garmin AHRS.

include procedures for leveling the aircraft and aligning the system for attitude.

A compass swing should be performed when the accuracy of the compass or compass system is in question, after certain modifications have been performed, after a lightning strike, or after a repair to the compass or compass system.

Systems using magnetometers have complex software that in turn uses mathematical models and Kalman filtering to remove distortions from the data. The system accounts for distortions by making a series of measurements. The system uses these measurements to model the hard iron and soft iron environment.

Figure 6-7-5. Cockpit of a Beechcraft King Air 350 that includes a flight management system.

Installation Project Management

Installing and integrating new equipment into an aircraft is a three-phase process. In large organizations, each phase may be handled by different personnel: administration or planning may be handled by engineering and logistics departments; execution by the installation department; delivery or completion by the sales department.

A project administrator or planner must take several factors into consideration. He or she must review aircraft records and documents. Planning an installation involves some engineering; therefore, the planner must read installation manuals, create lists of required tools, and identify consumables. He or she must create task lists, time lines, and simplified wiring diagrams.

Execution is the phase where the installation department and technicians become involved. The technician uses the plan and acceptable techniques and practices to install the equipment. This phase starts with disassembly and removal of interior parts, which are susceptible to damage, and ends with reassembly and testing of the newly installed systems, which is also the start of the third and final phase.

The third phase is completion, or delivery, when documents are updated, forms are filled out, and work orders are completed. This phase includes flight crew education and, in some cases, a check flight.

In a small business one person may be required to administer all phases of the project. This person wears many hats. He or she starts as a planner, becomes an engineer, transitions to a technician, returns to being an administrator and, perhaps, finishes as an educator.

Learning Objectives

DESCRIBE
- Aircraft acceptance, planning, and execution processes
- Methods of FAA approval
- Paperwork to complete at end of project

EXPLAIN
- Differences between findings and discrepancies
- Electrical load analysis
- How to determine if an alteration is major or minor

APPLY
- Recall avionics related standardized maintenance manual chapter codes
- Define RVSM, ETOPS
- List items factored into project cost

Left: Project management starts before the aircraft is rolled into the shop for the avionics installation and often continues well after new items are physically installed.

Section 1

Project Administration

Project Planning

The installation of avionics equipment and the integration with previously installed aircraft systems starts before the aircraft arrives on the ramp (Figure 7-1-1). The avionics shop's sales department makes a bid or quote, which the aircraft owner decides whether or not to accept. If accepted, this results in an agreement between the avionics shop and the customer that includes the cost of the project, a due date for completion and the warranty. The cost of the project to the customer is determined by several factors including equip-

Figure 7-1-1. Corporate jets on ramp.

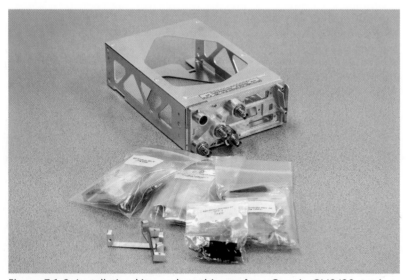

Figure 7-1-2. Installation kits, such as this one for a Garmin GNS430, typically include connectors and other small hardware.

ment, consumables, tooling, labor, approvals, and related work.

Cost

Cost of the equipment being purchased. Manufacturers of avionics equipment set a wholesale price for the installing shop and a list price for the customer. The list price is the suggested selling price to the customer. Many installers offer discounts off of the list price. While purchasing equipment from the manufacturer is a significant part of the cost of an installation and the shop owner wants to recover the purchase cost through the sale, many offer some level of discount to help entice customers to use their shop. In other cases the installer may purchase the unit from another dealer or distributor, which may make better prices possible. The longer an avionics system remains in stock, the more likely the dealer's sales department will reduce the price to get a sale.

Cost of consumables. Consumables include anything that is used in the installation and that cannot be used again. Examples of consumables include installation kits, cleaning and prep materials, paint and finishing materials, and may also include wiring and some types of connectors.

- **Installation kits.** Manufacturers often sell kits for installation that include hardware, connectors, and many other parts required to install the system (Figure 7-1-2). Some installation kits include prefabricated wire harnesses, however, most do not. An installation kit is considered a consumable because the components of the kit become part of the aircraft. The cost of the kit must be factored into the sales proposal.

- **Hardware.** Hardware includes items such as screws, nuts, washers or bolts, wire, clamps, lacing cord, or anything else that is installed in the aircraft but not included within the installation kit. Typically, the installing agency purchases wire in bulk. The amount necessary for the installation will be accounted for and the cost per install determined.

- **Chemicals and paint.** Not only does the cost of chemicals and paint need to be factored into the quote, but the shelf life of these materials must also be taken into consideration. Any chemical with an expired shelf life will end up creating a higher overall cost for shop operation because its cost cannot be recovered in a single job.

Cost of tooling. An installation project may require the shop to purchase additional tools. Moreover, existing tool costs may be amortized into estimates. In other words, the cost of an expensive wire marking machine may be spread over many jobs.

Cost of labor. Most quotes are made with an average amount of personnel hours factored in (Figure 7-1-3). For example, the management of a shop may have records indicating the past 10 similar GPS installations were completed in an average time of eight hours. It's likely that the next quote will figure the cost of eight labor hours. The pay rate of the assigned technician has an affect on the cost, as well, and requires a judgment call by management. A more experienced technician can complete a job quickly, but his or her hourly rate is more.

The condition of the aircraft upon arrival can have a large affect on the labor cost. Surprises will cost the installing agency, the aircraft owner, or both.

Cost of approvals. Often overlooked, the methods and costs of approvals for return to service must be factored into the pricing scheme. Depending on the complexity of the installation and integration, the approval method may be as simple as a log book entry or as complex as a new Supplemental Type Certificate. Obtaining the necessary approvals can add significantly to the cost of the installation. A shop with a faulty process for obtaining FAA approval will be faced with costly delays while negotiating with the FAA.

Overall cost of related work. During the planning and inspection process, the shop or owner may discover more work to be completed on the aircraft (Figure 7-1-4). A well planned installation and a well written quote can result in related items generating additional billable work. A poorly planned installation or a poorly written quote may cause related work to become a warranty problem.

There are multiple techniques for determining quotes. Some calculate a flat rate for consumables and tooling, while others bill for specific items used. In some cases, the installer may choose to cover costs in the difference between the wholesale and retail prices of the equipment. When quoting work, caution must be used with this method to cover labor costs, as there may be little or no margin to cover any additional work required.

Cost estimates and the resulting bids are most accurate when the potential installer has a chance to examine the aircraft. If a bid is accepted without the installer seeing the aircraft, then both the installing agency and

Figure 7-1-3. Technicians examine avionics equipment in a business-class aircraft.
Courtesy of Duncan Aviation

the customer must be prepared for changes to the agreement during the aircraft acceptance process.

Return To Service

Making an accurate plan requires the planner to acquire accurate and complete information. The planner needs to determine how the aircraft will be returned to service and what documents are necessary to do so. He or she must become familiar with the installation manual or manuals for the equipment being installed. In addition, aircraft documents and records should be scrutinized.

As described in the cost section, the method of approval can have a great affect on the cost of a project and the time required for its completion.

Figure 7-1-4. During a complex installation, additional required work may become apparent as old systems are removed and the underlying structure and wiring is revealed.

Alteration		
Appreciable affect to weight and balance	Yes	No
Appreciable affect to structural strength	Yes	No
Appreciable affect to performance	Yes	No
Appreciable affect to powerplant operation	Yes	No
Appreciable affect to flight characteristics	Yes	No
Appreciable affect to other qualities affecting airworthiness	Yes	No
Cannot be completed according to accepted practices	Yes	No
Cannot be accomplished by elementary operations	Yes	No
If any of the above are yes, then the alteration is major.		

Table 7-1-1. Major vs. minor alteration checklist.

A well planned installation determines early on the method to be used for returning the aircraft to service.

Major vs. Minor Alterations

By nature, most installations of avionics equipment either remove from or, more likely, add to a type-certificated aircraft's configuration. Installations that do not change the configuration of the aircraft are limited to the replacement of equipment with new equipment that has the same capabilities and functionality as the equipment being removed. For example, the replacement of an older model 760-channel communication radio with a newer 760-channel communication radio would not change the configuration described in the Type Certificate.

If the equipment changes the configuration, then a determination must be made as to whether the alteration is minor or major. The holder of a mechanic or repairman certificate, a person working under the supervision of a mechanic or certificate holder, the holder of a repair station certificate, the holder of an air carrier operating certificate or a certificate issued under FAA parts 121 or 135 is responsible for making the determination. To summarize, the technician doing the work is responsible for determining whether the alteration is major or minor.

An alteration is considered a major alteration if it is not listed in the aircraft, aircraft engine, or propeller specifications, and if one of the following conditions apply:

- It may appreciably affect weight, balance, structural strength, performance,
powerplant operation, flight characteristics, or other qualities affecting airworthiness, or

- It is not done according to accepted practices, or

- It cannot be completed by elementary operations

The long sentence above, which was derived from FAA CFR 14 1.1 can be used as a simple checklist, as shown in Table 7-1-1.

With the exception of the last item on the checklist, all of the checklist items can be verified by study of aircraft and equipment documentation. Some are simply common sense. For example, adding a second NAVCOMM to an instrument panel using accepted practices does not affect structural strength, performance, powerplant, or flight characteristics. If properly installed, the new NAVCOMM is also quite unlikely to change any other qualities affecting airworthiness. There will be an affect to weight and balance, but whether it's appreciable depends on how much the new unit weighs. The last item may depend on the technician. For an experienced technician, an operation may be elementary, but for an inexperienced technician, the operation may not seem elementary. In cases where no one has experience, the alteration becomes major.

FAA Advisory Circular AC 120-77 provides one means to ensure a contemplated alteration is in compliance with applicable regulations and existing policy. Appendix 1 to AC 120-77 is shown in Figure 7-1-5 and provides a different way of determining whether the alteration or repair is major or minor.

Since the technician performing the work is responsible for determining whether or not the alteration is major or minor, the planner must have a strong communication with the technician. In small organizations, the planner is the technician, but in larger organizations, there may be different levels of management between the sales and planning department and the hangar floor. Good communication leads to a good plan. If the alteration is determined to be major, then the work must be performed in accordance with approved data.

Approved Data

According to AC 120-77, approved data is, "Technical and/or substantiating data that has been approved by the FAA," or by an FAA delegation option authorization holder (DOA), designated alteration station (DAS), or an FAA designated engineering representative (DER).

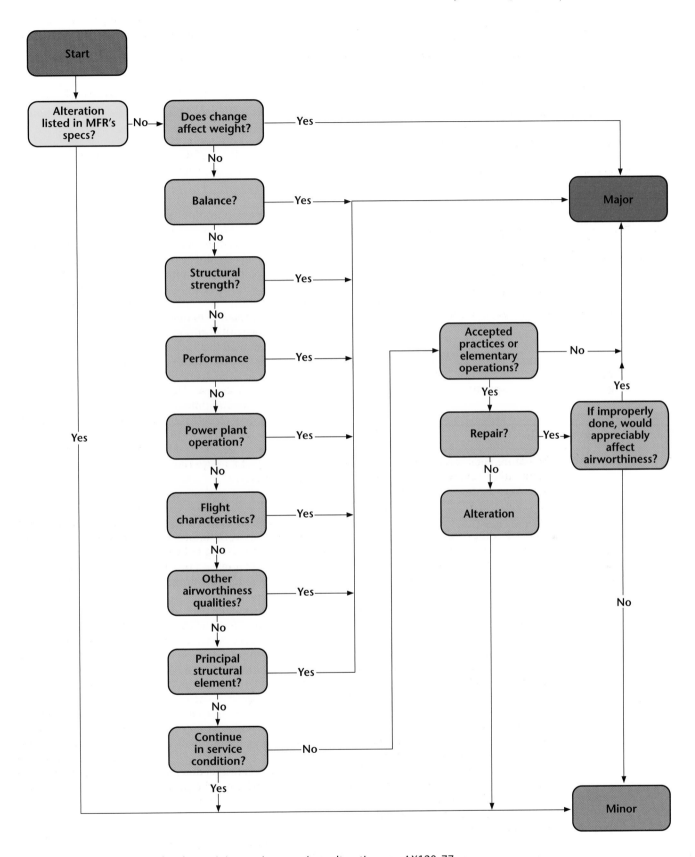

Figure 7-1-5. Decision tree for determining major vs. minor alteration per AX120-77.

Data may be approved by an airworthiness inspector or manufacturing inspection district office (MIDO). An STC or an airworthiness directive (AD) also contains approved data.

Approved data details a specific alteration to a specific engine or airframe. Approved data starts as acceptable data, which may come from *AC 43.13-1B: Acceptable Methods, Techniques,*

Figure 7-1-6. AC 43.13.

and Practices—Aircraft Inspection and Repair, AC 43.13-2B: Acceptable Methods, Techniques, and Practices—Aircraft Alterations (Figure 7-1-6) or manufacturer's installation manuals. The data is not approved until action is taken by the FAA or an FAA delegate, as listed above.

If the alteration is determined to be major, then the alteration must be documented on an FAA Form 337 (Figure 7-1-7). The data used on the 337 form must be FAA approved. The cost of

obtaining approved data varies widely. If the alteration is completed as part of an existing STC that was previously approved, then the cost will be low. In contrast, if the alteration requires your company to obtain a new STC, then the cost and the time involved will be high. Hiring a DER is a popular way to control cost and speed up the approval process.

Airplanes with Special Certifications

When planning an installation, the planner needs to be aware of any special certifications carried by the aircraft. An alteration may adversely affect one or more of these certifications. Two common extra certifications are described below.

Reduced vertical separation minimums. Barometric altimeters inherently have less precision as the altitude increases. To compensate for this, as aircraft operating altitudes increase, so has the vertical separation distance that air traffic control uses to maintain safe spacing between aircraft. The normal vertical clearance from sea level to 28,500 feet is 1,000 feet between aircraft. Prior to 1997 aircraft flying at altitudes above 28,500 feet operated with a minimum vertical separation of 2,000 feet. Aircraft operating above 41,000 feet operate with a minimum vertical separation of 4,000 feet.

Advances in avionics technology have increased the precision with which altitudes can be measured. Reducing the vertical separation from 2,000 feet to 1,000 feet gives air traffic control more options for handling the increasing numbers of aircraft at higher altitudes. Before aircraft can operate with reduced separation, each one is individually checked to verify the precision of its altitude measuring equipment. Starting in 1997 in Europe and implemented throughout Europe, North and South America, Africa and the Russia Federation by 2011, aircraft operating between 28,500 and 41,000 feet must be RVSM certified. This airspace now operates with a minimum vertical spacing of 1,000 feet, reduced from the previous minimum of 2,000 feet.

Figure 7-1-7. Example of an FAA Form 337.

Alterations to any airplane certified RVSM must be performed in close coordination with the aircraft owner's director of maintenance. RVSM certified airplanes must be able to measure altitude with a high degree of precision. These aircraft have an area marked as RVSM critical.

The marking surrounds the critical area and may be a solid line, like the one pictured in Figure 7-1-8, a dotted line or four corner markers. In this marked area, damage as minor as a paint scratch can introduce altimetry errors to great for flight in RVSM designated airspace.

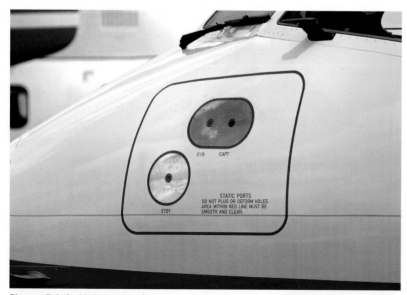

Figure 7-1-8. RVSM critical area marked with red solid line.

Alterations to the outer surface, even surfaces far removed from the RVSM critical area, can cause the same adverse affect. The aircraft owner's director of maintenance will be able to coordinate with the aircraft manufacturer to help the planner and installer avoid unintentional reductions in altimeter accuracy.

Extended operation. Extended operation (ETOPS) is also known as extended twin engine operation. All multi-engine passenger-carrying airplanes operated under Part 121 are required to comply with 121.161. This regulation imposes special requirements for ETOPS for these airplanes. For twin engine airplanes, ETOPS certification is required for flights with planned routing that contains a point farther than 60 minutes flying time from an adequate airport at an approved one-engine inoperative cruise speed under standard conditions in still air. For passenger-carrying airplanes with more than two engines, ETOPS certification is required for flights with planned routing that contains a point farther than 180 minutes flying time from an adequate airport at an approved one-engine inoperative cruise speed under standard conditions in still air.

To conduct ETOPS, the specified airplane-engine combination must be certificated to the airworthiness standards of transport-category airplanes and be approved for ETOPS. ETOPS-certified aircraft are operated by a company with a maintenance department and a director of maintenance. The installation planner must work with the director of maintenance to ensure that the alteration does not unintentionally and adversely affect ETOPS certification.

Document Review

A planner should review the following documents:

- Type certificate
- Airworthiness certificate (Figure 7-1-9)
- Registration certificate
- Flight manual
- Flight manual supplements

A review of these documents protects the installing agency from inadvertently committing a violation of FAA rules. The installer will find it in his or her interest to ensure the aircraft is legal and airworthy.

Record Review

For the same reasons listed under the documents review, a planner should search for and review the following records:

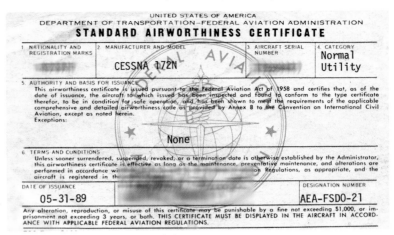

Figure 7-1-9. Airworthiness certificate.

- The aircraft logbook. This will contain maintenance records and inspection status (Figure 7-1-10).
- Weight and balance documents.
- Equipment list.
- Instructions for continued airworthiness (ICA).
- Field approvals (FAA Form 337).
- Supplemental Type Certificates (STC).

All aircraft have a logbook, weight and balance documentation, and an equipment list. ICAs, STCs, and 337 Forms only appear in aircraft that have had a major repair or an alteration requiring an ICA or STC.

Integration Planning

Integrating the new avionics equipment with the old equipment is where the avionics technician enters the engineering world. Some systems integrate easily, while other systems present a long list of challenges. An accurate integration plan is critical to the success of the overall project. For accuracy, the planner must acquire as much information as possible.

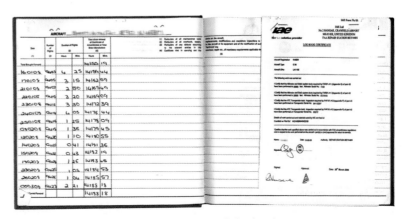

Figure 7-1-10. Sample page from an aircraft logbook.

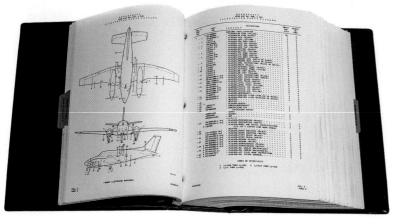

Figure 7-1-11. Sample page from a Hawker Beech parts manual.

The planner should acquire a copy of the maintenance and/or service manual as well as the illustrated parts manuals for the aircraft in which the equipment is to be installed (Figure 7-1-11). If the aircraft has been retrofitted previously, then schematics for the newer equipment installation should be required. For older aircraft, retrofit schematics may be difficult or impossible to find. If the schematics are not available, the planner must factor in the time required to reverse engineer the systems.

Reverse engineering can be relatively easy, if the technician is able to acquire installation manuals for the other equipment installed in the aircraft.

Installation manuals come with new equipment. The planner must read these in their entirety and become completely familiar with their contents. At this stage of the process, the planner should ask the following questions:

- Is there room in the panel for the controls, panel-mounted LRUs or instruments?
- Is there sufficient depth behind the panel for the panel-mounted equipment?
- Is there sufficient room in the equipment bay for remote-mounted LRUs?
- Where will the antennas (if required) fit?
- Where will external switches and enunciators be installed?
- Where will the circuit breakers be installed?
- Is there room for additional circuit breakers on the bus?
- Will the electrical system support the additional load?
- Will other equipment have to be moved?
- Where does the wiring fit?
- How will the wiring bundles be supported?
- Will the system interfere with any other equipment already installed on the aircraft?

Using the answers to the above questions, the planner should draw a wiring diagram that includes the connections to ground, the bus, and any other equipment. In addition, the planner should document how and where the wire bundles should be placed, how long the wires should be, and how they should be supported. The planner may need to draw up plans for how the equipment is to mounted to the airframe or instrument panel. A variety of documents will help the planner answer the questions above and any other questions that may arise when planning an installation.

Documents and Data

Both planners and installers must be familiar with a variety of documents and data, starting with the aircraft maintenance manual (MM).

Standardized Maintenance Manuals

The Air Transport Association, General Aviation Manufacturer's Association and the FAA have each created a list of standardized codes for use in MMs. As a result, three standards exist:

- Air Transport Association ATA 100 codes Listed in Appendix B

Figure 7-1-12. A technician examines a document on a typical microfiche reader.

- General Aviation Manufacturer's Association GAMA specification 2 Chapter codes
  Listed in Appendix C

- FAA Joint Aircraft System Component Code (JASC)
  Listed in Appendix D

The ATA 100 codes are referred to most often. Moreover, a great similarity exists between the three standards. In fact, the FAA hopes to "harmonize" the JASC and ATA 100 codes. The ATA codes for which avionics technicians must be most familiar are shown in Table 7-1-2.

An ATA specification manual has tabs labeled with the number. For example, information on the dependant navigation system can be found in 34-50, or under tab 34, subsection 50. Avionics supervisors encourage entry-level technicians to memorize basic ATA codes. With the codes memorized, technicians can find data quickly.

Other Commonly Used Documents

Both planners and technicians use the following documents often.

- AC 43.13-1B: Acceptable Methods, Techniques, and Practices–Aircraft Inspection and Repair

- AC 43.13-2B: Acceptable Methods, Techniques, and Practices–Aircraft Alterations

- Supplemental Type Certificates

- FAA Aircraft Specification / Type Certificate Data Sheet

- Manufacturer's installation manuals

- Manufacturer's structural repair manuals (SRM)

- Manufacturer's illustrated parts manuals

Forms of Documentation

Avionics technicians use documents from in a variety of media. Documents may be in a traditional paper form, on microfilm or microfiche, in PDF form on a CD, or on a computer network server. Paper documents must be handled with care, since pages can be torn easily or detached and lost. Microfilm and microfiche require a special reading machines, which shine a bright light through a lens onto a screen. A typical microfiche reader is pictured in Figure 7-1-12. Some microfilm and microfiche readers have the ability to print, but some do not. Manuals in PDF form vary widely in quality. Some

22	Auto flight
-00	General
-10	Autopilot
-20	Speed - attitude correction
-30	Auto throttle
-40	System monitor
-50	Aerodynamic load alleviating
-97	Wiring discrepancies
23	**Communications**
-00	General
-10	Speech Communications
-15	Satcom
-20	Data Transmission & Automatic Calling
-30	Passenger Address, Entertainment, and Comfort
-40	Interphone
-50	Audio Integrating
-60	Static Discharging
-70	Audio and Video Monitoring
-80	Integrated Automatic Tuning
-97	Wiring Discrepancies
24	**Electrical power**
-00	General
-10	Generator Drive
-20	AC Generation
-30	DC Generation
-40	External Power
-50	AC Electrical Load Distribution
-60	DC Electrical Load Distribution
-70	Primary and Secondary Power
-97	wiring Discrepancies
31	**Indicating and recording systems**
-00	General
-10	Instrument & Control Panels
-20	Independent Instruments
-30	Recorders
-40	Central Computers
-50	Central Warning Systems
-60	Central Display Systems
-70	Automatic Data Reporting Systems
-97	Wiring Discrepancies
34	**Navigation**
-00	General
-10	Flight Environment Data
-20	Attitude and Direction
-30	Landing and Taxiing Aids
-40	Independent Position Determining
-50	Dependent Position Determining
-60	Flight Management Computing
-97	Wiring Discrepancies

Table 7-1-2. ATA chapter codes commonly encountered by avionics technicians.

manuals are simply paper manuals that have been scanned into a computer then saved in PDF form. Other manuals have been created using a word processor and saved as an interactive PDF file. Still other documents are designed to reside on a server. Technicians access the server from computer work stations near the aircraft on which they are working.

Developing the Plan

With documents in hand, the planner is ready to develop a plan of execution. A good plan includes installation prints, parts lists, task lists, time table, and, if necessary, block diagrams to indicate where the equipment is to be located. A well drawn up plan is conducive, cost effective, timely, and error free installation.

Time Tables

A time table or schedule for installation completion is extremely important. A time table allows management and the technician to monitor the progress of an installation.

Developing a time table to complete an installation involves estimation, prediction and, to a small extent, guessing. There is always an amount of uncertainty involved in developing a time table. Weather, health, higher priority projects, and previously unknown problems can adversely affect a time table. For this reason, any time table should be reviewed often and revised as necessary.

To create a time table, the planner needs the following information.

- Description of the equipment to be installed
- Description of any other related alterations to the aircraft
- List of resources
- List of the steps required to complete the installation and related alterations
- Calendar of work days
- Personnel roster
- Deadlines
- Project risks

Installation manuals and records of past projects allow a planner to develop a list of steps or tasks required to complete the installation. Records of past projects also assist the planner in determining the number of person hours required to complete a project.

Some steps can be completed prior to the arrival of the aircraft. Jigs can be constructed, which will allow the technician to build wiring harnesses in advance. Since work on wiring harnesses can be completed in a well lit and temperature controlled work environment, building up wiring harnesses in this manner is cost effective, saves time, and is safe.

Parts and Supplies

For a technician to complete the task list on schedule, he or she will need consumables and tooling readily available. The planner must ensure that consumables are available in sufficient quantity and that items with limited shelf life are delivered in time to be used before expiration.

Installation Prints

With all the required documents and manuals available, the planner has a wealth of information available. In most cases, there is more information available than needs to be used. Often, installation manuals contain several pages of wiring diagrams. There may be diagrams for different variations of the system, and still more diagrams showing integration with various other equipment.

A good planner will draw a new diagram that shows only the connections to be made in the particular project being planned. Figure 7-1-13 shows an example of this simplification process.

The diagram on the left in Figure 7-1-13 shows a communication radio installation with an intercom and provisions for an audio input from an unspecified marker beacon receiver. On the right side of Figure 7-1-13, the diagram has been simplified for a particular installation that does not require an intercom and has a particular marker receiver installed. The diagram on the right is both simplified and more exact. In more complex installations, simplified and exact diagrams reduce the possibility of errors.

Aircraft Acceptance

Initial Inspection and Preparation

With the bid accepted and the job planned, it is time for the shop to accept the aircraft. Upon arrival of the aircraft to the shop, technicians should complete a detailed inventory of equipment installed and items that were carried on board. A good practice is to remove anything not attached to the aircraft and store it in a

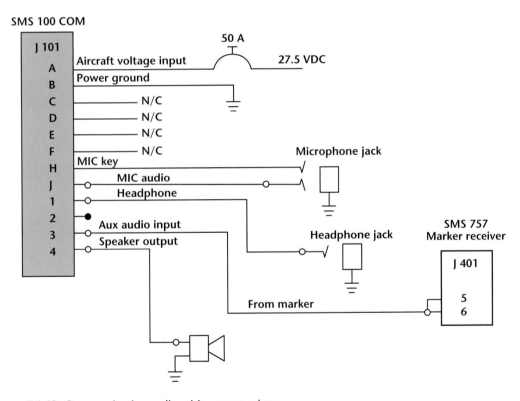

Figure 7-1-13. Communication radio wiring comparison.

properly marked container out of harm's way. At minimum, the container should be marked with the customer's name and aircraft registration number.

A digital camera is a useful tool to use at the acceptance stage of an installation project. The overall condition of the interior and exterior can be photographed and stored for reference later. Snapshots of the space behind the panel or in other hard to see areas may also be useful. A quick way of documenting the incoming settings of the avionics equipment is through use of a digital photo. The customer will appreciate the systems being set as they were when the aircraft came in.

Technicians should locate weight and balance documents, load analysis documents, and the flight manual. In any alteration, these documents will be needed for reference and, in many cases, modifications.

The technicians should perform visual or operational checks of:

- Airframe systems
- Powerplant
- Accessories
- Static system
- Pitot system
- Electrical system

Electrical Load

Any new avionic system installed in an aircraft presents a load to the electrical system. A basic electrical load calculation should be performed to ensure all continuous loads (current draw lasting for more than two minutes) do not add up to more than 80 percent of the alternator or generator capacity. In any operating condition, there must be enough system capacity to operate equipment and charge the battery.

An electrical load analysis accurately and completely examines all power sources (AC and DC) and electrical loads throughout the voltage range of the aircraft. The loads and power sources are analyzed under the most severe operating conditions under all phases of aircraft operation including start, warm up, taxi, takeoff, climb, slow cruise, normal cruise, and landing.

To perform the analysis via calculation, the technician must have data showing alternator or generator output in relation to engine r.p.m. In addition, the technician must have knowledge of the battery capacity in ampere-hours. Specific guidance for performing electrical load analysis is available in Military Specification MIL-E-7016F, "Electrical Load and Power Source Capacity, Aircraft, Analysis of."

The analysis produces average charging current for three rated-time intervals in each operating phase. The analysis yields current requirements for all operating phases under the most adverse operating conditions, in other words, when all equipment is drawing maximum amperage. In general, the current requirements should not exceed 80 percent of the alternator or generator capacity at minimum required engine r.p.m.

Findings and Discrepancies

The inspection and electrical load analysis may generate findings. A finding is a condition

Figure 7-2-1. A King Air 350 undergoing an upgrade.

that does not seem to conform to the Type Certificate or Supplemental Type Certificate. The technician may notice a clamp installation that may not conform to acceptable installation practices, wire chafing, inaccurate navigation systems, or a load analysis that does not meet current requirements. At this point, the discoveries made by the inspecting technician are considered findings. When the inspection and analysis are complete, the technician should use the list of findings and aircraft documents and records to determine whether or not these findings are a variation from the Type or Supplemental Type Certificate(s).

Some findings such as clamp installations or seemingly peculiar bundle routing may be part of the original type or supplemental type design; however, findings such as wire chafing, inaccurate navigation systems, or inadequate current capacity become discrepancies. Discrepancies describe conditions that deviate from the type design.

Before an aircraft can be declared airworthy, discrepancies must be addressed. If a technician determines that there are any discrepancies during the initial inspection or at any time during the installation process, then the owner or operator of the aircraft must be notified. Once the owner or operator has the discrepancy list, a plan can be developed to address each discrepancy.

In many cases, the customer will elect to hire the installing agency to address the discrepancies. In other cases, the customer will decide to have the work performed elsewhere.

Section 2
Project Execution

Installation

With the plan in hand, a technician is ready to execute the installation. He or she should take care to use acceptable practices. The Installation and Integration Chapter in this textbook is a good start for those learning to install avionics equipment.

Calibrated Tools

Some of the tools used by an avionics installer need to be calibrated. Commonly used calibrated tools are wire strippers and terminal

Figure 7-2-2. Circuit disabled and breaker collared.

crimpers. A technician must not start a project without calibrated tooling.

Preparing The Aircraft

During aircraft acceptance, loose items are removed from the aircraft and stored. In the execution phase the aircraft may be partially dismantled (Figure 7-2-1). Seats and interior parts that could interfere with work or which could easily be damaged must be removed, tagged and stored in a safe location. Any electric circuits that if inadvertently activated could cause damage, such as the landing gear circuit, should be disabled. These circuits can be easily disabled by deactivating the circuit breaker and installing a collar with a tag as shown in (Figure 7-2-2.)

As the installation progresses, panels, access panels, and any number of other items may need to be removed for work to continue. In each case, hardware and the parts must be stored properly and tagged. Be sure to examine the hardware as it is removed. Some of the hardware may need replacement. If this is the case, procure new hardware and throw out the old hardware. Make sure to make note of the hardware that is replaced, so costs can be tracked and, if necessary, the customer invoiced.

Noise Control

Modern aircraft can have a multitude of equipment installed, and each piece of equipment can generate electromagnetic interference, also known as noise. In addition, systems must be protected from outside electromagnetic interference.

HIRF Requirements: excerpts from 23.1308, 25.1317, 27.1317, and 29,1317	Failure condition	System HIRF certification level
Each electrical and electronic system that performs a function whose failure would prevent the continued safe flight and landing of the rotorcraft/airplane	Catastrophic	A
Each electrical and electronic system that performs a function whose failure would significantly reduce the capability of the rotorcraft/airplane or the ability of the flightcrew to respond to an adverse operating condition	Hazardous	B
Each electrical and electronic system that performs a function whose failure would reduce the capability of the rotorcraft/airplane or the ability of the flightcrew to respond to an adverse operating condition	Major	C

Table 7-2-1. HIRF failure conditions and system HIRF certification levels from AC 20-158.

Figure 7-2-3. A grounding strap installed on an aircraft.

High Intensity Radiated Fields

Concern for the protection of aircraft electrical and electronic systems has increased substantially in recent years. Modern aircraft have a great dependence on electrical and electronic systems performing functions required for continued safe operation. Moreover, advanced composite materials afford less shielding than aluminum. Research has shown aircraft systems using data buses, fast processor speeds, and high density circuit boards are more susceptible to interference from high intensity radiated fields. (HIRF) Worldwide, there has been expanded usage of frequencies near or above 1 GHz by high powered transmitters. These high-powered transmissions could be from radar, radio, television, shipborne, or other airborne transmitters.

Any electrical or electronic system required for continued safe flight and landing must not be affected when the aircraft is exposed to a HIRF environment.

Advisory Circular AC 10-158 provides information and guidance about complying with certification requirements for HIRF protection. Table 7-2-1 shows possible failure conditions and the resulting HIRF certification levels. If the system being installed could fail in a way described in (Figure 7-2-2), then a system certification may be necessary.

Bonding and Grounding

For general noise protection, the technician must work to ensure grounding points conform to manufacturer requirements. A grounding strap is pictured in Figure 7-2-3. A corroded surface cannot provide a good ground connection. A general discussion of bonding and grounding is included in the Installation and Integration chapter.

Corrosion Removal and Surface Preparation

Grounding points, the bases of antennas, and bonding points must be completely free of corrosion. For this reason, manufacturers recommend a chemical method of cleaning and preparing aluminum (Figure 7-2-4). For cleaning, the technician should use a phosphoric acid-based cleaner. Once the surface is clean, the technician must move on to the preparation step quickly, before any more dust or dirt can land on the part. Aluminum can corrode quickly. Waiting too long before moving on can allow corrosion to form again on the surface.

The next step is to apply a microscopically thin film of low resistance non-anodic protective coating to the surface just cleaned. Non-anodic means the material will not act as an anode and allow dissimilar metals corrosion to begin. The coating must have low resistance, so current can flow freely between the surfaces.

Many installation shops use MEK or acetone to initially clean the surface, followed by Alumiprep® for further cleaning. After the surface dries, Alodine® is applied as a protective coating. Alumiprep is a nonflammable, phosphoric, acid-based cleaner produced by Henkel Technologies. Alodine, also produced by Henkel Technologies, is a non-anodic protective coating.

Structure Penetration

Often, a new installation requires the technician to penetrate at least one surface within or on the outer surface of the aircraft. The technician needs to take special care to ensure the new hole does not adversely affect the airworthiness of the aircraft. Penetrating certain structural components may ground the aircraft until a very expensive repair can be completed.

On aircraft constructed of aluminum, an experienced maintenance technician can easily recognize which areas need to be left alone to preserve structural integrity; however, these areas are not quite so easily identified on a composite aircraft. In either case, a search of the aircraft manufacturer's documents will reveal where openings can be made and what size they can be.

If still in doubt, seek the opinion of an experienced airframe technician or get approval from a designated engineering representative before drilling any new holes.

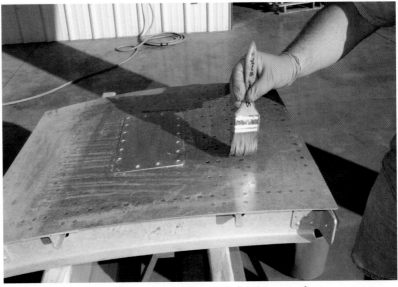
Figure 7-2-4. A technician treats a corroded aluminum surface.

Penetration of Composite Structures

Drilling through composite material requires special tooling. Since most composite materials are formed by placing a cloth material inside a matrix, special care must be taken to ensure the strands do not rip and tear causing unwanted damage. Always use a backing plate when drilling through composite structure.

Penetration of Pressurized Structures

Pressurized structures may need to be penetrated for antenna installations or for passing a bundle from an unpressurized area to a pressurized area of the airplane. Figure 7-2-5 shows a wire harness penetrating a

Figure 7-2-5. Wire harness penetrates a pressurized structure on an aircraft.

Figure 7-3-1. Technicians perform necessary software configurations/ updates or database updates after installing a new system.

Courtesy of Duncan Aviation

pressurized aircraft structure. Special care must be taken when planning to penetrate a pressure bulkhead or the outer skin of a pressurized airplane. Again, the aircraft manufacturer's documents reveal where openings can be made and what size they can be. In either case, the technician must use a special sealant to prevent air leakage.

A popular way of passing bundles through a pressure bulkhead is to use a connector. In general, sealing a connector is less time consuming than sealing a bundle. When sealing

Figure 7-3-2. DME SEL label pictured is an example of a placard.

a bundle, each wire must be separated and coated individually over the portion that is to pass through the structure.

Section 3

Project Completion

Once the equipment is installed and wired, then the completion phase of the project starts. The number of tasks to complete during this phase of the project varies depending on the type of installation.

Tasks

Pitot Static Interruptions

If during the installation process the pitot or static lines were opened, then a pitot static check must be performed to standards set forth in FAR Part 43, Appendix E. Advisory Circular 43-6B provides guidance for altitude reporting equipment and transponder system maintenance and inspection. Table 7-3-1 lists appropriate tests to assure pitot static system functionality after removal, replacement, or installation of altitude reporting equipment or transponder system components.

Function Checks

Before installing interior panels and seats, a complete functional check of the entire avionics system should be performed. Special attention should be paid to systems that interface or communicate with the newly installed equipment. The technician should perform a complete function check of all systems, in order to make sure none were damaged while the aircraft was in a partially disassembled state.

Software

The newly installed system may need immediate software configuration, software updates, or database updates. The technician should ensure any required updates or configurations are completed. (Figure 7-3-1)

Placards

New equipment may come with placards (Figure 7-3-2) that would need to be installed on the instrument panel or in another location as required by the installation manual. For example, some GNSS systems may require a placard reading *VFR ONLY*, placed in a prominent location.

Compass Swings

A large change and, in some cases a small change, can change compass calibration. Upon completion of the installation, a compass swing should be performed. If necessary, the compass can be recalibrated and a new compass correction card can be created.

Weight and Balance

The technician's approach to weight and balance depends on the scope of the project and the condition of the weight and balance documentation upon the aircraft's arrival. If the scope of the project is large or if the incoming documentation is poor, the most cost effective and accurate approach is to weigh the airplane, as described in the chapter, Aircraft Weight and Balance.

Alterations of a smaller scope may only require a calculated change to the weight and balance

Component	Descriptor	Test(s)
Altimeter	• Pilot reference	1. Field elevation verification 2. Correspondence test 3. Static leak test
Altimeter	• Pilot reference • Matched to pilot encoder prior to installation	1. Field elevation verification 2. Abbreviated correspondence test 3. Static leak test
Altimeter	• Other than pilot reference	1. Field elevation verification 2. Static leak test
Encoding altimeter	• Pilot reference	1. Field elevation verification 2. Abbreviated correspondence test 3. Static leak test
Encoding altimeter	• Other than pilot reference	1. Field elevation verification 2. Correspondence test 3. Static leak test
Encoding altimeter	• Other than pilot reference • Matched to pilot reference altimeter prior to installation	1. Field elevation verification 2. Abbreviated correspondence test 3. Static leak test
Blind altitude encoder	• Connected to transponder	1. Correspondence test 2. Static leak test
Blind altitude encoder	• Connected to transponder • Matched to pilot reference altimeter prior to installation	1. Abbreviated correspondence test 2. Static leak test
Blind altitude encoder	• Not connected to transponder	1. Abbreviated correspondence test 2. Static leak test
High reliability style connectors	• Connectors designed to or meeting Military or similar industry standards	
Pilot reference altimeter	• The altimeter normally used to maintain flight altitude	
Transponder	• High reliability style connector system	1. Transponder test and inspection
Transponder	• Non-high reliability style connector system	1. Transponder test and inspection 2. Abbreviated correspondence test

Table 7-3-1. Test association matrix for static systems and transponder components.

information. Table 7-3-2 shows how a change can be made on paper.

Inspection and Documentation

Visual Inspection

As a last check before flight or delivery, the technician should return all system settings to those recorded upon acceptance of the aircraft. Next, the technician should perform a pre-flight inspection, as if he or she were about to the fly the aircraft. Most likely, no problems will be found, but if one does appear, it can be solved before a dangerous situation develops.

Flight Checks

The FAA may require a flight check for certain systems. For example, area navigation systems cannot be certified for flight in instrument meteorological conditions until along

and cross track error is verified in flight. Flight checks must only be performed by a pilot with appropriate ratings. In most cases, the aircraft owner or the owner's professional flight crew will fly the aircraft at this time.

Paperwork

The job is not complete until several documents have been updated, forms completed, and logbook entries made.

Field approval. The following documents are required for field approvals:

- Completed FAA Form 337 with sufficient descriptive and detailed substantiating data to describe the alteration or repair.
- Completed airworthiness compliance checklist containing applicable data.
- Any other documentation required to describe limitations, emergency/abnormal procedures, normal operating procedures, performance, weight and balance, etc., such

Basic weight & balance record										
Airplane registration no. XXXXXXXXX		Weight & moment change						Total basic airplane		
Airplane serial no. XXX41		Added			Removed					
Date	Description of change	Wt. lb.	Arm in.	Moment lb.-In.	Wt. lb.	Arm in.	Moment lb.-In.	Wt. lb.	Arm in.	Moment lb.-In.
10/15/05	Previous aircraft empty weight						0	1560.0	84.5	131820
6/30/14	Full fuel	288	95.0	27360			0	1848.0	86.13636	159180
6/30/14	Oil	15	27.5	413			0	1863.0	85.66452	159593
6/30/14	Narco ADF 140 receiver			0	-2.5	58.3	-145.75	1860.5	85.70129	159447.25
6/30/14	Narco ADF 140 servo Ind			0	-1.3	61	-79.3-	1859.2	85.71856	159367.95
6/30/14	Narco ADF 140 loop Ant			0	-1.6	162	-259.2	1857.6	85.65286	159108.75
6/30/14	Narco ADF 140 cable, loop			0	-0.6	105.5	-63.3	1857.0	85.64645	159045.45
6/30/14	Narco ADF 140 sense Ant and cable			0	-0.4	147.5	-59	1856.6	85.63312	158986.45
6/30/14	Avo 15A GPS reciever	3.3	48.9	161.403			0	1859.9	85.56796	159147.853
6/30/14	Avo 15A wiring harness	1.2	43.0	51.6			0	1861.1	85.54052	159199.453
6/30/14	Avo 15A antenna cable	1.2	78.4	94.08			0	1862.3	85.53591	159293.533
6/30/14	AVO 22 antenna	1.5	84.5	126.75			0	1863.8	85.53508	159420.283
6/30/14	Ki 206 CDI	1.3	51.3	66.69			0	1865.1	85.51122	159486.973
6/30/14	Ki 206 wiring harness	0.9	49.3	44.37				1866.0	85.49375	159531.343
6/30/14	New empty weight, empty arm, and empty moment							1866.0	85.49375	159531.343

Table 7-3-2. Weight and balance documentation for a retrofit.

as would be contained within an Aircraft Flight Manual Supplement (AFMS).

- **Applicable ICAs**. New ICAs or revisions to ICAs that contain Airworthiness Limitations Section (ALS) of the ICA require FAA approval and must be coordinated with the Aircraft Certification Office (ACO). See paragraph 7f for restrictions on establishing, altering, or canceling airworthiness limitations. Submitted ICAs without ALS are only accepted by the FAA.

- **Aircraft documents.** The technician must ensure the following documents have been updated at the conclusion of the project.

- Logbooks.

- Electrical load analysis documents.

- Weight and balance records.

- Equipment list.

- Flight manual.

- Instructions for continued airworthiness.

Shop documents. The paperwork does not end with the aircraft and the FAA. Technicians will be required to complete paperwork so warranties can be honored, time and materials invoiced, and inventory controlled.

Warranty paperwork. New equipment will include cards or paperwork to be filed with the manufacturer, so the factory warranty can be honored. This is important, because later, if a piece of equipment fails, your shop can apply for reimbursement for the repair costs.

Work order. For the shop, a work order will need to be completed, which documents the time spent, the materials used, and a description of the work performed. Some shops use paper work orders, while others have a computerized system. Whichever system is in use, the technician must pay attention to this important document (Figure 7-3-3).

Flight Crew Education

The installing agency should not assume the aircraft or flight crew is completely familiar with the new equipment. At the very least, a representative of the shop should discuss the new equipment with the owner. Many manufacturers provide simulators or software to help train pilots on new systems. Any educational material available for the new system should be made available to the pilot. In addition, a representative of the installing agency may sit with the pilot in the cockpit or flight deck and demonstrate the new equipment.

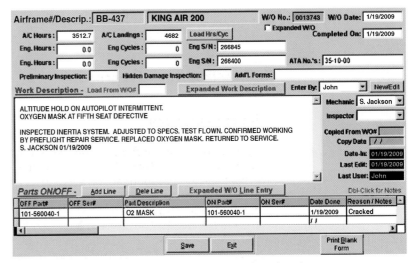

Figure 7-3-3. An example of a computer-based work order.

Section 4

Summary

Installing and integrating new equipment into an aircraft is a three-phase process. Planning or administration is the first phase, and the planner must take several factors into consideration. He or she must review aircraft records and documents. Furthermore, the planner must read installation manuals, create lists of required tools, and identify consumables. He or she must create task lists, time lines, and simplified wiring diagrams.

Execution is the second phase of the process. The technician uses the plan and acceptable techniques and practices to install the equipment. This phase starts with disassembly and removal of interior parts that are susceptible to damage, and this phase ends with reassembly and testing of the newly installed systems, which is also the start of the third and final phase.

The third phase is completion, in which documents are updated, forms are filled out, and work orders are completed. This phase also includes flight crew education and, in some cases, a check flight.

8

Installation and Integration

Installing avionics equipment and integrating it with the aircraft causes the technician to cross the line into the engineering realm. This chapter revisits the various configurations of avionics equipment, types of wire, and wire preparation, and it provides information on various types of connectors, including RF connectors. With careful study and practice in a laboratory setting, a technician should become proficient at soldering and crimping, along with the installation of hardware and wiring in an aircraft. This text pays special attention to methods of mounting avionics equipment. Section 1 covers some of the standard ways in which avionics are integrated, including channeling and data buses. Finally, there is a review of the paperwork that accompanies an installation, including a sample Form 337.

Section 1

Configurations

Before any wiring is done or any radio equipment is mounted, each radio installation must be planned. The installation manual must be read thoroughly. Typically, the technician is not given much leeway about where to mount remote LRUs, but in small aircraft, the pilot and technician should work together to plan the panel layout. The following questions must be answered before any wires are cut or holes are drilled.

- Is there room in the panel for the controls, panel-mounted LRUs or instruments?

- Is there sufficient depth behind the panel for the panel-mounted equipment?

Learning Objectives

DESCRIBE
- Pre-installation questions to consider

- Common avionics panel configurations

- Types of wire, cable, and connectors used

- A high quality soldering process

- Wire identification methods

- Data transmission methods, including channel selection

- LRU mounting methods

- Required installation documentation

- Antenna installations

EXPLAIN
- Cutting, terminating, and connecting methods for wire and cable

- Methods to route and support wire bundles

- Integration of avionic systems

- How to protect harnesses and wiring

Left. Transport aircraft can contain miles of wiring and large numbers of connectors that must all be accounted for.

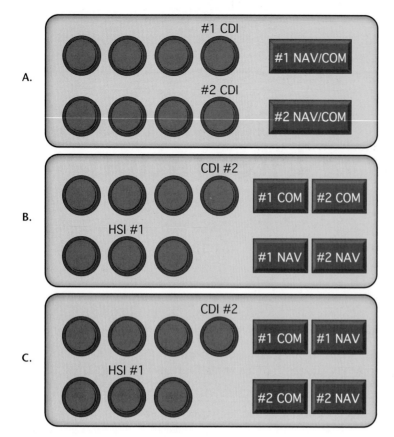

Figure 8-1-1. Typical preferred panel equipment locations.

- Is there sufficient room in the equipment bay for remote-mounted LRUs?
- Where will the antennas (if required) fit?
- Where will external switches and enunciators be installed?
- Where will the circuit breakers be installed?
- Is there room for additional circuit breakers on the bus?
- Will the electrical system support the additional load?
- Will other equipment have to be moved?
- Where does the wiring fit?
- How will the wiring bundles be supported?
- Will the system interfere with any other equipment already installed on the aircraft?

To help answer these questions, a technician needs to know the following requirements and conventions.

Circuit breakers must be labeled and installed within reach of the flight crew. Instruments must also be within view of the pilot during flight. Many aircraft have more than one com-

munication and navigation radio. The typical preferred layout locations for multiple radios are shown in Figure 8-1-1. In general, pilots prefer the No. 1 system either above the No. 2 system or to the left of the No. 2 system. Many navigation systems include moving map displays, and pilots prefer the unit with the moving map to be near the top of the panel. In small aircraft with limited space in the center opening, equipment may be placed on the right side of the instrument panel, often replacing the glove box.

Equipment certified for use under a Supplemental Type Certificate (STC) must be installed in accordance with the STC. No variation is allowed.

Section 2

Wire and Cable

Types of Wire

Avionics technicians and installers must work with several types of wire. The wire may be constructed of copper alloy, plated copper alloy, or aluminum. Wire used in aircraft is insulated. *Insulated wire* is a metal conductor covered with a *dielectric* or insulating material, as shown in Figure 8-2-1. Dielectric is another name for a nonconductor of electrical current. Insulated wire is commonly referred to as *wire*. Wires used in aircraft contain stranded conductors to allow flexibility and resistance to breakage. Insulation consists of several types of materials and layers to provide dielectric insulation, thermal protection, abrasion resistance, moisture resistance, and fluid resistance. Table 8-2-1 shows wires commonly used in aircraft.

Cable

Cable, or multi-conductor cable, has several definitions and types. The first definition for cable is two or more insulated conductors contained in a common covering or twisted together without a common covering, as shown in Figure 8-2-2. Another type of cable consists of one or more insulated conductors with a conductive shield covering and an additional layer of insulation over the shield. This type of cable is referred to as *shielded cable*. If two insulated conductors are twisted together, then technicians refer to them as a *twisted pair*. Yet another configuration of cable includes multiple insulated conductors twisted together with a conductive shield covering and an additional

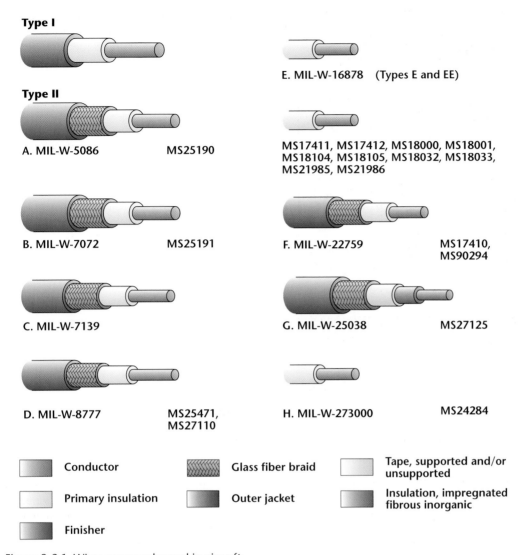

Type I

Type II

A. MIL-W-5086   MS25190

B. MIL-W-7072   MS25191

C. MIL-W-7139

D. MIL-W-8777   MS25471,
                       MS27110

E. MIL-W-16878   (Types E and EE)

MS17411, MS17412, MS18000, MS18001,
MS18104, MS18105, MS18032, MS18033,
MS21985, MS21986

F. MIL-W-22759   MS17410,
                       MS90294

G. MIL-W-25038   MS27125

H. MIL-W-273000   MS24284

Conductor	Glass fiber braid	Tape, supported and/or unsupported
Primary insulation	Outer jacket	Insulation, impregnated fibrous inorganic
Finisher		

Figure 8-2-1. Wires commonly used in aircraft.

layer of insulation over the shield. This cable is referred to as shielded twisted pair or shielded twisted triple, etc. Shielded wires are used to reduce electrical interference between systems.

A single insulated center conductor with a metallic braided outer conductor is a type of transmission line known as coaxial cable, which was described in Chapter 2. Technicians must never use coaxial cable in place of shielded wire and must check carefully to make sure this never happens.

Table 8-2-2 describes cables commonly used in aircraft. Typically, cables conform to military specifications. No cables using polyvinyl chloride (PVC) as insulation may be used, since PVC releases poisonous gas when heated.

Cutting Wire and Cable

A technician should ensure that he or she cuts all wires and cables to the appropriate lengths given on drawings or wiring diagrams. If the diagrams or drawings do not include lengths, as a general rule, the technician should add at least 50 percent to the estimated length measured in the aircraft. Keep in mind the old saying, "measure twice and cut once." In addition, splices reduce reliability; a long cable can always be shortened without adding a splice.

Cutting blades and tools are shown in Figure 8-2-3. Technicians should make sure all cutting tool blades are sharp and free from nicks, since a dull blade deforms and extrudes wire ends. To cut large diameter cables or heavy wires, the technician should use a circular saw with a cable cutting blade, which is similar to a meat slicing blade. A circular saw with teeth should not be used because the teeth catch and tear the cable. Heavy or light copper wires may also be cut with bench shears. If a few heavy gauge copper wires or cables are to be cut, then the technician may use a fine tooth hacksaw. Fine tooth hacksaws have 20 or more teeth per inch. When cutting with a hacksaw, a saw

Document	Voltage rating (maximum)	Rated wire temperature (˚C)	Insulation type	Conductor type
MIL-W-22759/1	600	200	Fluoropolymer insulated TFE and TFE coated glass	Silver coated copper
MIL-W-22759/2	600	260	Fluoropolymer insulated TFE and TFE coated glass	Nickel coated copper
MIL-W-22759/3	600	260	Fluoropolymer insulated TFE -glass-TFE	Nickel coated copper
MIL-W-22759/4	600	200	Fluoropolymer insulated TFE -glass-FEP	Silver coated copper
MIL-W-22759/5	600	200	Fluoropolymer insulated extruded TFE	Silver coated copper
MIL-W-22759/6	600	260	Fluoropolymer insulated extruded TFE	Nickel coated copper
MIL-W-22759/7	600	200	Fluoropolymer insulated extruded TFE	Silver coated copper
MIL-W-22759/8	600	260	Fluoropolymer insulated extruded TFE	Nickel coated copper
MIL-W-22759/9	1000	200	Fluoropolymer insulated extruded TFE	Silver coated copper
MIL-W-22759/10	1000	260	Fluoropolymer insulated extruded TFE	Nickel coated copper
MIL-W-22759/13	600	135	Fluoropolymer insulated FEP PVF2	Tin coated copper
MIL-W-22759/16	600	150	Fluoropolymer insulated extruded ETFE	Tin coated copper
MIL-W-22759/17	600	150	Fluoropolymer insulated extruded ETFE	Silver coated high strength copper alloy
MIL-W-22759/20	1000	200	Fluoropolymer insulated extruded TFE	Silver coated high strength copper alloy
MIL-W-22759/21	1000	260	Fluoropolymer insulated extruded TFE	Nickel coated high strength copper alloy
MIL-W-22759/34	600	150	Fluoropolymer insulated crosslinked modified ETFE	Tin coated copper
MIL-W-22759/35	600	200	Fluoropolymer insulated crosslinked modified ETFE	Silver coated high strength copper alloy
MIL-W-22759/41	600	200	Fluoropolymer insulated crosslinked modified ETFE	Nickel coated copper
MIL-W-22759/42	600	200	Fluoropolymer insulated crosslinked modified ETFE	Nickel coated high strength copper alloy
MIL-W-22759/43	600	200	Fluoropolymer insulated crosslinked modified ETFE	Silver coated copper
MIL-W-25038/3/2/	600	260	See specification sheet *	See specification sheet
MIL-W-81044/6	600	150	Crosslinked polyalkene	Tin coated copper
MIL-W-81044/7	600	150	Crosslinked polyalkene	Silver coated high strength copper alloy
MIL-W-81044/9	600	150	Crosslinked polyalkene	Tin coated copper
MIL-W-81044/10	600	150	Crosslinked polyalkene	Silver coated high strength copper alloy

Table 8-2-1. Open wiring.

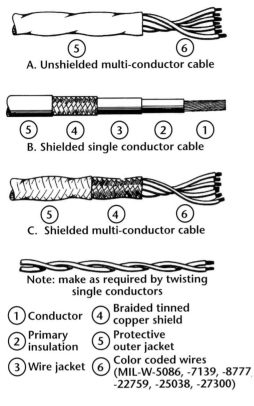

Note: make as required by twisting single conductors

① Conductor
② Primary insulation
③ Wire jacket
④ Braided tinned copper shield
⑤ Protective outer jacket
⑥ Color coded wires (MIL-W-5086, -7139, -8777, -22759, -25038, -27300)

Figure 8-2-2. Cables commonly used in aircraft.

MS number	MIL number	Definition
MS25192	MIL-C-7078	Single or multiple conductor using MS25190 wire and shielded with tinned copper braid
MS25313	MIL-C-7078	Similar to MS25912 but covered with a nylon jacket
NONE	MIL-W-22759	Single or multiple conductor using any commonly used wire; Sheilded with tinned, silver-coated, or nickel-coated copper braid and covered with the appropriate jacket
NONE	MIL-W-81381	Single or multiple conductor; Rubber insulated conductor with a rubber jacket

Table 8-2-2. Commonly used cables.

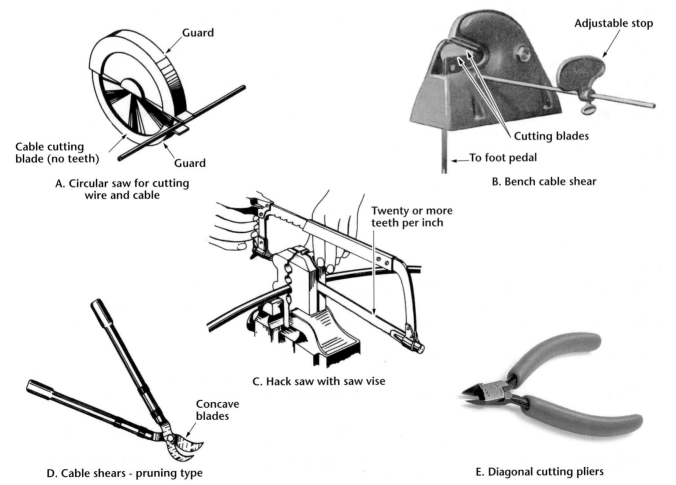

A. Circular saw for cutting wire and cable

B. Bench cable shear

C. Hack saw with saw vise

D. Cable shears - pruning type

E. Diagonal cutting pliers

Figure 8-2-3. Wire cutting tools.

Color	Code
Black	0
Brown	1
Red	2
Orange	3
Yellow	4
Green	5
Blue	6
Violet	7
Gray	8
White	9 (Also includes uncolored situations)

Table 8-2-3. Wire color code.

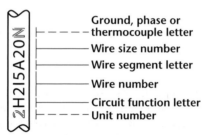

A. As Applied To All Circuit Functions Except R, S, T and Y

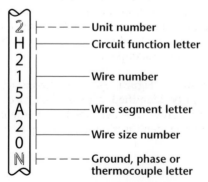

B. As Applied To Circuit Functions R, S and T

C. Vertical Stamping Of Wire Identification Code (Optional)

Figure 8-2-4. Examples of wire identification coding.

vice should be used to protect the wire. A saw vice, shown in Figure 8-2-3, is a standard vice modified with dies to hold wire firmly in place. There is space between the dies through which a saw blade may pass.

To cut light gauge copper wires, use diagonal cutting pliers. Do not attempt to cut wires larger than AN-8 with diagonal cutting pliers.

When cutting aluminum wire, the technician must be careful to avoid deforming the conductors. Aluminum wire is more brittle than copper and more susceptible to breakage. If deformed, the aluminum wire should be reshaped carefully. Aluminum wire should never be cut with tools that have reciprocating motion, such as a hacksaw. The reciprocating action hardens the aluminum, which leads to broken and torn strands. To cut a large number of aluminum wires, a power circular saw with a cable cutting blade should be used. Special shears with concave cutting edges, such as pruning or dehorning shears, may be used to cut aluminum wire safely.

Wire Identification

For ease of maintenance, each interconnecting wire and cable installed in an aircraft should be marked with a combination of letters and numbers that identify the wire, the circuit to which it belongs, its gauge, and other information necessary to relate the wire to a wiring diagram. This marking is called the *cable identification code*. Details of the code are given in Mil-Spec: MIL-W-5088. Wire is received from the manufacturer with the manufacturer's code designation printed on it in a light green color at intervals of one to five feet. The manufacturer's code designation includes: the MS number; the dash number of the wire (a number made up of dashes that indicates the wire size); and a one, two, or three digit number indicating the color of the basic wire insulation and the color of the stripes, if present. The color code is similar to the resistor color code and is shown in Table 8-2-3.

For example, a wire printed with number MS25190A20913 would designate a wire constructed in accordance with drawing MS25190, type A, size 20, with white insulation (9), a brown first stripe (1), and an orange second stripe (3).

When marking wires prior to installation, it is permissible to overstamp the manufacturer's printing. Examples of wire identification code marks are shown in Figure 8-2-4. Derived from a military standard, this basic wire identification code is presented as an illustration of one type of common wiring identification code. While this standard is used widely, some aircraft use unique codes developed by the individual aircraft manufacturer or avionics installation facility. Always consult the wiring diagram or installation manual for the aircraft or avionics on which you are working before attempting to interpret codes for a particular aircraft.

The basic code used for all circuits is as follows:

- **Unit number.** Prefixed where necessary to distinguish between wires in a circuit having identical items of equipment and identification numbers.

- **Circuit function** letter. Used to identify the function of the particular circuit. Details are contained in Mil-Spec 5088.

- **Wire number.** Used to distinguish between wires with the same circuit function letters.

- **Wire segment letter.** Used to distinguish between conductor segments in a particular circuit.

- **Wire size number.** Used to designate AN or AL gauge size of the wire. Wire size is not shown on coaxial cables. On thermocouple wire, the number is replaced with a dash.

- **Ground phase or thermocouple letter.** Used to denote a wire-to-ground phase of a wire in a three-phase system or material of a thermocouple pair.

In addition to the basic numbers and letters described in the previous paragraph, the wire identification codes R, S, and T stand for radio, radar, and special electronic circuits. If these letters are used, then the code includes another function letter known as the circuit designation letter, which further identifies the circuit inside the system, as shown in part B of Figure 8-2-4.

Identification Methods

The identification code may be stamped on the wires horizontally or vertically, as shown in Figure 8-2-4. The preferred method of identification is to stamp the marking directly on the wire or cable with a stamping machine or a laser wire-marking machine. Technicians should use this method whenever possible. If the insulation or outer covering does not stamp easily, a length of insulating tubing, known as a sleeve, may be stamped with the identification marking and installed on the wire or cable, as shown in Figure 8-2-5. Typically, shielded wire with no jacket, thermocouple wire, multiconductor cable, and high temperature wire are identified with sleeves. Otherwise, use sleeves only if the wire cannot be marked directly. Do

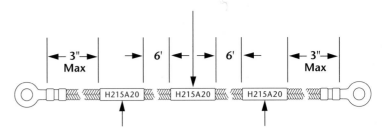

Figure 8-2-5. Location of identification sleeve.

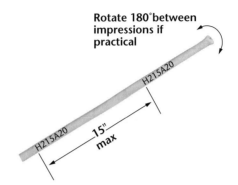

Figure 8-2-6. Spacing of identification stamping on wire and cable.

not use metallic markers or bands for identification, since the metal is likely to damage the wire. Furthermore, do not use sleeves to change the identification of wire or cable that has been previously marked. Sleeves marked with the identification number should be placed at each terminating end. For ease of troubleshooting and wire tracing, place sleeves at regular intervals throughout the entire length of the cable.

When marking wires, make sure the marking is legible and in a color contrasting with the insulation or sleeve. For example, use black stamping on light colored backgrounds and vice versa. Allow sufficient time for the marking to dry before working with the cable. As shown in Figure 8-2-6, stamp wires at intervals of not more than 15 inches along the entire length. Furthermore, stamp wires within 3 inches of each junction and at each terminating point. If the splice is permanent, the three-inch rule does not apply. Wires less than 3 inches long need not be stamped.

As shown in Figure 8-2-7, multiconductor cables can be identified with marked sleeves installed as previously described. Immediately following the identification code, stamp letters

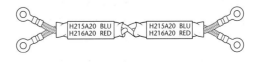

Figure 8-2-7. Multi-conductor cable identification.

Abbreviation	Color
BLK	Black
BLU	Blue
BRN	Brown
GY	Gray
GRN	Green
ORN	Orange
PR	Purple
RED	Red
WHT	White
YEL	Yellow

Table 8-2-4. Color abbreviations.

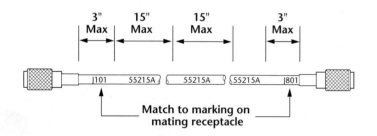

Figure 8-2-8. Coaxial cable identification.

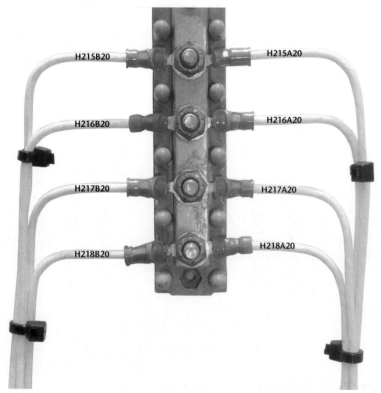

Figure 8-2-9. Wire identification at terminal board.

indicating the conductor color using abbreviations shown in Table 8-2-4.

Coaxial cable may be identified by stamping or with sleeves, as shown in Figure 8-2-8. The technician must take care to avoid flattening the cable during the stamping process because flattening adversely affects the cable properties causing standing waves. In addition to marking the coaxial as previously described, the terminating ends should be marked to match the equipment to which the cable is connected.

If possible, mark wires attached to terminal boards and equipment terminals between the termination and the point where the wire is brought into the wire bundle, as shown in Figure 8-2-9. If the enclosure permits, then identify the wires inside.

Clear or opaque flexible vinyl sleeving is adequate for general purpose wiring. For high temperature applications (over 100° C), silicone rubber or silicone fiberglass sleeving should be used. Where resistance to synthetic hydraulic or other solvents is necessary, nylon sleeving, either clear or white opaque, should be used. Heat shrinking polyethylene tubing may also be used to identify wire that cannot be marked directly. Table 8-2-5 lists the sizes of identification sleeving.

Automatic marking machines are preferable for stamping large numbers of long wires. Figure 8-2-10 shows an automated laser wire-marking machine with a 15-station [dereeler]. A dereeler is a device used to unwind wire on a spool and supply it to the wire-marking machine.

Figure 8-2-11 shows a manually operated laser wire-marking machine with a single dereeler. For short wires on repair or maintenance work, a hand-operated wire-marking machine, like the one pictured in Figure 8-2-12, may be more convenient and economical. With this type of machine, the desired amount of wire is fed through by hand and stamped by operating the handle for each marking. Wire guide holders are available in sizes for wires, and slot holders are supplied to hold the appropriate size of type. Marking machines come with operating manuals, which should be followed to allow for proper marking of wires.

Wire and Cable Preparation

Before wire can be assembled into connectors, terminals, splices, or other devices, the insulation must be stripped from the conducting ends to expose the bare conductor. For attachment to connectors, enough insulation is stripped so the conductor bottoms in the solder cup or

MIL-W-5086 Types I and II AN	Wire size MIL-W-5086 Type III AN	MIL-W-7072 AL	Sleeving size	
			NO.	Nominal ID (inches)
#22			11	.095
#20	#22		10	.106
#18	#20		9	.118
#16	#18		8	.133
#14	#16		7	.148
#12	#14		6	.166
#10	#12		4	.208
#8	#10		2	.263
#6	#8	#8	0	.330
#4	#6	#6	3/8	.375
#2	#4	#4	1/2	.500
#1	#2	#2	1/2	.500
#0	#1	#1	5/8	.625
#00	#0	#0	5/8	.625
#000	#00	#00	3/4	.750
#0000	#000	#000	3/4	.750
	#0000	#0000	7/8	.875

Table 8-2-5. Sizes of identification sleeving.

Figure 8-2-10. Automated Nova 860 laser marking machine.

Courtesy of Spectrum Technologies, PLC

fits properly in the crimping die. For solder cup terminal connections, there should be a small gap left between the top of the solder cup or loop terminal and the cut end of the insulation, as shown in Figure 8-2-13.

Copper wire may be stripped in a number of ways, depending on its size and insulation material. Table 8-2-6 shows various strippers available for copper wire. The use of hand strippers is not recommended on wires that will be installed in connectors utilizing a rubber sealing grommet.

A knife should be used to strip aluminum wire, and it must be stripped very carefully. The technician must take extreme care not to nick aluminum wire when stripping it because a nick in the wire will cause it to break more easily.

Figure 8-2-11. Manual Nova 800 laser marking machine.

Courtesy of Spectrum Technologies, PLC

Figure 8-2-12. Hand-operated wire marking machine.

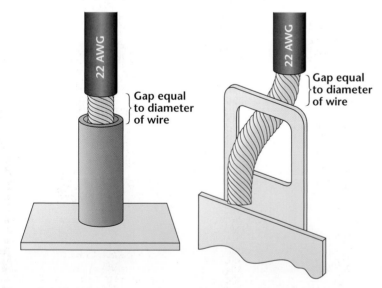

Figure 8-2-13. Wire strip gap above solder loop terminal.

When stripping any wire with the tools shown in Figure 8-2-14, observe the following instructions:

- When using a hot blade stripper, make sure the blades are clean. If necessary,

clean the blades with a brass wire brush. The hot blade stripper will not strip wire with glass braid insulation.

- Make sure all stripping blades are sharp and free from nicks or dents.

- When using any type of wire stripper, hold the wire perpendicular to the cutting blades.

- Adjust automatic stripping tools carefully and follow the manufacturer's instructions.

- Examine stripped wires for damage and re-adjust tools as necessary. Damage limits are shown in Table 8-2-7.

- Make sure insulation is cut cleanly with no frayed or ragged edges. If necessary, trim the insulation.

- Ensure all insulation is removed from the stripped area.

- When using hand plier strippers, use two or more operations to remove lengths of insulation longer than 3/4 inch.

- Retwist copper strands by hand or with pliers, if necessary, to restore natural lay and tightness of the strands.

Figure 8-2-15 demonstrates the correct way to strip a wire with a hand-held stripper.

Before copper wires are soldered to connectors, the ends exposed by stripping must be tinned to hold the strands solidly together and to encourage thorough heat transfer during the soldering process. The tinning operation is considered satisfactory when the ends and sides of the wire strands are fused together with a coat of solder. Do not tin wires that are to be crimped to Class K (fireproof) connectors, wires that are to be attached to solderless terminals or splices, or wires that are to be crimped to removable crimp-style connector contacts.

Copper wires are usually tinned by dipping them into flux and then into a solder bath (Figure 8-2-16). In the field, copper wires can be tinned with a soldering iron and rosin core solder. Tin the conductor for about half its exposed length. This is enough to take advantage of the closed part of the solder cup. Tinning or solder on wire above the cup encourages *wicking*. Wicking is a process where solder fills in openings between strands, much like water fills in openings between sponge fibers. The wicking process causes both solder and water to apparently defy gravity and rise into the openings. Solder wicking causes the wire to be stiff at a point where flexing should take place. This stiffness results in wire breakage.

Wire stripper	An gauge number	Insulation
Hot Blade	# 26 - # 4	All types except glass braid
Rotary Electric	# 26 - # 4	All types
Bench	# 20 - # 6	All types
Hand Pliers	# 26 - # 8	All types
Knife	# 2 - # 0000	All types

Table 8-2-6. Wire strippers for use on copper wire.

Wire	Nickel or broken strands
Copper	
AN #22 - #12	None
#10	2
#8 - #4	4
#2 - #0	12
Aluminum	
All sizes	None

Table 8-2-7. Wire damage limits.

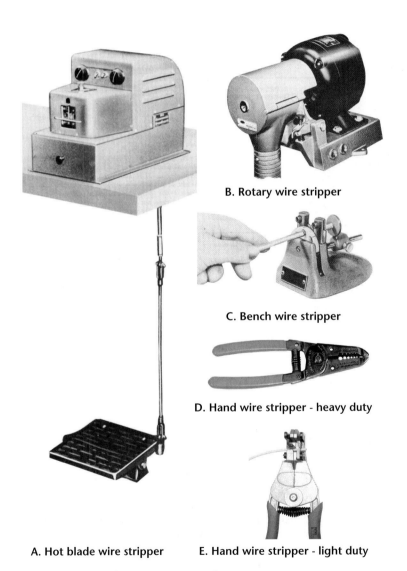

B. Rotary wire stripper

C. Bench wire stripper

D. Hand wire stripper - heavy duty

A. Hot blade wire stripper   E. Hand wire stripper - light duty

Figure 8-2-14. Typical wire stripping tools.

Step 1

Select correct hole to match wire gauge

Step 2

Blades remain open until wire is removed

Figure 8-2-15. Stripping wire with a handheld stripper.

Solder flux is available from many electrical, electronic, and aviation supply houses. Do not use acid, since acid will prematurely corrode the wire. The most common solder used in the aviation industry is a wire that consists of 60 percent tin and 40 percent lead, and it may be marked Sn60. In some cases, *eutectic solder* may be used. The term eutectic describes a material that becomes liquid at the lowest temperature possible. Eutectic solder consists of 63 percent tin and 37 percent lead. Eutectic solder melts and solidifies more quickly than Sn60 solder.

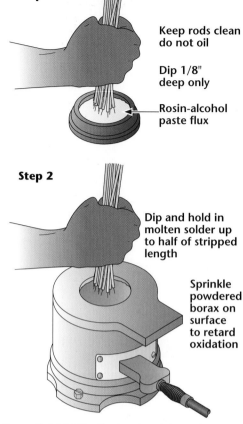

Step 1

Keep rods clean
do not oil

Dip 1/8"
deep only

Rosin-alcohol
paste flux

Step 2

Dip and hold in
molten solder up
to half of stripped
length

Sprinkle
powdered
borax on
surface
to retard
oxidation

Figure 8-2-16. Dip tinning in solder pot.

Wire size (AN gauge)	Soldering iron size (heat capacity)
#20 - #16	65 Watts
#14 & #12	100 Watts
#10 & #8	200 Watts

Table 8-2-8. Approximate soldering iron sizes for tinning.

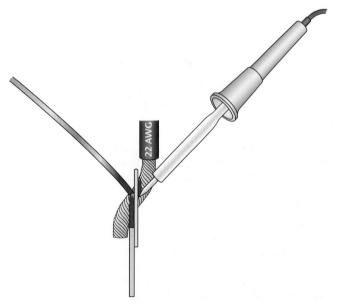

Figure 8-2-17. Solder iron and solder placed on either side of a wire.

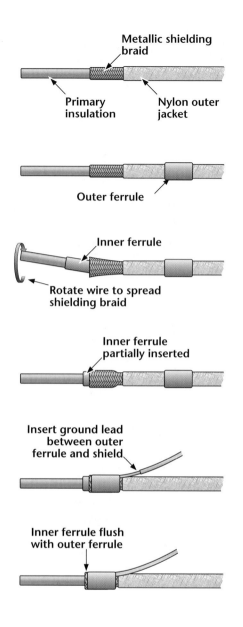

Metallic shielding braid

Primary insulation

Nylon outer jacket

Outer ferrule

Inner ferrule

Rotate wire to spread shielding braid

Inner ferrule partially inserted

Insert ground lead between outer ferrule and shield

Inner ferrule flush with outer ferrule

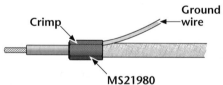

Crimp

Ground wire

MS21980

Figure 8-2-18. Two piece grounding connection for terminating shielded wire.

Wires may also be tinned by the use of a soldering iron and rosin core solder. When tinning wire using a soldering iron, select an iron with suitable heat capacity for the wire size (Table 8-2-8).

Prime by holding the tip and the solder together until a bead of solder forms on the tip of the iron. Place the soldering iron tip on one side of the wire and the solder on the other side, as shown in Figure 8-2-17. Heat until the wire draws in the solder. Pull the solder away before removing the heat.

Part number	Color code	Sleeve ID (inches) Nominal	Installing tools (Thomas & Betts)
MS21980-101	Tin	0.101	WT - 219
-128	Blue	0.126	-200
-149	Purple	0.149	-201
-156	Yellow	0.156	-202
-175	Blue	0.175	-203
-187	Orange	0.187	-206
-194	Red	0.194	-206
-199	Tin	0.199	-206
-205	Yellow	0.206	-208
-219	Green	0.219	-208
-225	Purple	0.225	-209
-232	Orange	0.233	-210
-261	Yellow	0.261	-211
-275	Tin	0.275	-212
-281	Purple	0.281	-214
-287	Blue	0.287	-214
-299	Green	0.299	-214
-312	Yellow	0.312	-215
-327	Tin	0.327	-216
-346	Orange	0.346	-217
-359	Purple	0.359	-221
-375	Yellow	0.375	-222
-405	Red	0.405	-218
-415	Blue	0.415	-218
-460	Tin	0.460	-220
-500	Green	0.500	-223

Table 8-2-9. Shielded wire terminations—uninsulated outer sleeves and installing tools.

Shielded Cable Termination

Shielded cable has a metallic braid over the insulation to provide a barrier around the conductor through which electrostatic energy cannot pass. Electrostatic energy causes noise or interference. To obtain good results from shielded cable, the shield must be unbroken and must extend to a point as near to the end of the conductor as practical. Shielded cable may not be grounded at both ends. Equipment installation manuals may require grounding at only one end to prevent static electricity from discharging along the shield. Read the equipment installation manual carefully to determine how to terminate shielded wire properly.

Some shielded cable has a thin coating of extruded plastic over the shielding braid. Strip the plastic off as far as necessary with a hot blade stripper. The length of strip depends on the method of shield termination and type of wire connection. Strip the outer jacket back far enough to make the work easy. If no hot blade stripper is available, use plier-type hand strippers for sizes No. 22 through No. 10 and a knife for larger sizes. You must take care not to damage the shielding braid.

If the metallic braid of the shielded cable can be flared out easily, then terminate the shield by crimping it, with or without a ground jumper lead. Standard shield grounding ferrule MS25311 and the MS25312 crimping tool may be used.

Military standard two-piece crimp-type grounding connectors are also available for terminating shielded cable, as shown in Figure 8-2-18, Table 8-2-9 and Table 8-2-10 in both insulated and non-insulated varieties.

Part number	Color code	Sleeve ID (inches) Nominal	Installing tools (Thomas & Betts)
MS18120-101	Tin	0.101	WT-200
-128	Blue	0.128	-201
-149	Purple	0.149	683-51135
-156	Yellow	0.156	WT-206
-175	Blue	0.175	-208
-187	Orange	0.187	-210
-194	Red	0.194	-210
-199	Tin	0.199	-210
-205	Yellow	0.205	-211
-219	Green	0.219	-211
-225	Purple	0.225	-211
-232	Orange	0.232	-212
-261	Yellow	0.261	-214
-275	Tin	0.275	-215
-281	Purple	0.281	-217
-287	Blue	0.287	-217
-297	Green	0.297	-217
-312	Yellow	0.312	-222
-327	Tin	0.327	-222
-348	Orange	0.348	683-51014
-359	Purple	0.359	WT-216
-375	Yellow	0.375	683-51-15
-405	Red	0.405	683-51141-1
-415	Blue	0.415	683-51141-1
-460	Tin	0.460	683-51141-2
-500	Green	0.500	683-51141-3

Table 8-2-10. Shielded wire terminations—insulated outer sleeves and installing tools.

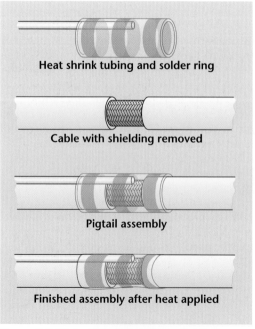

Figure 8-2-19. Insulated pigtail terminations.

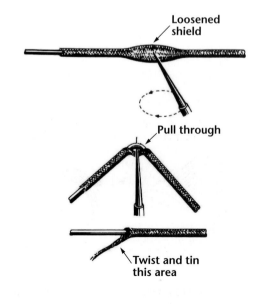

Figure 8-2-20. Pigtail termination for shielded wire.

A.

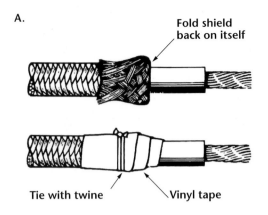

Fold shield
back on itself

Tie with twine   Vinyl tape

B.

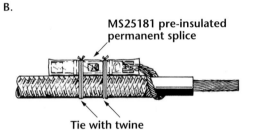

MS25181 pre-insulated
permanent splice

Tie with twine

Figure 8-3-21. (A) Dead ending shielding with tape wrap, (B) Dead ending shielding with permanent splice.

Insulated pigtail terminations constructed of heat shrink tubing and solder are also available, as shown in Figure 8-2-19. Once the termination is in place, a heat gun can be used to melt the solder ring and shrink the tubing.

If necessary, pigtails may also be constructed manually, as shown in Figure 8-2-20. Once the center conductor has been pulled through the loosened shield, it may be spliced to a longer piece of wire to allow proper grounding.

In cases where the termination of the shielded wire is not to be grounded, it must be *dead ended*. Several methods are available to dead end the shield. The key step in all of the methods is to insulate the shielding so it does not make contact with ground. Figure 8-2-21 shows two methods of dead ending shielded wires.

Section 3

Connectors

Connectors provide a means of quickly connecting and disconnecting harnesses to simplify installation and maintenance of electric and electronic equipment. Connectors consist of two parts, a plug assembly and a receptacle assembly. The plug assembly contains a coupling device.

Military Specification Connectors

Several connectors are available that are constructed to military specification (MS) or Army/Navy specifications (AN). Standard AN-type connectors are coupled with a threaded coupling ring, except for MS3107, which has a friction coupling. Miniature MS connectors are a small lightweight version of the AN type and

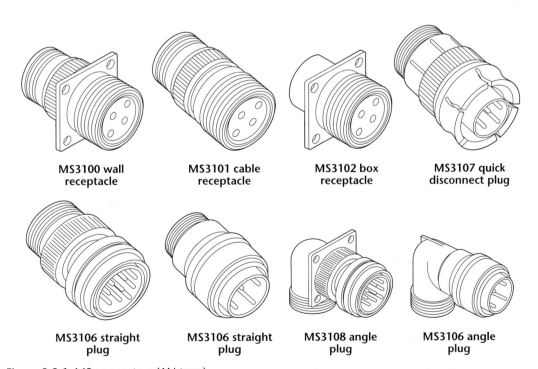

MS3100 wall
receptacle

MS3101 cable
receptacle

MS3102 box
receptacle

MS3107 quick
disconnect plug

MS3106 straight
plug

MS3106 straight
plug

MS3108 angle
plug

MS3106 angle
plug

Figure 8-3-1. MS connectors (AN type).

A. Miniature connectors MIL-C-26482 - solder and crimp-type contacts

Wall mounting receptacle
Solder: MS3110 & MS3130
Crimp: MS3120 & MS3140

Box mounting receptacle
Solder: MS3112 & MS3132
Crimp: MS3122

Jam nut receptacle
Solder: MS3114 & MS3134
Crimp: MS3124 & MS3144

Straight plug
Solder: MS3116
Crimp: MS3126

Thru-bulkhead receptacle
Solder: MS3119 & MS3139

Short plug
Solder: MS3147
Crimp: MS3147

Class E
grommet seal

Class F
strain relief clamp

Class P
potting seal

Class J
gland seal

B. Miniature connectors MIL-C-26500 - crimp-type contacts only

Flange mounting
receptacle MS24264

Single-hole mounting
receptacle MS24265

Straight plug
MS24266

Figure 8-3-2. MS connectors (miniature).

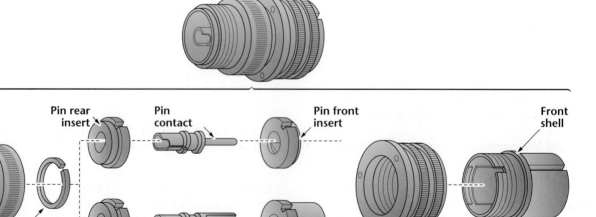

MS3106A

Back shell

Pin rear insert

Pin contact

Pin front insert

Front shell

Retaining ring

Socket rear insert

Socket contact

Socket front insert

Coupling ring

Figure 8-3-3. Exploded view of an MS connector plug.

MS3106A

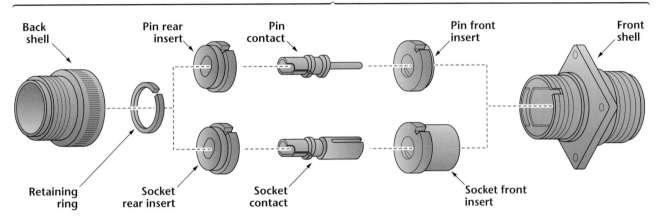

Back shell

Pin rear insert

Pin contact

Pin front insert

Front shell

Retaining ring

Socket rear insert

Socket contact

Socket front insert

Figure 8-3-4. Exploded view of an MS connector receptacle.

are coupled by means of a threaded ring, bayonet lock, or push-pull coupling.

Figure 8-3-1 illustrates several AN-type connectors. Figure 8-3-2 illustrates miniature MS connectors.

The receptacle is usually the fixed part of the connector and may be attached to a bulkhead or equipment case. The plug is usually the removable part of the connector and includes the coupling ring. When the two parts of the connector are joined by the coupling device, the electric circuit is made by pin-and-socket contacts inside the connector. Usually, the "live" or "hot" side of the circuit is connected through the socket (female) contacts. The contacts are held in place and insulated from each other and the shell by a dielectric insert. The insert and contacts are housed in a metal shell. Figure 8-3-3 shows an exploded view of a typical plug, and Figure 8-3-4 shows an exploded view of a typical receptacle.

AN and MS connectors are separated into types and classes, with manufacturers variations within each type and class. These variations are found in the method of complying with specification requirements and in appearance. The variations are minor and do not affect the ability to mate plugs and receptacles constructed by different manufacturers. There are six AN types of standard MS connectors, as listed in Table 8-3-1. The connectors are further separated into six classes, which are listed in Table 8-3-2.

MS Type	Nomenclature
MS3100	Wall mounting receptacle
MS3101	Cable connecting plug
MS3102	Box mounting receptacle
MS3106	Straight plug
MS3107	Quick disconnect plug
MS3108	90 Degree angle plug

Table 8-3-1. AN types of standard MS connectors.

As shown in Figure 8-3-1, the following six types of standard AN-type connectors used in aircraft:

- **MS3100.** A receptacle with a flange for mounting to a bulkhead. The device contains a front shell, insert retaining ring, insert contacts, and a back shell. Connectors with resilient inserts omit the insert retaining ring. Figure 8-3-4 shows the exploded view of the typical MS3100 receptacle.

MS Class	Application	Shell	Availability					
			3100	3101	3102	3106	3107	3108
A	General purpose	Solid aluminum alloy	Yes	Yes	Yes	Yes	Yes	Yes
B	General purpose	Split aluminum alloy	Yes	Yes	No	Yes	Yes	Yes
C	Pressurized receptacle	Solid aluminum alloy	Yes	No	Yes	No	No	No
E	Environmental resistant	Solid aluminum alloy with strain relief clamp	Yes	Yes	Yes	Yes	No	Yes
K	Fire and flame resistant	Solid steel	Yes	No	Yes	Yes	No	Yes
R	Environmental resistant	Solid aluminum alloy	Yes	Yes	Yes	Yes	No	Yes

Table 8-3-2. Classes of AN-type connectors.

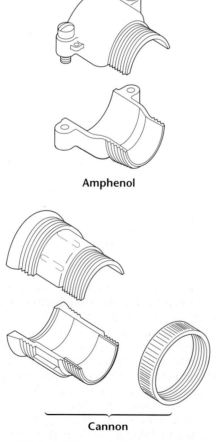

Amphenol

Cannon

Figure 8-3-5. Split-back shell connector.

- **MS3101.** A plug used at the end of a wire or wire bundle where mounting is not required. The device is similar to the MS3100, except for the lack of a mounting flange.

- **MS3102.** A receptacle with a flange for mounting to a junction box or equipment case. The device is similar to the MS3100, except for the lack of a back shell.

- **MS3106.** A straight plug used at the end of a wire or bundle. The device consists of a front shell, coupling nut, insert retaining ring, insert, contacts, and a back shell. Connectors with resilient inserts omit the retaining ring, as shown in Figure 8-3-2.

- **MS3107.** A quick-disconnect plug used where fast pull disconnection from the receptacle is necessary. Similar to a MS3106, the MS3107 is coupled to the receptacle by means of a friction ring rather than a coupling unit.

- **MS3108.** A right-angle plug used where wiring must make an abrupt change in direction as it leaves the plug.

There are six classes of AN and MS connectors. All have shells made of aluminum alloy, except the K Class, which has a steel shell to achieve fire resistance.

MS Type	Nomenclature	Availability				
		Class				
		E	F	P	H	J
Bayonet coupling						
MS3110	Wall Mounting Receptacle	Yes	Yes	Yes	No	Yes
MS3112	Box Mounting Receptacle	Yes	No	Yes	Yes	No
MS3114	Rear Mounting Jam Nut Receptacle	Yes	No	Yes	Yes	No
MS3116	Straight Plug	Yes	Yes	Yes	No	Yes
MS3119	Thru-bulkhead Mounting Receptacle	Yes	No	Yes	No	No
Push-pull coupling						
MS3130	Wall Mounting Receptacle	Yes	No	Yes	No	Yes
MS3132	Box Mounting Receptacle	Yes	No	No	Yes	No
MS3134	Single-hole Mounting Receptacle	Yes	No	Yes	Yes	Yes
MS3137	Short Plug	Yes	No	Yes	No	Yes
MS3138	Lanyard Plug	Yes	No	Yes	No	Yes
MS3139	Thru-bulkhead Mounting Receptacle	Yes	No	No	No	No

Table 8-3-3. Types and causes of MIL-C-26482 miniature MS connectors with solder contacts.

- **Class A.** A general-purpose connector with a solid, one-piece back shell. All the receptacles shown in Figure 8-3-1 are Class A.

- **Class B.** A connector with the back shell split in two lengthwise, as shown in Figure 8-3-5, and used where it is important to be able to access soldered connections with ease. The two halves of the back shell are held together by a clamping ring or screws.

- **Class C.** A pressurized connector used on equipment walls and bulkheads. It looks the same as a Class A receptacle, but the inside sealing arrangement is different. Inserts of Class C connectors cannot be removed. Mating Class C receptacles to other class plugs does not affect the sealing qualities of the Class C receptacle.

- **Class E.** An environment-resisting connector used in areas where changes in temperature may cause condensation or in areas where vibration is likely. Class E connectors have a sealing grommet in the back shell. The wires pass through tight fitting holes in the grommet, which seal against moisture. The contacts are supported in a resilient insert. Class E receptacles must mate to Class E plugs.

- **Class K.** A fireproof connector used where it is vital that current continues to flow, even though the connector may be exposed to a continuous open flame. Class K connectors are longer in overall length than other class connectors and have a shell made of steel. Inserts in Class K connectors are made of special fire-resistant material and have crimp-type contacts. Crimping pressure forms the metal of the contact around the conductor, creating a low resistance and a mechanically strong connection.

- **Class R.** A lightweight environment-resisting connector similar to the Class E connector. It is intended to replace the Class E connector where shorter length and lighter weight are required. For additional sealing, an O-ring is provided with MS3106 and MS3108 plugs for additional sealing.

Miniature MS connectors are covered by two standards. The most commonly used in aircraft are MIL-C-26482 and MIL-C-26500. Connectors manufactured to MIL-C-26482 may have contacts of either solder or crimp types. MIL-C-26500 connectors have crimp-type contacts only. Connectors to both specifications have contacts in sizes 20, 15, and 12 only. The types and classes of miniature MS connectors with solder-type contacts are listed in Table 8-3-3. Miniature MS connectors with crimp-style contacts are listed

MS Type	Nomenclature
1. MIL-C-26482	
Bayonet coupling:	
MS3120	Wall mounting receptacle
MS3122	Box mounting receptacle
MS3124	Rear mounting jam nut receptacle
MS3126	Straight plug
Push-pull coupling:	
MS3140	Wall mounting receptacle
MS3144	Single-hole mounting receptacle
MS3147	Plug
MS3148	Lanyard plug
2. MIL-C-26500	
MS24264	Flange mounting receptacle
MS24265	Single hole mounting receptacle
MS24266	Straight plug

Table 8-3-4. Types of miniature MS connectors with crimp contacts.

in Table 8-3-4 and are of the environment-resisting classes.

The following types of miniature MS connectors with solder contacts are used in aircraft.

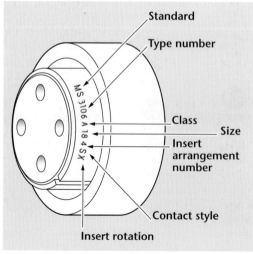

Figure 8-3-6. MS connector marking.

- **MS3110.** A receptacle with a flange for mounting to a bulkhead, coupled by means of a *bayonet* lock. A bayonet lock consists of pins on one half of the connector, which align with L-shaped slots on the other half of the connector. Spring tension holds the pins in the slots. Clockwise rotation locks the connector in place. Counterclockwise rotation releases the connector.

- **MS3112.** A receptacle with a bayonet lock coupling similar to an MS3110, except it has no back shell, that is used for mounting to a junction box or equipment case.

- **MS3114.** A rear-mounting receptacle with a jam nut, instead of a flange, and a bayonet lock coupling.

- **MS3116.** A straight plug for end of wire or wire bundle with a bayonet lock coupling.

- **MS3119.** A receptacle with a bayonet-lock coupling made for passing wires and cables through a bulkhead.

- **MS3130.** A receptacle similar to the MS3110, except it has a push-pull, ball-lock coupling.

- **MS3132.** A receptacle similar to MS 3112, except it has a push-pull coupling.

- **MS3134.** A single-hole, mounting receptacle similar to the MS3114, except it has a push-pull coupling.

- **MS3137.** A straight plug similar to MS3116, except it has a push-pull coupling.

- **MS3139.** A through-bulkhead mounting receptacle similar to the MS3119, except it has a push-pull coupling.

Miniature MS connectors with crimp contacts are similar to the solder type, but they have removable contacts to which wires are crimped using a standard crimping tool. Connectors with crimp-type contacts are available in the following types.

- **MS3120.** A bayonet-coupled receptacle with a flange for mounting to a bulkhead.

- **MS3122.** A bayonet-coupled receptacle for mounting to a junction box or equipment case. The connector is similar to a MS3120, except it has no back shell.

- **MS3124.** A rear-mounting, bayonet-coupled receptacle with a jam nut instead of a flange.

- **MS3126.** A bayonet-coupled straight plug for use at the end of a wire or wire bundle.

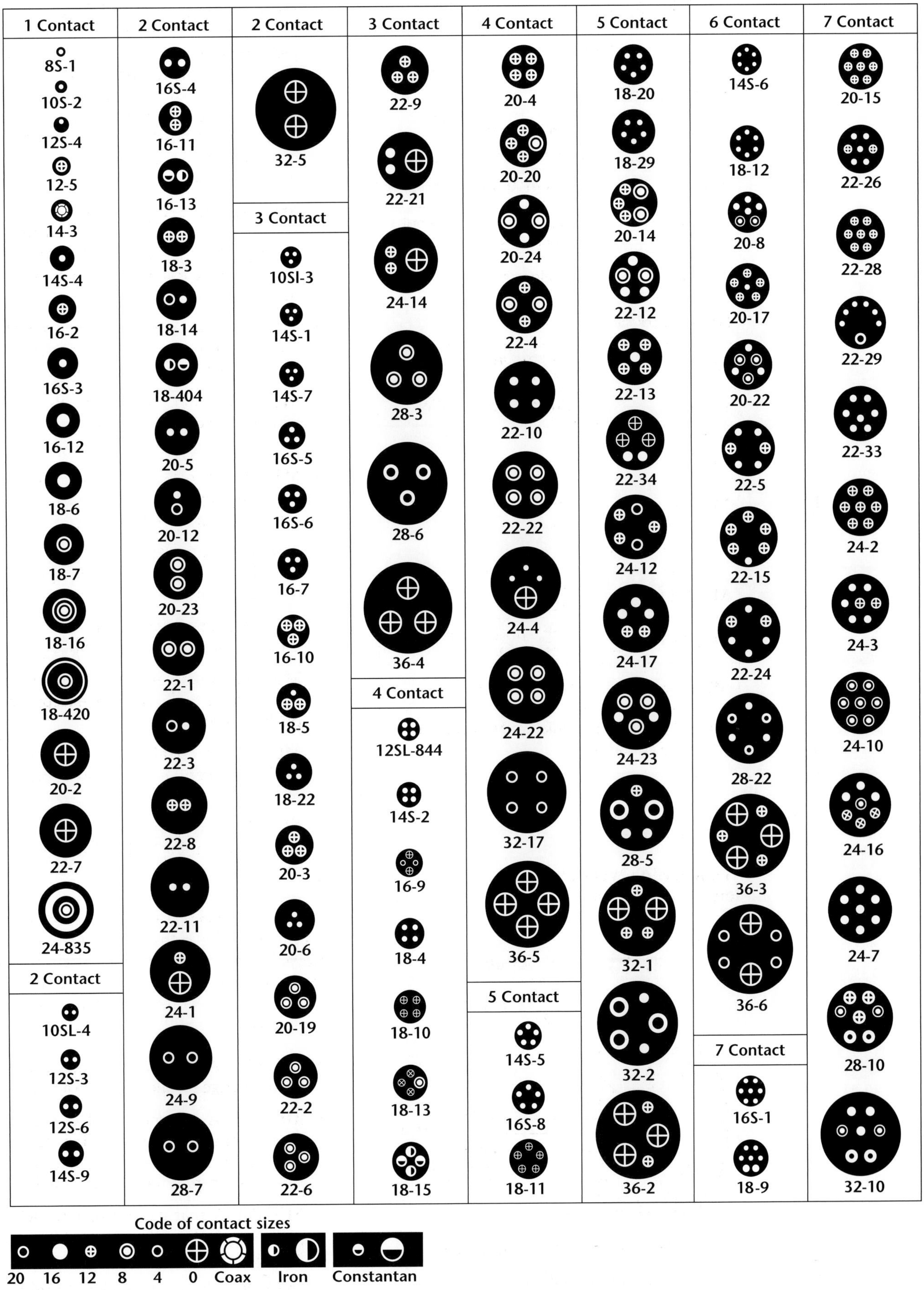

Figure 8-3-7A. Insert arrangements (AN-type connectors, MIL-C-5015).

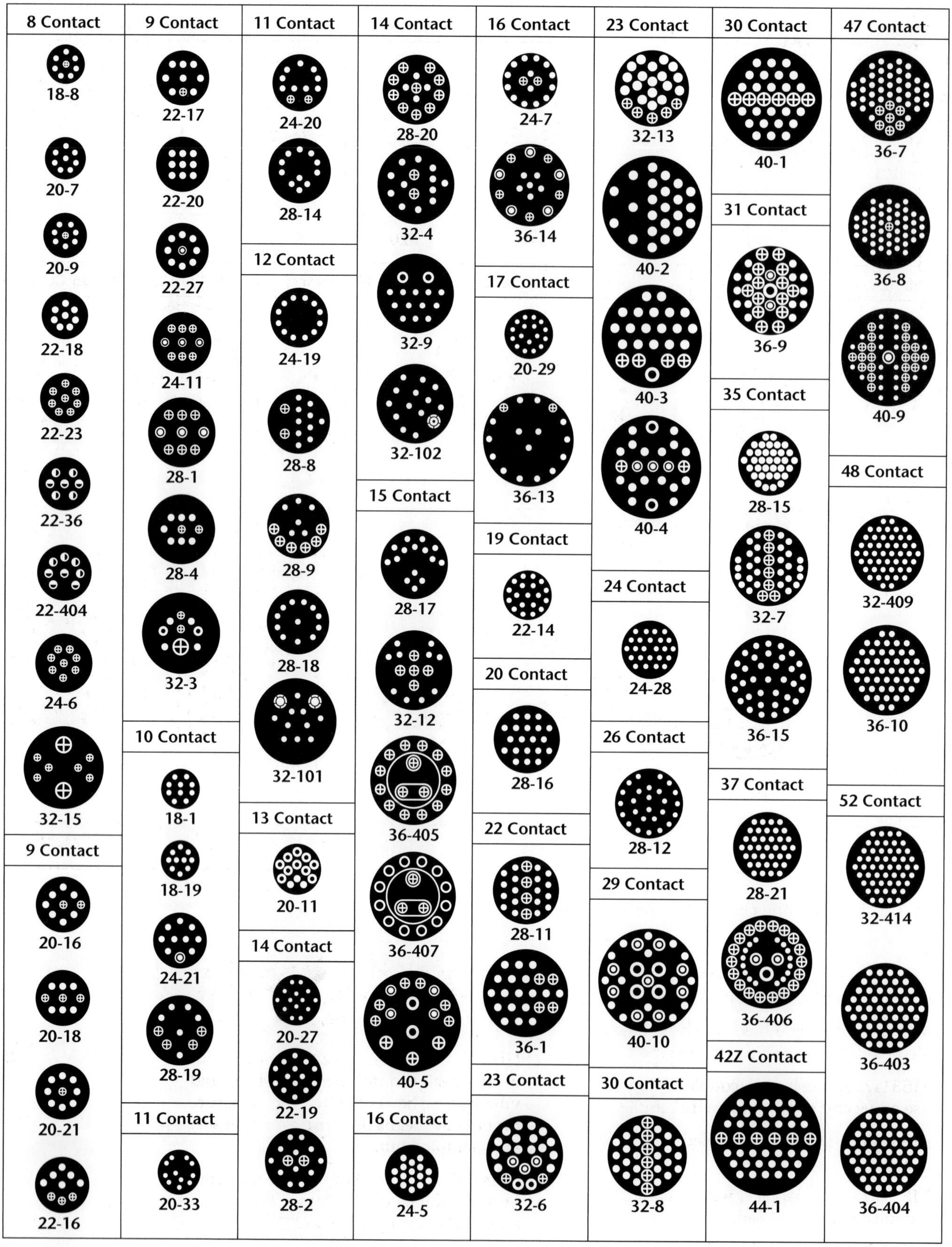

Figure 8-3-7B. Insert arrangements (AN-type connectors, MIL-C-5015) continued.

Shell size	3 Contacts		4 Contacts	5 Contacts	6 Contacts	8 Contacts	10 Contacts	11 Contacts
Insert arrangement number	8-3	12-3	8-4	14-5	10-6	16-8	12-10	18-11
Number and size of contacts	3-20	3-16	4-20	5-16	6-20	8-16	10-20	11-16

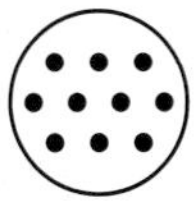

Shell size	12 Contacts	15 Contacts	16 Contacts	19 Contacts	21 Contacts	26 Contacts
	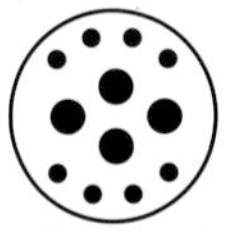		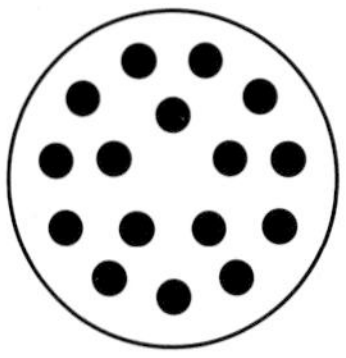	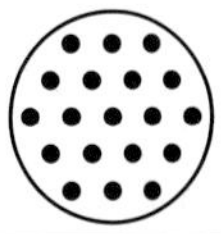	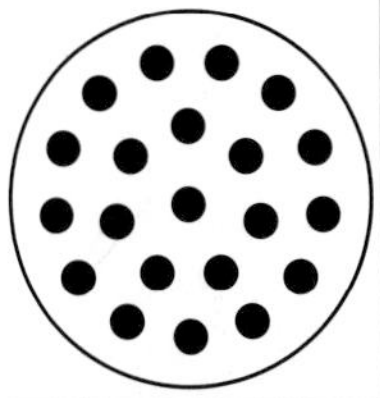	
Insert arrangement number	14-12	14-15	20-16	14-19	22-21	16-26
Number and size of contacts	8-20 4-16	14-20 1-16	16-16	19-20	21-16	26-20

Shell size	32 Contacts	39 Contacts	41 Contacts	55 Contacts	61 Contacts
	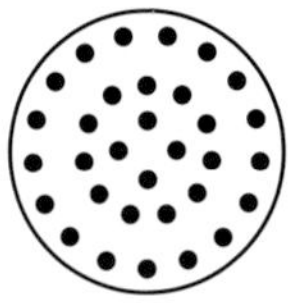	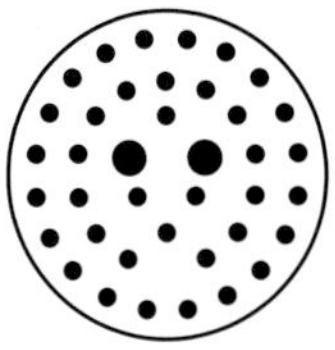	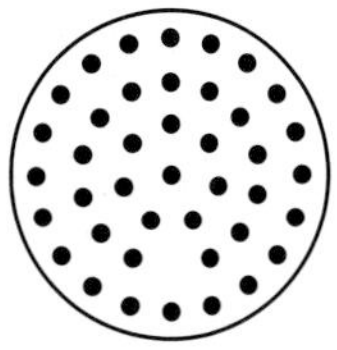	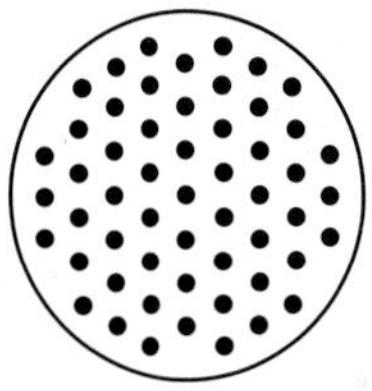	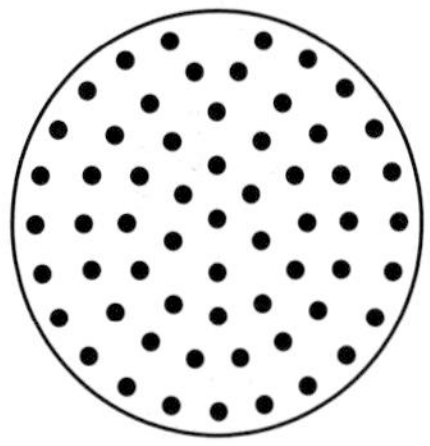
Insert arrangement number	18-32	20-39	20-41	22-55	24-61
Number and size of contacts	32-20	37-20 2-16	41-20	55-20	61-20

Figure 8-3-8. Insert arrangements (MS miniature connectors, MIL-C-26482).

- **MS3140.** A flange-mounted push-pull coupled receptacle similar to the MS3120.
- **MS3144.** A single-hole, push-pull coupled receptacle similar to the MS3124.
- **MS3147.** A push-pull coupled plug for use at the end of a wire or wire bundle.
- **MS3148.** A push-pull coupled plug with a lanyard.
- **MS24624.** A receptacle with a flange for mounting to a bulkhead.
- **MS24625.** A receptacle with a jam nut for panel mounting.
- **MS24266.** A straight plug used at the end of a wire or wire bundle.

Like AN connectors, miniature MS connectors come in classes. There are five classes of miniature MS connectors with solder-type contacts.

- **Class E.** An environment-resisting connector designed to resist moisture and vibration. The connector is moisture proofed by means of a wire grommet seal and clamping nut.
- **Class F.** An environment-resisting connector, similar to the Class E but with a strain relief clamp added.
- **Class H.** A hermetically sealed receptacle with a glass insert fused to the contacts and the shell.
- **Class J.** A connector with a *gland seal* incorporated for sealing a jacketed cable.

	Shell size					
	10	**12**	**14**	**16**	**18**	**22**
Size 20 contacts Rated 7.5 amperes For wire sizes 24-22-20 AWG insulation O.D. Max:=.090in. Min: = .040 in.	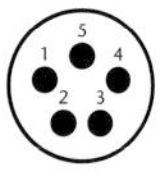 *(insert)*	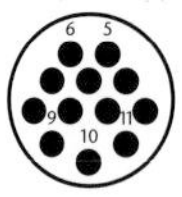 *(insert)*	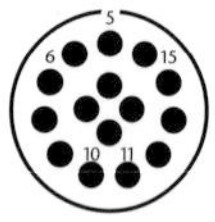 *(insert)*	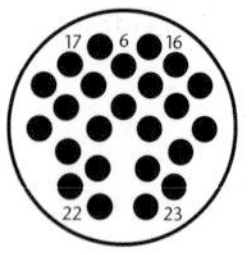 *(insert)*	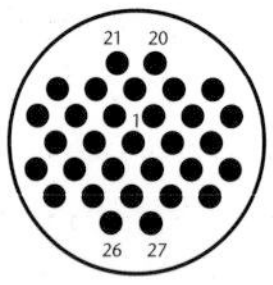 *(insert)*	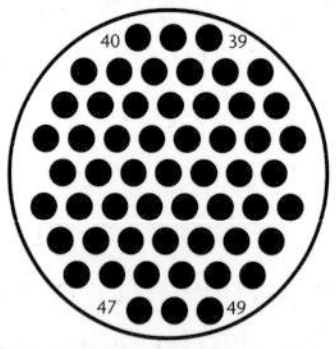 *(insert)*
	5 Contacts	12 Contacts	15 Contacts	24 Contacts	31 Contacts	55 Contacts
Size 16 contacts Rated 20 amperes For wire sizes 18-16 AWG insulation O.D. Max: = .130 in. Min: = .064 in.		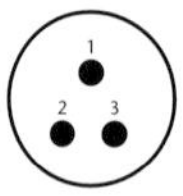 *(insert)*	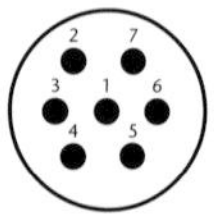 *(insert)*		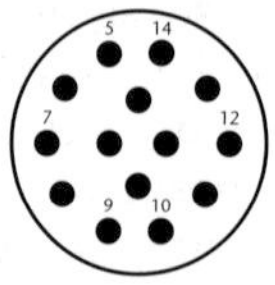 *(insert)*	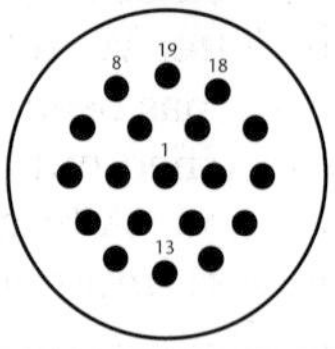 *(insert)*
		3 Contacts	7 Contacts		14 Contacts	19 Contacts
Size 12 contacts Rated 35 amperes For wires sizes 14-12 AWG insulation O.D. Max: .170 in min: = .106			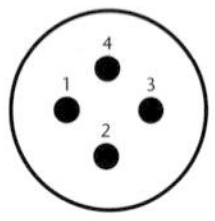 *(insert)*			
			4 Contacts			
Size 16 contacts See above wire accommodations #2 Shielded contact Rated 7.5 amperes			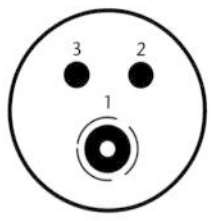 *(insert)*		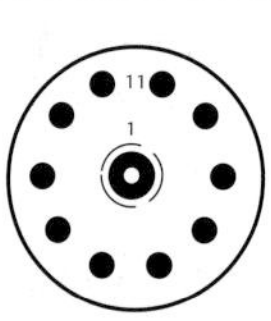 *(insert)*	
			3 Contacts		11 Contacts	
For shielded cable size 20 per MIL-C-7078, type II			2 #16 1 #2 Shielded		10 #16 1 #2 Shielded	
	Back face of pin insert as shown					

Figure 8-3-9. Insert arrangements (MS miniature connectors, MIL-C-26500).

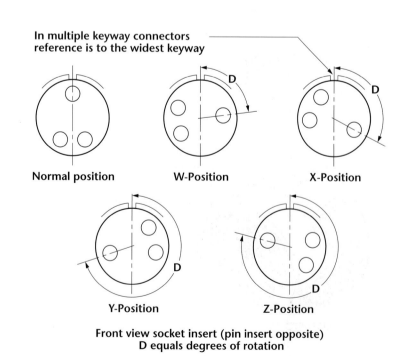

In multiple keyway connectors reference is to the widest keyway

Normal position **W-Position** **X-Position**

Y-Position **Z-Position**

Front view socket insert (pin insert opposite)
D equals degrees of rotation

Figure 8-3-10. Alternate positions of connector inserts.

A gland seal is a resilient device designed to make the junction between stationary and moving parts waterproof or airtight

- **Class P.** Connectors supplied with plastic potting mold, so the connector may be sealed by the application of potting compound

MS connectors are marked on the shell or coupling ring, as shown in Figure 8-3-6, with a code of letters and numbers that give all the information necessary to identify the connector. For example, a connector coded MS3114 E 12-10 P W is made according to military specifications, indicated by (MS). The next four numbers (3114) indicate the type of shell and whether it is a plug or receptacle; in this case, the part is a rear-mounting bayonet coupled receptacle with a jam nut. The letter that follows indicates the connector's class; so (E) in this example designates this part as an environmental connector. The next two numbers (12) indicate the shell size as measured by the outside diameter of the mating part of the receptacle in 1/16 inch increments or by the diameter of the coupling thread in one-sixteenth in increments; the connector in this example has an outside diameter or coupling thread of 3/4 an inch. The number following the hyphen (10), indicates the insert arrangement, as illustrated in Figure 8-3-7A and B, Figure 8-3-8 and Figure 8-3-9. The next letter indicates the contact style of the connector, whether it is a plug (P) or socket (S)—a plug is indicated in this example. The last character in the code mark (W) indicates the insert rotation or position of the connector (either W, X, U, or Z are used); so the letter W in this case signifies the connector insert has been rotated with respect to the shell a specified number of degrees from the normal position. Alternate positions are specified to prevent improper connections when connectors of identical size and contact arrangement are installed adjacent to each other. These alternate positions vary and are shown on the governing MS drawings. If no letter appears, then the insert is in the normal position. If a connectors has multiple keyways, the degree of rotation is measured from the widest keyway, as shown in Figure 8-3-10. In addition, the letter C following the code marking stamped on MS3100 through MS3108 connectors indicates that the connector has passed a damage test.

MIL-C-26500 connectors have an added letter between the shell size and the insert arrangement code numbers to indicate the type of coupling. The letters used are T for thread coupling, B for bayonet coupling, and Q for push-pull coupling. For example, the letter B in the code marking MS24264R18B30P6 indicates a bayonet coupling. Alternate insertion or position indications on MIL-C-265100 connectors are indicated by numbers 6 through 10 instead of by letters. The letter C after the code marking stamped on MS3100 through MS3108 connectors indicates that the connector passed a damage test conducted with a prod.

Crimp type contacts on MS and AN connectors are removable; however, solder-type contacts may not be removable. Contact sizes are related to AN wire sizes, but not all wire sizes have corresponding contacts. Contacts may accommodate a range of wire sizes, as shown in Table 8-3-5. Use only contacts designed for use with the particular connector. When replacing contacts, make sure the replacement contact is identical to the contact being replaced.

With the exception of potted connectors, cable clamps are used at the back of MS connectors to support wiring and to prevent twisting or pulling on the connections. As shown in Figure 8-3-11, there are three types of MS cable clamps.

- **MS3057.** This clamp consists of a clamp body, two washers, and a clamp saddle held on the clamp body by two screws and lock washers.

Contact size	Wire size range
*20	*24-20
*16	*22-16
*12	*14-12
8	10-8
4	6-4
0	2-0
*Available in crimp type connectors	

Table 8-3-5. Contacts and their wire size range.

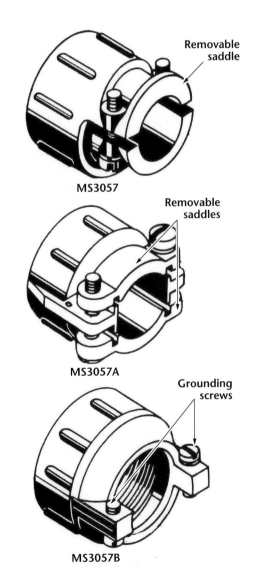

Figure 8-3-11. MS3057 connector cable clamp types.

MS3103

MS25183

Figure 8-3-12. Potting connectors.

- **MS3057A.** Used with an AN3420 telescoping bushing, this device consists of a clamp body and two saddles held on by screws and lock washers.
- **MS3057B.** This one-piece clamp has no separate cap or saddles and is used with AN3420A bushings.

MS potting connectors are used only where potting is required. They are similar to other standard types, except they have a shorter body shell and include a potting boot, as shown in Figure 8-3-12. There are three types of MS potting connectors:

- **MS3103.** A receptacle with a flange for mounting to a bulkhead.
- **MS25183.** A straight plug used at the end of a wire or wire bundle.
- **MS25183A.** Similar to a MS25813 with the addition of a grounding screw.

Special Purpose Connectors

There is a wide variety of special purpose connectors used in the avionics industry. They may be rectangular, round, or D-shaped. Many are considered light duty and may not be used in areas or circuits that are critical to the safety of flight. Some of these connectors look very much like MS or AN connectors but do not have aluminum alloy or steel shells. Light duty connectors are not designed for high environmental or mechanical stress.

Many avionic devices connect with D subminiature connectors (D connectors), like those shown in Figure 8-3-13. For aviation use, the connectors use crimp-type contacts and have locking mechanisms.

A very common type of connector used with panel mounted avionic systems is the edge connector. The edge connector plug is formed out of the edge of a printed circuit board with the contacts made from the circuit board trace. The receptacle may have solder-type contacts; however, crimp-type contacts are much more common. As shown in Figure 8-3-14, edge connector receptacles come in two different types, single sided and double sided. Although the contacts are similar in shape and size, as shown in Figure 8-3-15, they are not interchangeable. A polarizing key or tab may be inserted between contact openings in the receptacle housing to ensure the connector is not installed upside down.

Assembly of Wires to Solder-Type Connectors

A properly soldered connection will last the life of the airframe. For a technician to ensure a high quality solder connection, he or she must use the proper soldering process, and if necessary, practice to maintain soldering skills.

Shown in Table 8-3-6, five types of wire or cable are normally fastened to connectors. The choice of wire is determined by the installation requirements and is indicated in the appropriate installation manual. When assembling wire to connectors, the technician must remember to slide any shells, nuts, ferrules, sleeves, or keepers over the wire or harness, cable or wire before soldering. Solder is chosen based on the type of wire. Sn60 solder is appropriate for tin-coated copper wire and coaxial cable. Soft solder-lead-

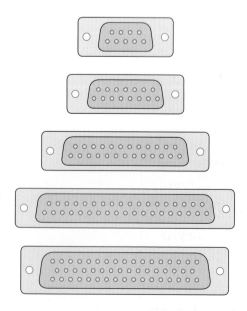

Figure 8-3-13. D subminiature connectors.

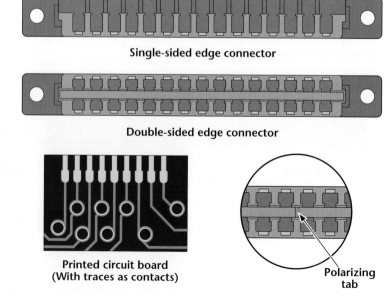

Single-sided edge connector

Double-sided edge connector

Printed circuit board (With traces as contacts)

Polarizing tab

Figure 8-3-14. Edge connectors.

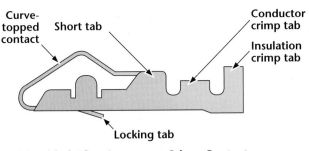

Figure 8-3-15. Edge connector crimp contacts.

Wire type	Military specification number(s)	Solder requirement
Tin-coated copper wire	MIL-W-5086	Sn60
Silver-coated copper wire	MIL-W-7139 MIL-W-8777 MIL-W-16878 MIL-W-22759	Sn96 Ag2.5 Cu0.5 Bi1 (lead free) Sn94.5 Ag5.5 (lead free)
Nickel-plated copper wire	MIL-W-22759 MIL-C-25038 MIL-W-27300	Crimp only
Coaxial cable	MIL-C-17	Sn60
Thermocouple wire	MIL-W-5845 MIL-W-5846	Varies

Table 8-3-6. Specification numbers and solder requirements for wire.

silver conforming to J-STD-006, composition Ag 2.5 or Ag 5.5 (2.5 percent or 5.5 percent silver alloy) is used for silver-coated copper wire.

Solder cup contacts on AN-MS connectors are silver or gold plated to provide low contact resistance. Silver-plated contacts on these connectors have pre-tinned solder cups. Gold-plated contacts are not pretinned because the gold prevents oxidization; therefore, it is easy to solder without tinning.

Prior to soldering the wires to the connector cups, each wire must be cut and stripped. Typical strip dimensions are shown in Table 8-3-7. Once stripped the wires should be tinned as described earlier.

Contact size	Stripped length (inches)
20	1/8
16	1/4
12	5/16
8	5/8
4	5/8
0	3/4

Table 8-3-7. Stripping lengths for solder connections.

Temperature range	Material	MIL Specification
Up to 160°F	Vinyl, transparent Nylon, transparent	MIL-I-7444 or MIL-I-631
160°F-400°F	Silicone-impregnated fiberglass Silicone-rubber Fiberglass	MIL-I-3190 or MIL-I-18057
400°F-600°F	Extruded TFE TFE-impregnated fiberglass	—

Table 8-3-8. Insulating sleeving material.

AN Wire Size	Number	ID (inches)	Length (inches)
16-14	7	0.148	3/4
12	5	0.186	3/4
10	3	0.234	3/4
8	1	0.294	1
6	0	0.330	1-1/4
4	7/16	0.438	1-1/4
2	1/2	0.500	1-1/4
0	5/8	0.625	1-1/4

Table 8-3-9. Insulating sleeving sizes.

Insulating sleeves are installed over the soldered connections to protect the connection against vibration and reduce the possibility of arc-over between contacts. If the connector is to be potted, then insulating sleeves are not necessary. Moreover, insulating sleeves are not used in most AN-type Class E or R connectors, since they have sealing grommets over the soldered connection. Types of sleeve material are

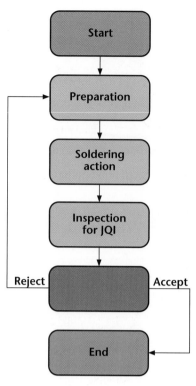

Figure 8-3-16. Block diagram of a high quality soldering process.

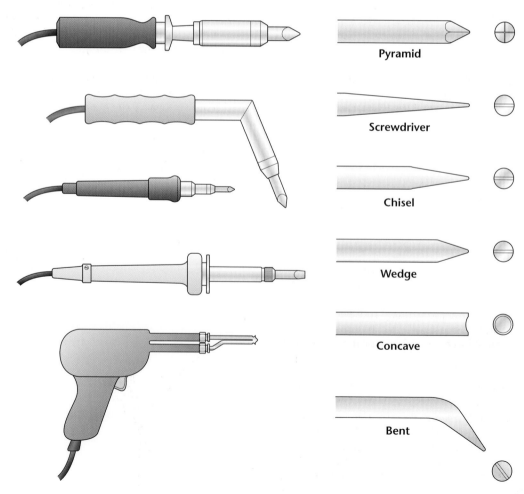

Figure 8-3-17. Types of hand soldering irons and various tip shapes.

Figure 8-3-18. Soldering iron holder.

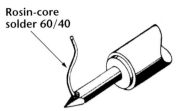

Rosin-core
solder 60/40

Note: tin while iron is heating

Figure 8-3-20. Tinning soldering iron tip.

Figure 8-3-19. Vice.

In order for high quality soldering to take place, the solder tip must be cleaned and tinned. Furthermore, the contacts must also be cleaned and, if necessary, tinned. A double-cut mill file or brush may be used to prepare the soldering iron tip before the iron is turned on. File or brush the tip until it is smooth and of a bright color. Turn the iron on, and before the tip reaches full temperature, apply a small amount of solder, as shown in Figure 8-3-20. Tip preparation varies by tip type and manufacturer, therefore, follow the manufacturer's guidelines for tip preparation.

The tip cleaning process should be repeated as necessary throughout the soldering job. When the solder tip is ready and the connector is secured properly in the vice, then the connector solder cup can be tinned, as shown in Figure 8-3-21. Keep in mind that gold-plated contacts do not require tinning.

High quality soldering involves safe and precise control of heat. The most common tool used to create heat is the hand soldering iron, like the ones shown in Figure 8-3-16. The hand soldering iron includes a handle, an electrically heated reservoir, and a tip to transfer the heat to the work being soldered. Many soldering irons have a thermal switch and an adjustment knob to control tip temperature.

Solder

**Connector
solder cup**

Figure 8-3-21. Position of soldering iron.

listed in Table 8-3-8 and recommended sleeve sizes are shown in Table 8-3-9. Heat shrinkable tubing is often used as insulating sleeves in light duty connectors.

When using either insulating sleeves or heat shrinkable tubing, the sleeve or tubing must be cut to the appropriate length and placed on the wire prior to soldering. The technician must slip the tube or sleeve away from the end to be soldered, so heat from the soldering process does not affect the insulator.

The proper soldering process is shown in the block diagram in Figure 8-3-16 and involves preparation, the action of soldering, and inspection for job quality indications. Before the soldering process can begin, the technician must have an understanding of soldering theory.

Preparation for high quality soldering involves having the appropriate tools and equipment on hand before continuing the process. The technician should assemble at the work station, the soldering iron with an appropriate tip, as shown in Figure 8-3-17, a caddy or holder as shown in Figure 8-3-18, solder, flux, tip cleaning tools, a vice (Figure 8-3-19), and, of course, the wires and connector to be soldered.

Figure 8-3-22. Heat balance.

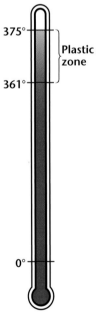

375°

**Plastic
zone**

361°

0°

Figure 8-3-23. Sn 60 melting temperatures and plastic zone.

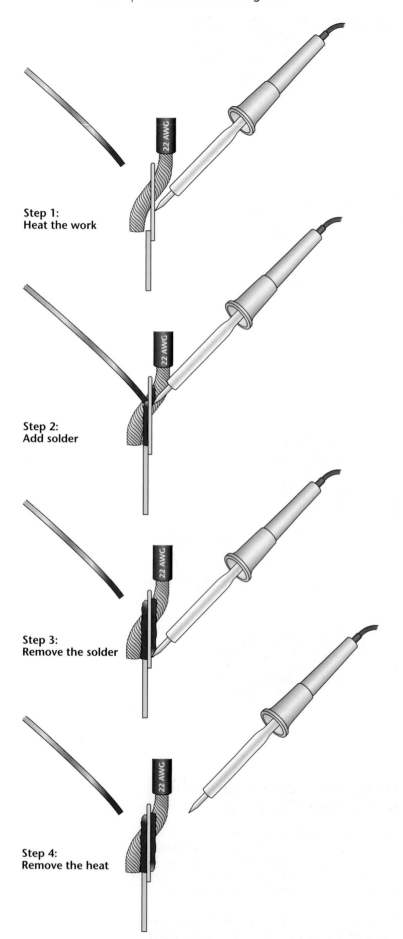

Step 1:
Heat the work

Step 2:
Add solder

Step 3:
Remove the solder

Step 4:
Remove the heat

Figure 8-3-24. Four steps in the soldering process.

If a soldering iron of the proper wattage is being used, then the electric element replenishes the heat in the heating element to balance the flow of heat to the work, as shown in Figure 8-3-22. If the iron is of insufficient wattage, then the element is not able to replenish the heating element and the iron becomes too cold to accomplish the task.

When properly soldered, the solder combines with the terminals to create a new alloy. In other words, the terminals and the wire become one continuous piece of metal. This combining process is known as *wetting action*. Wetting action cannot occur on corroded surfaces. Small amounts of corrosion, even amounts smaller than what is visible to the naked eye, can prevent the wetting action from occurring.

To remove corrosion and allow the wetting action to take place, technicians use flux or rosin. Wires may be dipped into a basin containing flux, or flux may be brushed onto the contact, or the technician may use solder with a rosin core may be used. Acid should not be used since it will cause more corrosion.

Sn60 solder begins to melt at 361°F and completes melting at 375°F. As shown in Figure 8-3-23, the range of temperatures between 361°F and 375°F is called the *plastic zone* because the solder is neither a complete solid nor a complete liquid. To achieve a high quality solder connection, the wire and connector must not move until after the connection has completely solidified.

If any piece of the work moves before the solder joint has cooled past the plastic zone, then rapid cooling occurs, causing premature solidification and cracks in the joint.

With the soldering iron tip at the proper temperature, the soldering iron tip tinned, the connector solder pot tinned, and everything clamped in place, the soldering action may begin. Holding the solder in one hand and the iron in the other, the technician should place the soldering iron tip on the solder pot and bring the solder in from the other side. As soon as enough solder has flowed into the pot, he or she should remove the solder and then immediately remove the heat. As shown in Figure 8-3-24, these four steps should take no more than two seconds on a small connector. If the process takes longer, the solder tip may not be hot enough. Odd as it may seem, soldering with a solder tip too low in temperature may cause more damage than soldering with a tip too hot. If the tip is too cold, the whole connector may become heat soaked and damaged before the solder melts.

Once the connection has cooled, the technician can inspect the joint for job quality. A quality

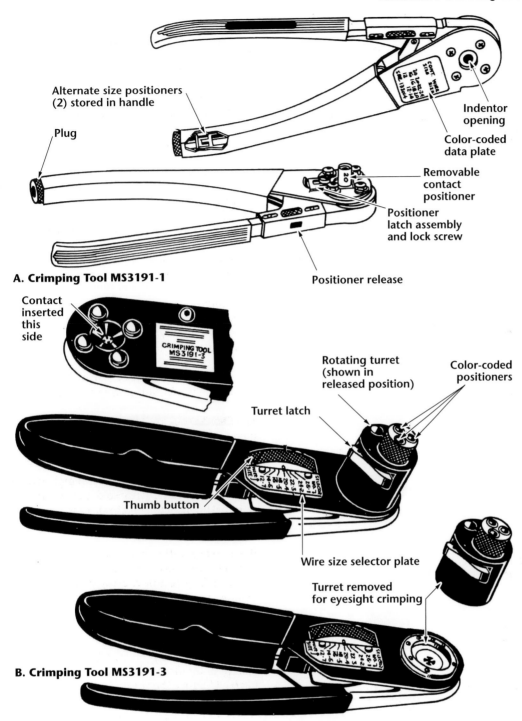

Figure 8-3-25. MA3191 standard crimping tools.

solder joint is smooth, shiny, and symmetrical with no cracks or pits. Furthermore, there should not be any drips, sags, or spikes on the connector. If the connection does not pass visual inspection, the solder should be removed using a desoldering wick or a heated vacuum, and then the process should be repeated.

When soldering a connector with multiple contacts, the technician should avoid soldering adjacent pins to avoid heat soaking any one area of the connector.

Wire-to-Connector Assembly with Crimp Contacts

Connectors using crimp-type contacts are received from the manufacturer with the contacts packaged separately, so the wires can be crimped to the contacts with a crimping tool before they are inserted into the connector.

The tools used for crimping MS electrical connector contacts are designed to MIL-C-22520D. The tools shown in Figure 8-3-25 are hand

Contact size	Color code
#20	Red
#16	Blue
#12	Yellow

Table 8-3-10. Contact size crimping color code.

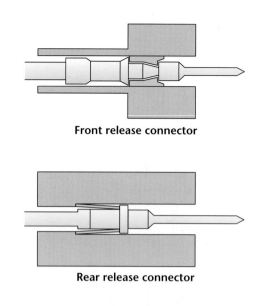

Front release connector

Rear release connector

Figure 8-3-26. Front and rear release connectors.

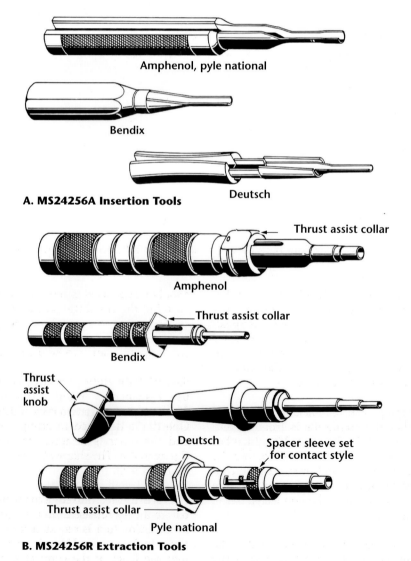

Amphenol, pyle national

Bendix

A. MS24256A Insertion Tools

Deutsch

Thrust assist collar

Amphenol

Thrust assist collar

Bendix

Thrust assist knob

Deutsch

Spacer sleeve set for contact style

Thrust assist collar

Pyle national

B. MS24256R Extraction Tools

Figure 8-3-27. Insertion and extraction tools for crimp-type contacts.

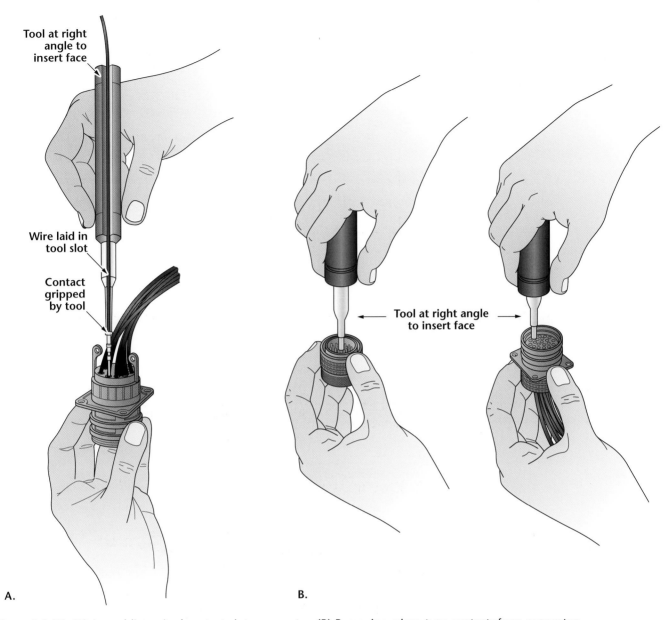

Figure 8-3-28. (A) Assembling wired contacts into connector, (B) Removing crimp-type contacts from connector.

operated and cycle controlled by a ratchet that does not release until the crimping cycle is complete. The tools may have a separate position for each contact size, and these are color coded, as shown in Table 8-3-10. These crimpers contain four dies to compress the pin from four directions simultaneously.

Before crimping, the technician must determine whether the connector is front or rear release, as shown in Figure 8-3-26. In other words, he or she must determine whether the pin slides in from the front or rear of the connector. If the connector is front release, then the wire must pass through the connector barrel before crimping.

In most cases, once the wire is crimped to the pin, a tool must be used to insert the pin into the barrel of the connector. Once a pin is installed,

a tool must be used to remove the pin from the barrel of the connector. A variety of insertion and extraction tools are shown in Figure 8-3-27. The use of insertion and extraction tools for MS connectors is shown in Figure 8-3-28.

Several light duty and edge connector pins use F-shaped crimping surfaces. Crimpers for these pins have two dies of different sizes. One die is designed to crimp the conductor and the other is designed to crimp around the insulator. The shape of the die is shown in Figure 8-3-29.

Pins are inserted into edge connectors from the rear, but they release from the front. Although no insertion tool is required for edge connectors, a tool is required for release and is inserted into the front of the connector, as shown in Figure 8-3-30.

Wire stripped, inserted, and ready to crimp

End view of die shaped to curl tabs

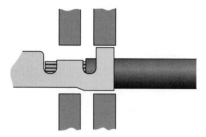

**Die on left crimps conductor;
die on right crimps insulation**

Figure 8-3-29. Wire insertion and crimp die shapes.

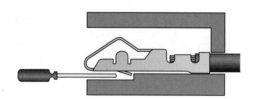

Figure 8-3-30. Edge connector removal.

RF connectors

RF connectors are used with coaxial cable and are available as plugs, jacks, panel jacks, and receptacles. For aviation use, these connectors are designed with a surge impedance of 50 Ω. Plugs and jacks are attached to the ends of coaxial cables; panel jacks and receptacles are mounted to panels or chassis. Some panel jacks are fastened by screws to the structure, as shown in Figure 8-3-31, Figure 8-3-3, Figure 8-3-33. Other panel jacks are fastened to the structure by means of a single nut threaded over the jack body, as shown in Figure 8-3-34. Panel jacks and receptacles may be front- or rear-mounted. Plugs always have male contacts, and jacks always have female contacts. Examples of a plug, a panel jack, and a jack are shown in Figure 8-3-35.

The BNC series of connectors shown in Figure 8-3-31 are small, lightweight, bayonet-type connectors for use with small coaxial cables. The

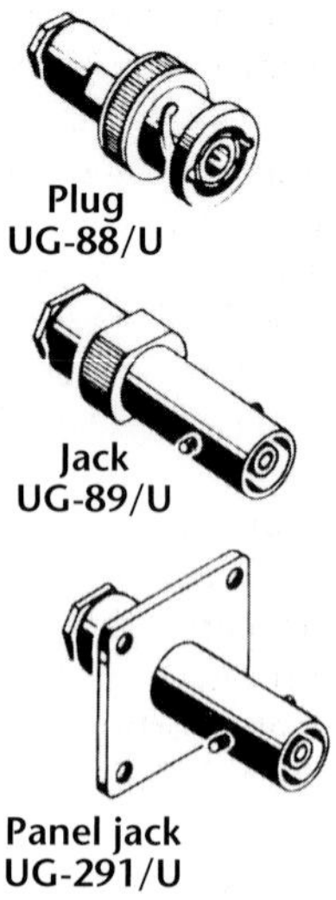

**Plug
UG-88/U**

**Jack
UG-89/U**

**Panel jack
UG-291/U**

Figure 8-3-31. Typical BNC connectors.

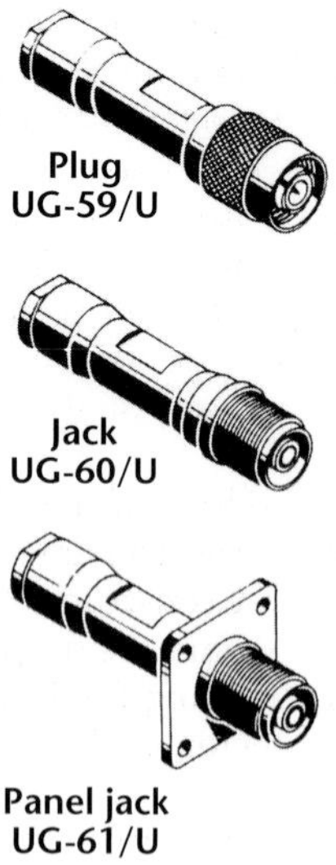

**Plug
UG-59/U**

**Jack
UG-60/U**

**Panel jack
UG-61/U**

Figure 8-3-32. Typical HN connectors.

**Plug
UG-21/U**

**Jack
UG-20/U**

**Panel jack
UG-19/U**

Figure 8-3-33. Typical N connectors.

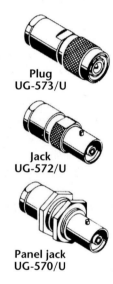

**Plug
UG-573/U**

**Jack
UG-572/U**

**Panel jack
UG-570/U**

Figure 8-3-34. Typical C connectors.

**Plug
UG-180/U**

**Panel jack
UG-181/U**

**Jack
UG-174/U**

Figure 8-3-35. Typical pulse connectors.

**Plug
KA51-03 (king)**

**Jack
KA31-02 (king)**

**Panel jack
KA11-03 (king)**

Figure 8-3-36. Typical TNC connectors.

HN series is a screw-on-type connector for use with medium sized coaxial cables. The N series of connector is also of the screw-on-type, and it is used with medium sized coaxial cables. The C series is a bayonet-type connector for use with medium sized coaxial cables. The TNC series (Figure 8-3-36) is similar to the BNC, but it has a screw on connection and better noise level reduction and vibration resisting characteristics.

A variation of the BNC, HN, and TNC connector is the triaxial connector. Triaxial connectors are constructed so coaxial cables with dual shields may be properly terminated. Each layer of shielding fits into a separate portion of the connector, as shown in Figure 8-3-37.

RF connectors may be crimp type or solder type for the center conductor, with a nut and die to clamp the coaxial shield. Care must be taken with all types of RF connectors not to damage the shield or dielectric while assembling the connector. Always check the RF connector with an ohmmeter after construction for both shorts between the center conductor and the shield and open connections from end-to-end.

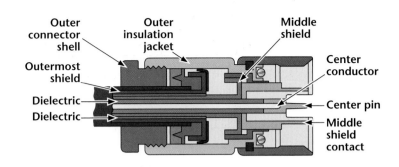

Figure 8-3-37. A cross section of a triaxial connector.

Section 4
Bonding and Grounding

Bonding is the electrical connection between two or more conducting objects that are not adequately connected. *Grounding* is the electrical connection of a conducting object to the primary structure for a current source.

Aluminum terminal and jumper							
Structure	**Screw or bolt; Lock-nut**	**Plain nut**	**Washer A**	**Washer B**	**Washer C & D**	**Lock-washer E**	**Lock-washer F**
Aluminum alloys	Cadmium plated Steel	Tin plated brass	Aluminum alloy	Aluminum alloy	Cadmium plated steel or aluminum	Cadmium plated steel	Cadmium plated steel
Magnesium alloys	Cadmium plated Steel	Cadmium plated steel	Magnesium alloy	Magnesium alloy	Cadmium plated steel or aluminum	Cadmium plated steel	Cadmium plated steel
Steel, cadmium plated	Cadmium plated Steel	Cadmium plated steel	None	None	Cadmium plated steel or aluminum	Cadmium plated steel	Cadmium plated steel
Steel, corrosion resisting	Corrosion resisting steel	Cadmium plated steel	None	None	Cadmium plated steel or aluminum	Corrosion resisting steel	Cadmium plated steel
Tinned copper terminal and jumper							
Aluminum alloys	Cadmium plated Steel	Cadmium Plated Steel	Aluminum Alloy	Aluminum Alloy	Cadmium plated steel	Cadmium plated steel	Cadmium plated steel or aluminum
Avoid connecting copper to magnesium							
Magnesium alloys steel, cadmium plated	Cadmium plated Steel	Cadmium plated steel	None	None	Cadmium plated steel	Cadmium plated steel	Cadmium plated steel
Steel, corrosion resisting	Corrosion resisting Steel	Corrosion resisting steel	None	None	Cadmium plated steel	Corrosion resisting steel	Corrosion resisting steel

Table 8-4-1A. Hardware for stud bonding or grounding to flat surface.

Aluminum terminal and jumper					
Structure	Screw or bolt; nut plate	Rivet	Lock washer	Washer A	Washer B
Aluminum alloys	Cadmium plated steel	Aluminum alloy	Cadmium plated steel	Cadmium plated steel or aluminum	None
Magnesium alloys	Cadmium plated steel	Aluminum alloy	Cadmium plated steel	Cadmium plated steel or aluminum	None or magnesium alloy
Steel, cadmium plated	Cadmium plated steel	Corrosion resisting steel	Cadmium plated steel	Cadmium plated steel or aluminum	None
Steel, corrosion resisting	Corrosion resisting Steel or cadmium plated steel	Corrosion resisting steel	Cadmium plated steel	Cadmium plated steel or aluminum	Cadmium plated Steel
Tinned copper terminal and jumper					
Aluminum alloys	Cadmium plated steel	Aluminum alloy	Cadmium plated steel	Cadmium plated steel	Aluminum alloy
Magnesium alloys	Avoid connecting copper to magnesium				
Steel, cadmium plated	Cadmium plated steel	Corrosion resisting steel	Cadmium plated steel	Cadmium plated steel	None
Steel, corrosion resisting	Corrosion resisting Steel	Corrosion resisting steel	Cadmium plated steel	Cadmium plated steel	None

Table 8-4-1B. Hardware for plate nut bonding or grounding to flat surface.

Aluminum terminal and jumper					
Structure	Screw or bolt; lock nut	Lock washer	Washer A	Washer B	Washer C
Aluminum alloy	Cadmium plated steel	Cadmium plated steel	Cadmium plated steel or aluminum	None	Cadmium plated steel or aluminum
Magnesium alloy	Cadmium plated steel	Cadmium plated steel	Magnesium alloy	None or magnesium alloy	Cadmium plated steel or aluminum
Steel, cadmium plated	Cadmium plated steel	Cadmium plated steel	Cadmium plated steel	Cadmium plated steel	Cadmium plated steel or aluminum
Steel, corrosion resisting	Corrosion resisting steel or cadmium plated steel	Cadmium plated steel	Corrosion resisting steel	Cadmium plated steel	Cadmium plated steel or aluminum
Tinned copper terminal and jumper					
Aluminum alloy	Cadmium plated steel	Cadmium plated steel	Cadmium plated steel	Aluminum alloy	Cadmium plated steel
Magnesium alloy	Avoid connecting copper to magnesium				
Steel, cadmium plated	Cadmium plated steel	Cadmium plated steel	Cadmium plated steel	None	Cadmium plated steel
Steel, corrosion resisting	Corrosion resisting steel or cadmium plated steel	Cadmium plated steel	Corrosion resisting steel	None	Cadmium plated steel

Table 8-4-1C. Hardware for plate nut bonding or grounding to flat surface.

Bonding and grounding connections serve several purposes:

- To protect the aircraft and personnel against the hazards from lightning discharges

- To provide power and current return paths

- To prevent the development of unwanted RF potentials

- To protect personnel from shock hazards

- To prevent accumulation of static charges, including those from precipitation static (P-static)

- To provide fault current return paths

Unwanted RF potentials and static charges can cause noise in avionics signals. This noise may be heard while the pilot is listening to audio, it may be seen as random navigation needle deviations, or it may be felt as unpredictable autopilot performance. When the aircraft is flying through precipitation, the additional friction on the airframe from contact with the rain or snow causes a high amount of static electricity and associated RF potentials and noise known as precipitation static. To prevent these occurrences, equipment must be properly grounded or bonded.

When making grounding or bonding connections the technician should observe the following general precautions and procedures:

- Bond or ground parts to the primary aircraft structure where practical

- Make bonding or grounding connections in such a way as to not weaken any part of the aircraft structure

- Install bounding or grounding connections so vibration, expansion or contraction, relative movement incident to normal service will not break or loosen the connection

- Locate bonding and grounding connections in protected areas when possible. Whenever possible, locate connections near hand holes, the inspection door, or other accessible areas

- Do not compression-fasten bonding or grounding connections through any nonmetallic material

Hardware used to make bonding or grounding connections is selected on the basis of mechanical strength, current to be carried, and ease of installation. Where a connection is made by aluminum or copper jumpers to a structure of dissimilar material, a washer of suitable material is installed between the dissimilar metals so any corrosion will occur in the washer rather than in the structure. When repairing

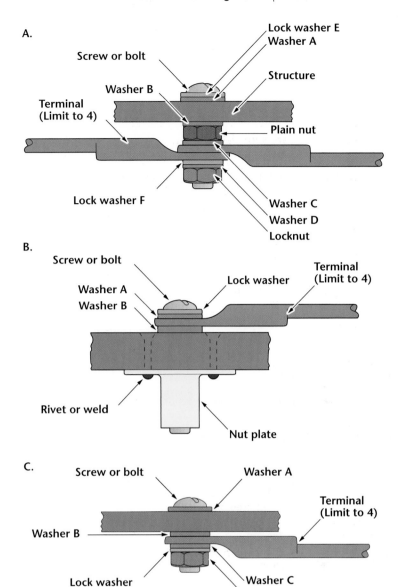

Figure 8-4-1. (A) Stud bonding or grounding to a flat surface, (B) Plane nut bonding or grounding to a flat surface, (C) Bolt and nut bonding or grounding to a flat surface.

existing grounding or bonding connections the technician must be sure to use the same type of hardware used in the original connection. Table 8-4-1 shows various types of hardware used for grounding and bonding.

Before any grounding or bonding connection is made, the surfaces should be thoroughly cleaned and all oil, grease, paint, anodic film, or any other nonconducting material removed from an area slightly larger than the connection. Do not use abrasives such as emery cloth, crocus cloth, steel wool, etc. These materials can leave corrosive particles embedded in the surface being cleaned.

Methods of making connections to a flat surface are shown in Figure 8-4-1. If necessary, a

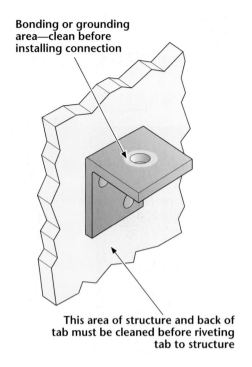

Bonding or grounding area—clean before installing connection

This area of structure and back of tab must be cleaned before riveting tab to structure

Figure 8-4-2. Bonding tab riveted to structure.

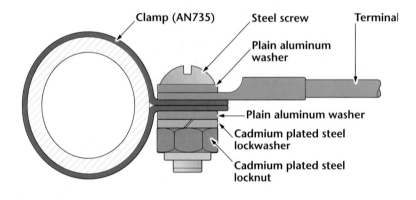

Clamp (AN735)   Steel screw   Terminal

Plain aluminum washer

Plain aluminum washer

Cadmium plated steel lockwasher

Cadmium plated steel locknut

Figure 8-4-3. Example of an aluminum jumper connection to tubular structure.

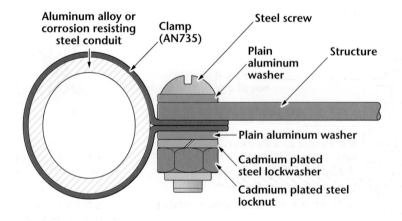

Aluminum alloy or corrosion resisting steel conduit   Clamp (AN735)   Steel screw

Plain aluminum washer   Structure

Plain aluminum washer

Cadmium plated steel lockwasher

Cadmium plated steel locknut

Figure 8-4-4. Bonding conduit to structure.

tab can be riveted to the structure, as shown in Figure 8-7-2, for grounds required to carry high current.

An example of methods to make connection to a tubular structure is shown in Figure 8-4-3. Always make sure all connections are tight as evidenced by the split-lock washers being completely compressed. When the terminal is under the head of a screw or bolt, as shown in Figure 8-4-1, avoid installing more than one terminal, since a loose screw with more than one terminal may cause malfunctions.

Methods of bonding aluminum or steel conduit to a structure are shown in Figure 8-4-4. If necessary, an AN742 clamp may be used in place of the AN437 clamp using the same hardware.

To accomplish the purpose of bonding or grounding, the technician must provide a conductive path where direct electrical contact does not exist. For this purpose, jumpers are used between moving parts, between shock mounted equipment and structure, and between electrically conducting objects and structure. Keep jumpers as short as possible and, if practical, under 3 inches. Never use two or more jumpers in series.

The resistance across a bonding or grounding jumper must be less than 0.1 Ω. The technician should make the test after the mechanical connection is completed by measuring the resistance between the cleaned areas of the object and the structure.

As shown in Figure 8-4-5, a special ohmmeter may be required to make this test.

Section 5

Electrical Hardware and Wire Support

Using standard procedures for installing equipment in aircraft provides the best possible protection for equipment and personnel.

Bus bars are used in aircraft for power distribution and for grounding. Small aircraft may have only one bus bar; however, it is common practice to have a main bus and a switchable avionics bus. Larger aircraft have AC and DC buses, essential and nonessential busses, and split busses. The most commonly used materials for bus bars are bare electrical-grade aluminum, plated electrical-grade aluminum, or plated copper.

Bus bar preparation varies according to the materials used. Unplated aluminum requires more preparation than aluminum and copper bus bars. Bus bars for power distribution must be insulated from the grounded structure of the airframe. Figure 8-5-1 illustrates a method of mounting a bus bar to the aircraft structure.

Both rigid and flexible conduit is used in large aircraft to protect wires and cables. Typically, the conduit is installed before the wiring is routed. Nonmetallic conduit is usually installed at the same time the wiring is routed.

Bend rigid conduit as required to the limits shown in Table 8-5-1 before installation into the airframe. Make sure the conduit is not overstressed in the installation and there is no strain on the ferrules. Install the conduit so there is no vibration flexing at the ferrules.

Conduit is attached to the aircraft structure using plain aluminum clamps of the proper size, as shown in Table 8-5-2. If the flexible metallic conduit is rubber covered, then use a cushioned clamp, as shown in Table 8-5-3.

When mounting conduit, attach the clamps to the rigid surface of the structure, so there will be no relative motion between the conduit and the aircraft structure. Install clamps so the mounting screw is above the conduit, as shown in Figure 8-5-2. The clamps and conduit should be installed so the conduit slants downward at one end while the aircraft is on the ground. This allows condensation to drain. If attached to equipment, then the slant should be downward toward the open end and away from the equipment.

Do not tighten clamps holding conduit in such a way that will damage or collapse the conduit. If during inspection, collapsed or damaged conduit is found, it must be replaced.

Support rigid metallic conduit with clamps close to each end and at a maximum spacing of 3 feet along the entire conduit run, as shown in

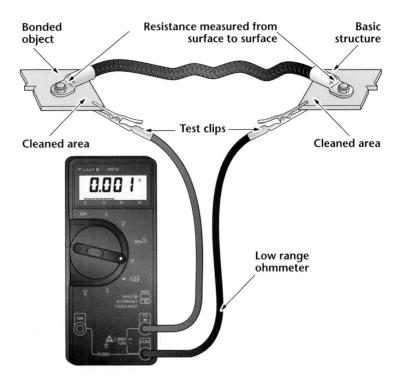

Figure 8-4-5. Special milliohm meter and clip leads for testing bond resistance.

Nominal ID of conduit (inches)	Minimum bending radius inside (inches)
3/16	2-1/4
1/4	2-3/4
3/8	3-3/4
1/2	3-3/4
5/8	3-3/4
3/4	4-1/4
1	5-3/4
1-1/4	8
1-1/2	8-1/4
1-3/4	9
2	9-3/4
2-1/2	10

Table 8-5-1. Minimum bending radii for flexible aluminum or brass conduit.

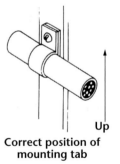

Figure 8-5-2. Installation of supporting clamps for conduit.

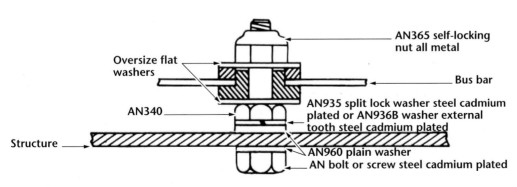

Figure 8-5-1. Example of a bus bar mounting on a structure.

Nominal OD of conduit	AN Clamp
3/16	AN742D3
1/4	AN742D4
3/8	AN742D6
1/2	AN742D8
5/8	AN742D10
3/4	AN742D12
1	AN742D16
1-1/4	AN742D20
1-1/2	AN742D24
1-3/4	AN742D28
2	AN742D32
2-1/2	AN742D40

Table 8-5-2. Support clamps for rigid or flexible bare aluminum conduit.

MS Clamp number	Nominal ID of clamp (inches)
MS 21919D5	0.313
MS 21919D6	0.375
MS 21919D7	0.438
MS 21919D8	0.500
MS 21919D9	0.563
MS 21919D10	0.625
MS 21919D11	0.688
MS 21919D12	0.750
MS 21919D13	0.813
MS 21919D14	0.875
MS 21919D15	0.938
MS 21919D16	1.000
MS 21919D19	1.888
MS 21919D21	1.313
MS 21919D23	1.438
MS 21919D25	1.563
MS 21919D27	1.688
MS 21919D29	1.812
MS 21919D31	1.938
MS 21919D33	2.062
MS 21919D35	2.188
MS 21919D37	2.312
MS 21919D43	2.688
MS 21919D45	2.812

Table 8-5-3. Support clamps for rubber covered flexible aluminum or brass conduit.

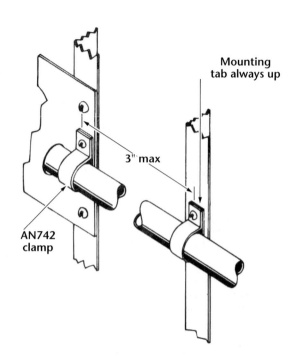

Figure 8-5-3. Spacing clamps for rigid metallic conduit.

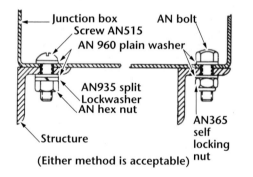

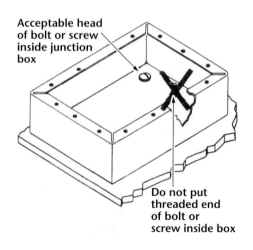

Figure 8-5-4. Attaching junction box to structure.

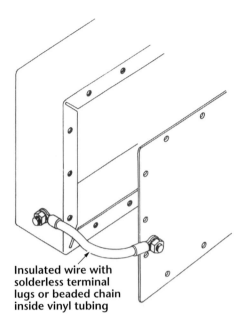

Insulated wire with
solderless terminal
lugs or beaded chain
inside vinyl tubing

Figure 8-5-5. Attaching cover to a junction box.

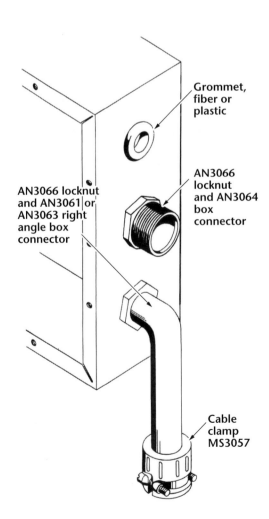

Grommet,
fiber or
plastic

AN3066
lyocknut
and AN3064
box
connector

AN3066 locknut
and AN3061 or
AN3063 right
angle box
connector

Cable
clamp
MS3057

Figure 8-5-6. Wire entry holes in a junction box.

Figure 8-5-3. Flexible metallic conduit should be supported with clamps close to each end and spaced at least 6 inches apart at a minimum to 24 inches apart at a maximum. Spacing of support clamps within the limits given is determined by conditions and structure.

Bond the conduit to the structure at each terminating or breaking point by means of a plain metal clamp or a clamp and jumper.

Junction boxes are containers with hinged or removable covers. Junction boxes are used to provide a protected area for electrical power distribution of equipment, such as bus bars and terminal boards. Junction boxes may be made of metal or fiberglass, however, fiberglass is not allowed in areas subjected to high heat.

Use standard AN bolts or screws of the appropriate size to attach junction boxes to the aircraft structure, as shown in Figure 8-5-4. Junction boxes must be installed on a bulkhead or ceiling, so loose hardware falls away from the contacts. Insert screws or bolts so the head of the screw or bolt is inside the junction box. Do not allow the threaded part of the screw or bolt to protrude inside the junction box. The sharp threaded edges will damage wire insulation.

The inside of metallic junction boxes should be coated with a material to insulate wiring from the metal, improve visibility, and facilitate inspection. Nonmetallic junction boxes do not need to be insulated.

Junction box covers may be hinged or attached by means of screws, camlocks, or Dzus fasteners. Camlock and Dzus fasteners are two different styles of locking fasteners. The camlock features a cam mounted in the airframe. The Dzus includes the cam in the fastener and a wire mounted in the airframe. Screw threads must not extend into the box. If junction box covers are not hinged, secure the covers to the box with insulated bead chain or No. 14 wire, as shown in Figure 8-5-5. Make the attachment outside the box, so when the cover is secured the chain or wire does not interfere with the internal contacts.

To prepare wire entry holes into the junction box, determine the outside diameter of the wire or bundle and make sure the opening is at least 1/8 inch larger in diameter to allow for later enlargement of the bundle. Use a box connector and a cable clamp to protect the wiring. When not using a box connector, use a plastic or fiber grommet to protect the wire from the box edges, as shown in Figure 8-5-6.

Like conduit, condensation may form inside the junction box. To allow drainage, drill one

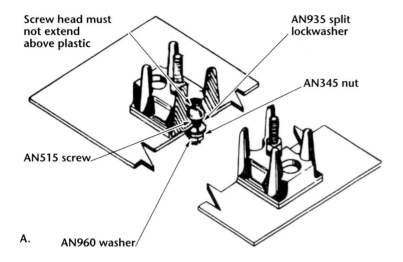

A.

B.

C.

Figure 8-5-7. (A) Mounting of terminal board, (B) Alternate mounting of terminal board, (C) Insulation of terminal board.

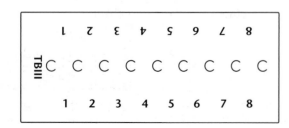

Figure 8-5-8. Identification of terminal board.

or more holes with a minimum diameter of 3/16 inch at the lowest point of the box when the aircraft is on the ground. Always deburr any holes drilled in the junction box. Bond or ground junction boxes to the structure by direct metal-to-metal contact or by means of a bonding jumper.

Terminal boards must be mounted so they are insulated from the aircraft structure, including junction box walls, as shown in Figure 8-5-7. Terminal boards should be identified by numbers and letters. Typically, wiring diagrams label terminal boards with the letters TB. The terminal board should be so lettered as shown in Figure 8-5-8.

Section 6
LRU Fasteners and Installation

Remote mounted line replaceable units are installed in a tray-type holder and may be shock mounted. If shock mounted, the tray must be bonded by means of a bonding jumper. Typically, remote mounted LRUs are fastened with a thumbscrew-type fastener, as shown in Figure 8-6-1. The fastener may require safety wire to prevent loosening under vibration. The insertion/extraction fastener has an extra cam to push the unit out of the connector.

Panel mounted LRUs designed for small aircraft are mounted in a tray designed to fit a standard opening of 6.3 inches. Technicians should note this standard has changed. Older aircraft may have a standard opening of only 6.25 inches. In order to facilitate a panel that is pleasing in appearance, the standard practice is to utilize fasteners that can be adjusted up or down, as shown in Figure 8-6-2. Do not rivet panel-mounted LRU trays in place. Pay particular attention to the spacing requirements between LRUs, since mounting the trays too close causes the units not to fit properly. In addition, make sure that the tray, itself, is straight, since a distorted tray forces the radio to bind when inserted. A binding radio may be damaged and is difficult to remove.

Most panel-mount LRU racks also have a hole predrilled near the back of the tray for rear support, as shown in Figure 8-6-3. The preferable method is to suspend the racks from above; however, if no structure is available to suspend from, aluminum can be bent to provide sufficient strength to hold the LRU when mounted

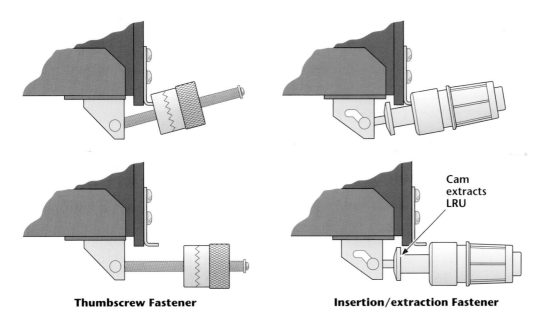

Thumbscrew Fastener

Insertion/extraction Fastener

Cam extracts LRU

Figure 8-6-1. Thumbscrew fasteners for remote LRUs.

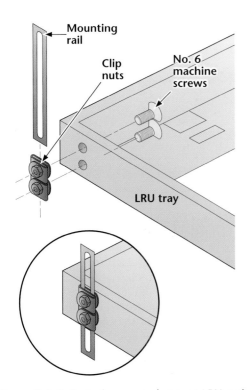

Mounting rail

Clip nuts

No. 6 machine screws

LRU tray

Figure 8-6-2. Fastening a panel-mount LRU rack.

from below. Without rear support, vibration exerts a bending moment on the mounting rail and clip nuts, causing the tray and LRU to sag in the rear. Sagging could interfere with other harnesses or with the aircraft controls. In aircraft with a tube frame, an adel clamp could be used for rear support.

Some aircraft have standardized width MS25121 5.75 inch Dzus rails for panel-mounted LRUs, as shown in Figure 8-6-4. These fasteners have a wire spring in the receptacle and a cam in the stud. LRUs constructed to the MS25121 standard do not have mounting trays. The Dzus rails are sufficiently strong and the LRUs are sufficiently short, so no back support is necessary. When properly installed, the screwdriver slots on the cam studs should line up with each other.

The equipment constructed to the MS25121 standard mount with Dzus fasteners do not require a mounting tray; however, other panel mounted LRUs must be held into a mounting

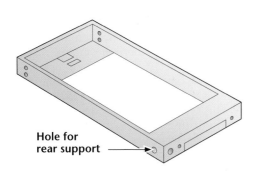

Hole for rear support

Figure 8-6-3. LRU tray with hole for rear support.

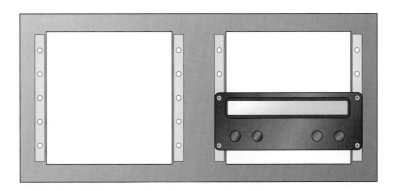

Figure 8-6-4. Standard MS25121 opening and standard unit installed.

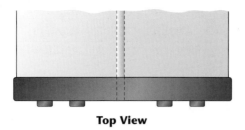

Top View

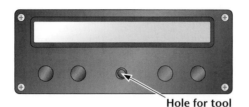

Hole for tool

Front View

Figure 8-6-5. Screw mounting mechanism.

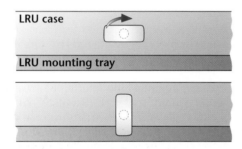

LRU case

LRU mounting tray

Figure 8-6-6. A simple mounting pawl.

Pawl pulls radio in

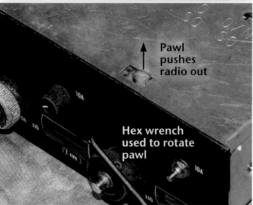

Pawl pushes radio out

Hex wrench used to rotate pawl

Figure 8-6-7. A complex mounting pawl.

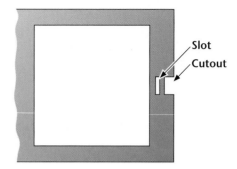

Slot

Cutout

Figure 8-6-8. Mounting rack with cutout and slot.

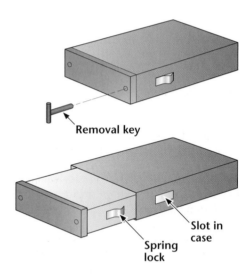

Removal key

Slot in case

Spring lock

Figure 8-6-9. Spring lock fastening.

tray. There are several tray-fastening methods. These methods fall into three basic categories: the screw, pawl, and spring lock types are all popular among manufacturers.

The screw-type method uses a machine screw accessible from the front panel that protrudes through the back of the LRU and fastens to a nut attached to the rack. A few older pieces of equipment use a slotted or Phillips head screw, but a hex screw is more prevalent. Figure 8-6-5 shows a radio with a machine screw mounting mechanism.

Mounting pawls are more common than mounting screws. Mounting pawls can be divided into two categories: complex cam type and simple type. Furthermore, mounting pawls can be constructed of plastic or metal. The simple pawl, as shown in Figure 8-6-6, simply rotates into a slot cut into the LRU mounting rack. This type of pawl does not assist the technician in seating the radio into the connector or in extraction. If the pawl is made of plastic, the technician must exercise caution and not over torque the mechanism because damage to the equipment will occur.

General purpose	1. 600 volts or under		
	Aluminum	High temperature	Fire resistant
MIL-W-5086 Types I, II and III	MIL-W-7072	MIL-W-7139 MIL-W-8777 MIL-W-18678, Type E *MIL-W-22759 MIL-W-27300	MIL-W-25038
—	2. Over 600 volts		
	MIL-W-5086, Type IV MIL-W-16878, Type EE *MIL-W-22759		
	3. Cabled shielded and jacketed		
	MIL-C-5767 MIL-C-7078 MIL-C-27500		
*MIL-W-22759 covers wire rated at 600 volts-and 1000 volts.			

Table 8-7-1. Wire types.

Figure 8-6-7 shows a complex mounting pawl that, when rotated, either pulls the radio into the tray and the rear connector or pushes the radio out. Racks designed for a complex mounting pawl include a cutout and a slot similar to that shown in Figure 8-6-8.

Some panel mount LRUs are mounted with spring locks fastened inside the mounting rack, as shown in Figure 8-6-9. In these cases, the radio locks itself into the rack when pushed. To remove the unit, keys are inserted into the holes, which pushes the spring out of the slot cut into the side of the radio. Once the spring is out of the slot, the ejector mechanism pushes the radio out.

Section 7

Wiring Installation

Any wiring not enclosed in a conduit is considered open wiring. Two or more wires going to the same location, no matter whether or not they are in conduit, are considered a wire group and should be tied together to retain group identity. A bundle consists of two or more groups of wires going in the same direction. A wire harness is a wire group or wire bundle tied together as a compact unit or contained in an outer jacket. Wire harnesses, such as those for avionics, may be prefabricated then installed into the aircraft as a single assembly. Any wire not protected by a fuse, circuit breaker, or other current limiting device is considered unprotected wiring. Table 8-7-1 shows wires commonly used in aircraft electrical systems.

Some wire groups or bundles should remain separated from each other. For example, wires supplying duplicate vital equipment should not be bundled together. Furthermore, unprotected power wiring should not be grouped or bundled with protected wiring. Wire not supplied through a circuit breaker or fuse is unprotected wire. In some aircraft, wires between the battery and the bus are unprotected. Other examples of unprotected wiring include the alternator field wire or wires leading to the magnetos in piston aircraft.

Most approved installations and good practice limits the size of a wire bundle to 75 wires or 2 inches in diameter, whichever is smaller. When several wires are grouped at junction boxes, terminal boards, panels, etc., the identity of the group within the bundle should be maintained with spot ties, as shown in Figure 8-7-1.

Before tying bundles, the wires should be combed smooth, so they run parallel with each other. The technician may construct a wire

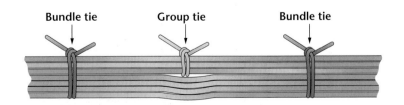

Figure 8-7-1. Group and bundle ties.

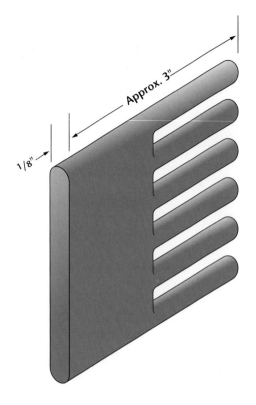

Figure 8-7-2. Comb for straightening wires in bundles.

comb, as shown in Figure 8-7-2. The wire comb is made from a piece of 1/8-inch nylon or other smooth insulating material. All sharp edges should be rounded smooth to protect the wires when constructing a wire comb

Pairs of wires may be twisted together to reduce induction and capacitance with other nearby wires or equipment. Typically, the following wires are twisted together:

- Wires in the vicinity of the magnetic compass or flux detector
- Three-phase AC distribution wiring
- Sensitive circuit avionics wiring
- Any other wiring required by engineering drawings to be twisted

When twisting wires, twist them so they lie snugly against each other, making approximately the number of twists shown in Table 8-7-2. Inspect the wire group for damage after twisting, and replace it if necessary.

In general, avoid making splices within a group or bundle; however, if splicing is necessary, then locate the connections so they may be inspected. Stagger the splices, as shown in Figure 8-7-3, to ensure the bundle does not become excessively large. Make sure all noninsulated splices are covered by shrinkable tubing or by plastic sleeves securely tied at both ends.

When installing wires or wire bundles, the technician must ensure they have the proper amount of slack. Wires or bundles with either too much slack or too tight should not be installed. Slack between support points, such as cable clamps, should not exceed 1/2 inch of deflection with moderate hand force, as shown in Figure 8-7-4. Although this 1/2 inch of deflection may be exceeded if the wire bundle is thin, and the clamps are far apart, the slack must never be great enough to allow the wire bundle to touch any surface. Allow a sufficient amount of slack near each end for any or all of the following:

- To permit ease of maintenance
- To allow replacement of terminals at least twice
- To prevent mechanical strain on the wires, junctions, and supports
- To permit free movement of shock-and-vibration mounted equipment
- To permit shifting of equipment for purposes of maintenance while installed in the aircraft

Often when space allows, panel mounted indicators, such as CDIs, are connected to a harness with sufficient slack to allow the unit to be plugged in after removal from the panel. The bundle is looped and the wire tied. This loop is known as a service loop.

Wires and bundles should not be bent too sharply or damage to the insulation and the wire may occur. Individual wires must have a minimum bend radius of 10 times the outside diameter of the wire. A wire bundle's minimum bending radius is 10 times the diameter of the bundle diameter. The minimum bending radius for coaxial cable can be six times the outside diameter of the cable.

The general rule for wiring is that it must be installed so that it is mechanically and

Wire size	#22	#20	#18	#16	#14	#12	#10	#8	#6	#4
2 Wires	10	10	9	8	7-1/2	7	6-1/2	6	5	4
3 Wires	10	10	8-1/2	7	6-1/2	6	5-1/2	5	4	3

Table 8-7-2. Twists per foot.

electrically sound and does not cause harm to itself, other wiring, or other parts of the airplane. Furthermore, the wiring should be neat in appearance. Whenever practical, route the wires and bundles parallel with or at right angles to stringers or ribs, as shown in Figure 8-7-5.

In contrast, coaxial cable must be routed as directly as possible. Avoid unnecessary bends and locate attachments at each frame rib on cable runs along the length of the fuselage or at each stiffener on cable runs through the wings. This method is necessary to prevent excessive signal reduction within the transmission line.

Observe the following precautions when installing electrical wiring:

- Do not permit the wire or wire bundles to have moving, frictional contact with any other object, since the friction will eventually wear through the insulation and damage the wire

- Do not permit the wire or wire bundles to contact sharp edges of structure, holes, or anything else

- Do not use any installing tools other than those specifically authorized in maintenance or installation manuals

- Do not damage threads of attaching hardware by over tightening or cross threading

- Do not subject wire bundles to sharp bends during the installation process, since doing so may damage the bundle prior to the completion of the installation

- Do not allow dirt, chips, loose hardware, lacing tape scraps, or anything else to accumulate in enclosures or wire bundles. If necessary, lay a cloth over wire bundles to protect from flying metal chips when drilling

- Do not hang anything on wire bundles

- Do not install wire bundles where they may be used as footrests, steps, or hand holds. Furthermore, do not use them as such

- Do not compensate for wires that are too long by folding them back onto themselves and attempting to hide the folds in the bundle

- Do not twist or pull excessively on wire bundles during assembly or installation, since this may cause damage to the wires or the pins to be pulled from connectors

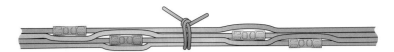

Figure 8-7-3. Staggered splices in wire bundle.

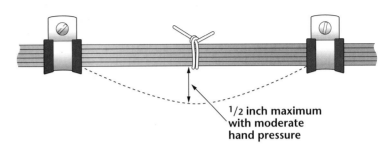

½ inch maximum with moderate hand pressure

Figure 8-7-4. Slack between supports.

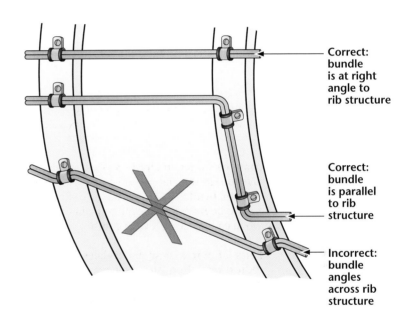

Correct: bundle is at right angle to rib structure

Correct: bundle is parallel to rib structure

Incorrect: bundle angles across rib structure

Figure 8-7-5. Routing bundles.

- Do not stretch wires to mate connectors; allow sufficient slack to permit easy mating

Bundles and wire must be properly supported and bound. When supporting wire or bundles, observe the following guidelines:

- Prevent chafing of cables

- Secure wires and wire bundles routed through bulkheads and structural members

- Fasten wires in junction boxes, panels, and bundles for proper routing and grouping

- Prevent mechanical strain that tends to break the conductors and connections

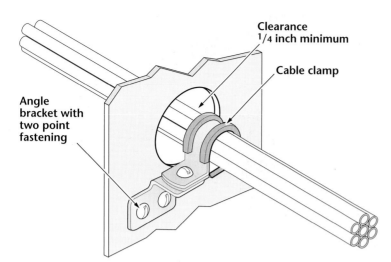

Figure 8-7-6. Cable clamp at bulkhead hole.

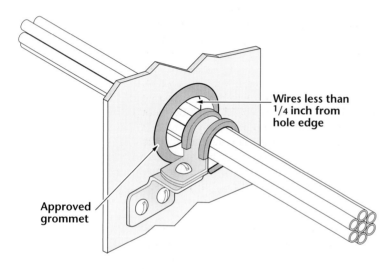

Figure 8-7-7. Cable clamp and grommet of bulkhead hole.

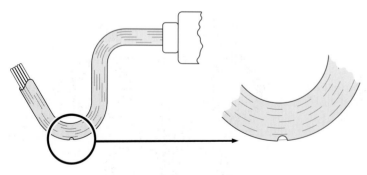

A drainage hole 1/8 inch diameter at lowest point in tubing.
Make the hole after installation is complete and lowest point is firmly established.

Figure 8-7-8. Drainage hole in low point of tubing.

- Facilitate re-assembly to equipment and terminal boards
- Prevent interference between wires and other equipment
- Permit replacement or repair of individual wires without removing the entire bundle
- Prevent excessive movement in areas of high vibration

When installing or routing wires, protect them from the following:

- Chafing or abrasion
- High temperature
- Use of wire bundles as handholds, footholds, foot rests, steps, or any other type of support for personal belongings or equipment
- Damage by personnel moving within the aircraft
- Damage from cargo stowage or shifting
- Damage from battery acid fumes, spray, or spillage
- Damage from solvents and fluids
- Abrasion in wheel wells from exposure to rocks, ice, mud, and other debris

Install wires and wire groups so they are protected against chafing or abrasion in locations where contact with sharp surfaces or other wires would damage the insulation. Damage to the insulation may result in short circuits or equipment malfunctions. Use MS 21919 cable clamps to support wire bundles at each hole through a bulkhead, as shown in Figure 8-7-6. If the wire bundle is closer than 1/4 inch from the end of a hole, install a grommet, as shown in Figure 8-7-7. Do not depend on vinyl sleeves as protection against abrasion or chafing or as a substitute for good routing practice.

Wire and wire bundles must be protected against high temperatures. To prevent wire insulation deterioration, keep wires separate from high temperature equipment, such as resistors, exhaust stacks, heating ducts, etc. The amount of separation may be indicated in installation or maintenance manuals. If the wires must be routed through hot areas, insulate the wires with high temperature material, such as fiberglass, Teflon®, or conduit. Never use low temperature wire to replace high temperature wire.

Many coaxial cables have soft plastic insulation, which is especially subject to deformation and deterioration at high temperatures. Avoid all high temperature areas with transmission lines.

Cables and wire bundles should be installed so they are protected by structure. Use the structure or conduit to prevent pinching against the airframe by cargo. Locate the wire bundles so personnel are not tempted to use sections of the wire as handholds or ladder rungs.

Never route any wires below a battery. Inspect wires in battery areas frequently, and replace any wires discolored by battery fumes.

Avoid areas where wires will be subjected to damage from fluids. Wires and cables installed in aircraft bilges should be installed at least 6 inches from the aircraft centerline. If there is a possibility a wire without a protective outer jacket may be soaked in any location, use plastic tubing to protect it. The tubing should extend past the wet area in both directions and be tied at each end, if the wire has a low point between the tubing ends. The lowest point of the tubing should have a draining hole, as shown in Figure 8-7-8.

Wires in wheel wells are subject to many additional hazards, such as exposure to fluids, pinching, and severe flexing. All wire bundles in wheel wells should be protected by sleeves of flexible tubing held securely at each end. There should be no relative movement at points where the tubing is secured. Inspect these wires and tubing careful at very frequent intervals. Replace them at the first sign of wear. When the gear is fully extended, there should be no strain on the wires, and when the gear is retracted, the slack should not be excessive.

When wiring must be routed parallel to combustible fluid or oxygen lines for short distances (never run parallel for long distances), maintain as much fixed separation as possible but at least 6 inches or more. Route the wires on a level with

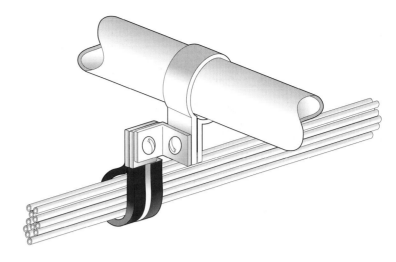

Figure 8-7-9. Separation of wires from plumbing lines.

or above the plumbing lines. Space clamps so if a wire is broken at a clamp it will not contact the line. Where a 6-inch separation is not possible, clamp both the wire bundle and the plumbing line to the same structure to prevent any relative motion. If the separation is less than 2 inches but more than one-half inch, use a nylon sleeve over the wire bundle to give additional protection. Use two cable clamps back-to-back, as shown in Figure 8-7-9, to maintain rigid separation, not for bundle support. Do not route any wire so it can possibly come closer than one-half inch to a plumbing line, and never support any wire or bundle from a plumbing line carrying flammable fluids or oxygen. Clamps may only be used to ensure separation.

Route wiring to maintain a minimum clearance of 3 inches from control cables. If this is not possible, install mechanical guards to prevent contact with the wiring by the control cables.

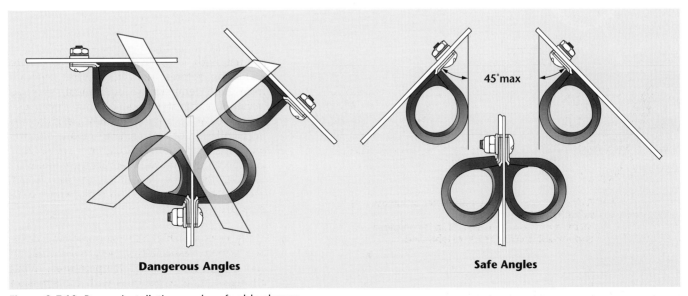

Dangerous Angles   **Safe Angles**

Figure 8-7-10. Proper installation angles of cable clamps.

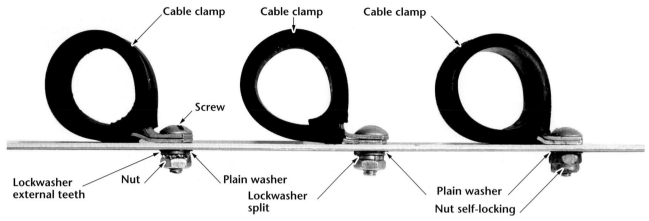

Figure 8-7-11. Attaching cable clamp to structure.

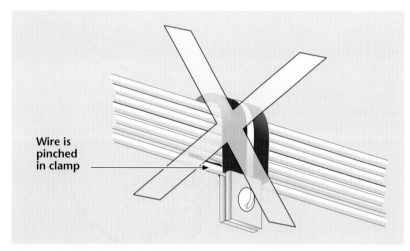

Figure 8-7-12. Wire pinched due to improper clamping.

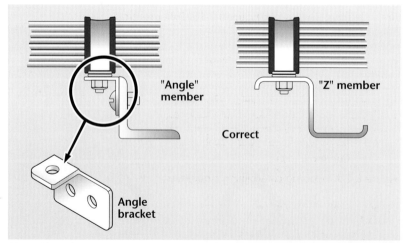

Figure 8-7-13. Mounting cable clamps to Z member and angle structural member.

Once the wire is routed, it must be clamped. Install MS21919 cable clamps, as shown in Figure 8-7-10. MS21919 cable clamps are cushioned with insulating material to prevent abrasion. Never use metal clamps without cushions. The mounting screw should be above the bundle, so the weight of the bundle does not exert a bending or pulling force on the machine screw and nut.

Use hardware, as shown in Figure 8-7-11, to mount the cable clamps to the structure. Make sure no wires are pinched in the flange of the clamp (Figure 8-7-12). If the wire bundle is smaller than the nearest clamp size, wrap the wire bundle with the necessary number of turns of vinyl tape so the bundle is held securely.

If the wire bundle is 2 inches in diameter or less and the ambient temperature is less than 235°F, then nylon clamps, MS25281, may be used. When installing nylon clamps, use a large diameter metal washer under the screw head or nut adjacent to the clamp.

Mount cable clamps directly to Z *members* of the structure. A Z member is a piece of aluminum bent into the Z shape and used to stiffen or strengthen the fuselage. If the structural member is of the angle type, as shown in Figure 8-7-13, then use an angle bracket with two mounting screws.

A tool to facilitate the installation of cable clamps is shown in Figure 8-7-14. Similar to conventional slip joint pliers, the tool compresses and holds the clamp with the securing bolt in place while a nut is being installed on the bolt. The tool is particularly useful for installing clamps in restricted areas and for installing groups of two or three clamps.

Use AN735 clamps without cushions for clamping to a tubular structure. The clamps must fit tightly but should not deform when locked into place. Once the AN735 clamp is installed, attach the wire bundle using a MS21919 clamp with AN hardware, as shown in Figure 8-7-15.

MS grommets are available in rubber, nylon, and Teflon®. MS grommets and their temperature limits are shown in Table 8-7-3. If a nylon

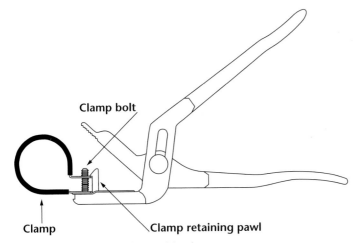

Figure 8-7-14. Tool for installing cable clamps.

Standard	Material	Upper temperature limit
MS35489	Rubber, hot oil and coolant resistant	250°F
MS35490	Rubber, general purpose	250°F
MS21265 and MS21266	Nylon	235°F
MS21265 and MS21266	TFE	500°F

Table 8-7-3. Grommets-temperature limitations of material.

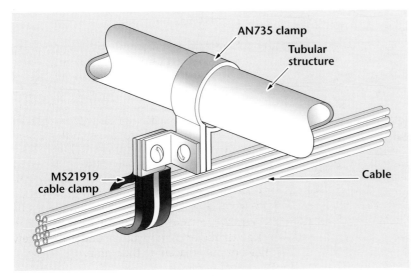

Figure 8-7-15. Installing cable clamps to tubular structure.

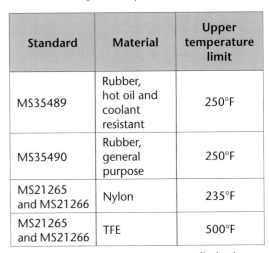

Figure 8-7-16. Split grommet.

grommet must be cut to install it, then make the cut at a 45° angle, as shown in Figure 8-7-16. Cement the grommet in place with the cut at the top of the hole using general purpose cement. When installing caterpillar-type grommets, cut the grommet to the required length, making sure to cut square between the teeth, as shown in Figure 8-7-17. Cement the caterpillar grommet in place using general purpose cement, with the cut at the top of the hole.

As shown in Figure 8-7-18, install terminal lugs on terminal boards MS25123 or MS2712 in a way that locks them against moving in a loosening motion. Table 8-7-4 shows terminal board specifications.

Terminal Boards

MS25123 terminal boards have studs secured with AN960 flat washers and MS20341 steel nuts. Place copper terminal lugs directly on top

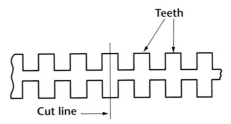

Figure 8-7-17. Cutting caterpillar grommet.

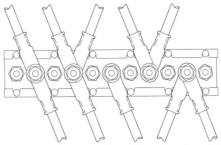

Note: All terminals should be placed so that movement will tighten nut

Figure 8-7-18. Connecting terminals to terminal board.

Terminal board MS part number	Stud thread	Number of studs	Cover part number
MS27212-1-20	6-32UNC-2A	20	MS18029-1-20
MS27212-2-16	10-32UNF-2A	16	MS18029-2-16
MS27212-3-8	1/4-28UNF-2A	8	MS18029-3-8
MS27212-4-8	5/16-24UNF-2A	8	MS18029-4-8
MS27212-5-8	3/8-24UNF-2A	8	MS18029-5-8

Note: Terminal boards and covers are procured in full lengths with number of studs indicated. Cut to suit needs at installation.

Table 8-7-4. MS27212 terminal boards and covers.

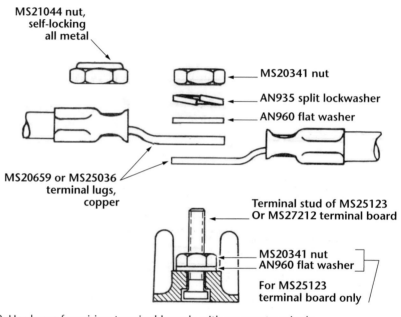

Figure 8-7-19. Hardware for wiring terminal boards with copper terminals.

MS Number	Terminal size	Stud size
MS25440-3	8, 6, 4	No. 10
-4	8, 6, 4, 2, 1, 1/0	1/4
-5	8, 6, 4, 2, 1, 1/0, 2/0	5/16
-6	8, 6, 4, 2, 1, 1/0, 2/0	3/8
-6A	3/0, 4/0	3/8
-8	2, 1, 1/0, 2/0, 3/0, 4/0	1/2

Table 8-7-5. Washers for use with aluminum terminal lugs.

of the MS20341 nut. Follow with an AN960 flat washer, an AN935 split-steel lock washer, and either an MS20431 steel nut or an MS21044 self-locking all-metal nut, as shown in Figure 8-7-19.

MS27212 terminal boards have studs molded into the structure and do not require stud attaching hardware. The lug attachment is the same as the MS25123 terminal board.

If aluminum terminal lugs are used, place them over MS25440 plated, flat washers of the cor-

rect size. Aluminum washer sizes are matched with terminal sizes and stud sizes, as shown in Table 8-7-5.

Figure 8-7-20 shows a mix of terminal types or wiring boards with aluminum terminals. Torque values for terminal board nuts are shown in Table 8-7-6.

When connecting a terminal lug to a bus bar, a high efficiency, low resistance connection is necessary for the maximum transfer of power;

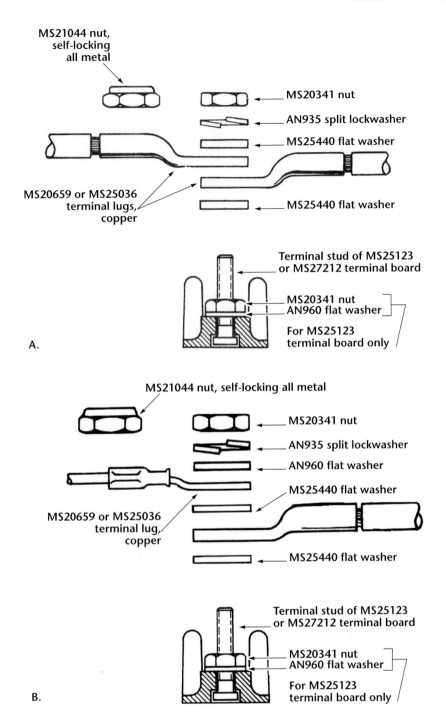

Figure 8-7-20. Hardware for wiring terminal boards: (A) With aluminum terminals, (B) With a combination of terminals.

Stud size	Inch-pounds of torque	
	Plain nuts	Self-locking nuts
3/8-24	110-120	115-125
1/2-20	135-150	150-170

Table 8-7-6A. Installation torques for copper terminals.

Stud size	Inch-pounds of torque
#10	32
1/4	100
5/16	150
3/8	250
1/2	480

Table 8-7-6B. Installation torques for aluminum terminals.

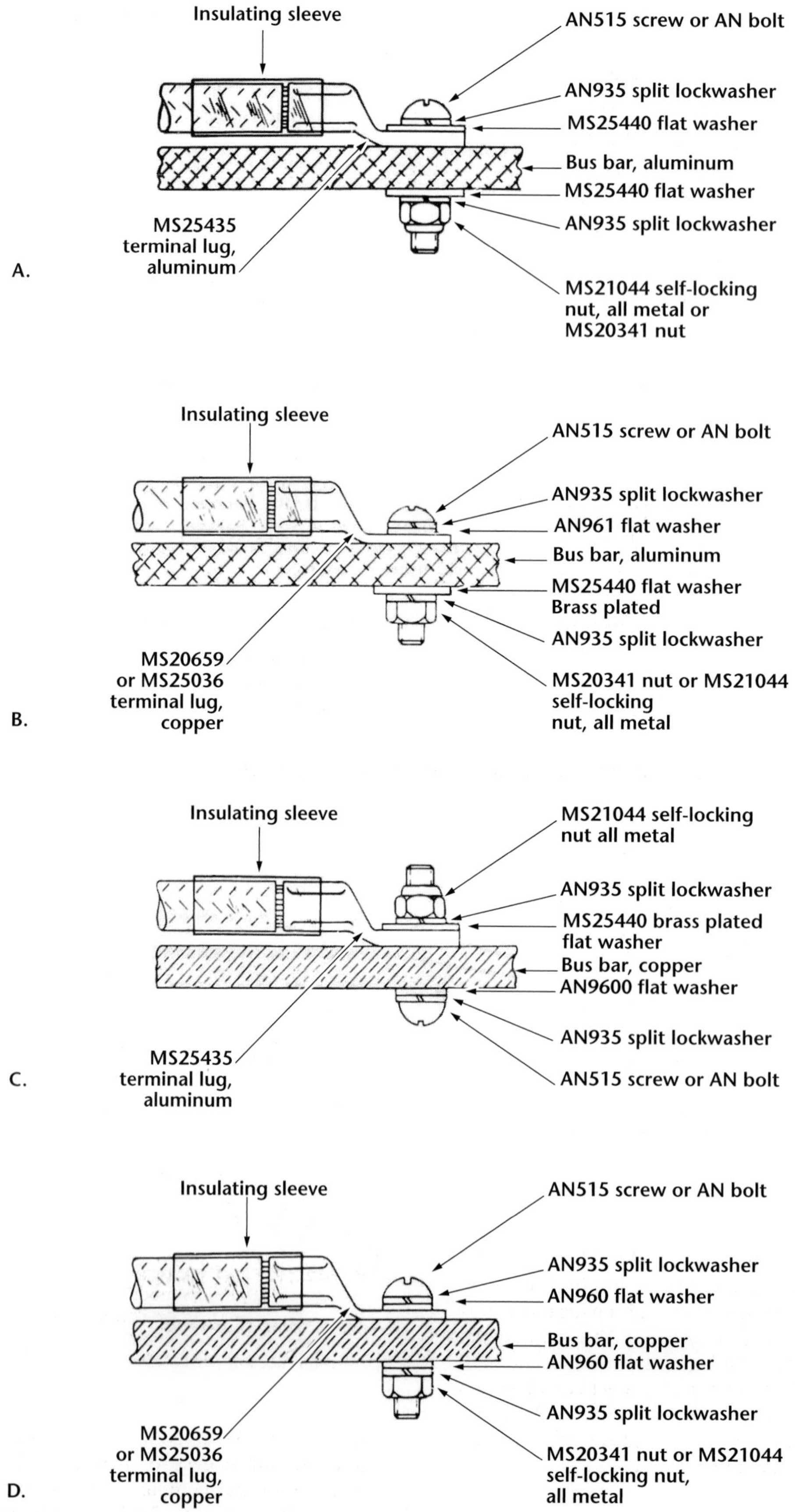

Figure 8-7-21. Techniques for connecting terminal to bus bar: (A) Aluminum terminal to aluminum bus bar, (B) Copper terminal to aluminum bus bar, (C) Aluminum terminal to copper bus bar, (D) Copper terminal to copper bus bar.

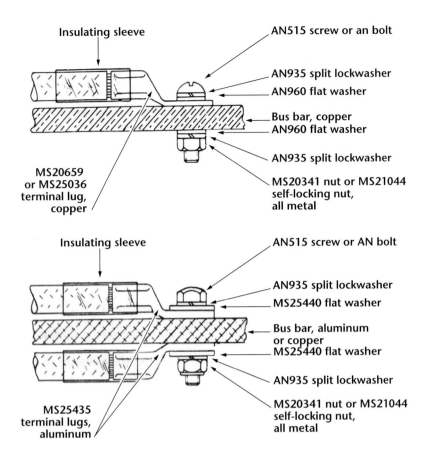

Figure 8-7-22. Connecting two terminal to the same point on bus bar note.

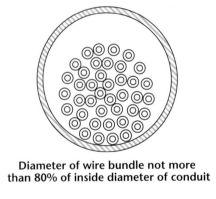

Diameter of wire bundle not more than 80% of inside diameter of conduit

Figure 8-7-23. Conduit capacity.

therefore, the technician should ensure the terminal lug and the bus bar are in direct contact. The technician should ensure the bus bar is clean before making the connection. Techniques for making connections are shown in Figure 8-7-21. If it is necessary to connect two terminals to the same point on the bus bar, connect one terminal on top and the other on the bottom, as shown in Figure 8-7-22.

Wires in Conduit

Wire bundles are not allowed to take up more than 80 percent of the space inside conduit, as

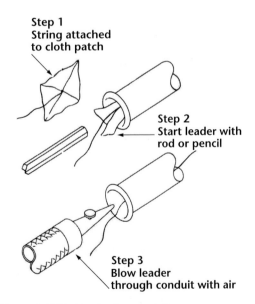

Figure 8-7-24. Leader for conduit.

shown in Figure 8-7-23. So, before installing a bundle in conduit, measure the outside diameter of the wire and compare it to the inside diameter of the conduit. The inside diameter of conduit can be calculated by subtracting the two wall thicknesses from the outside diameter. In addition, no wire ties or splices are allowed inside conduit.

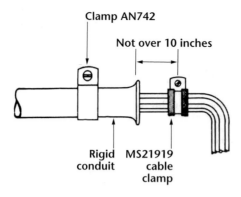

Figure 8-7-25. Support for wire at conduit end.

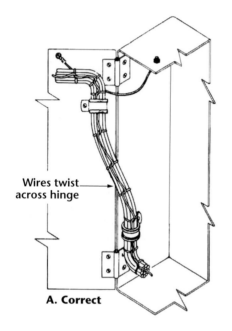

A. Correct

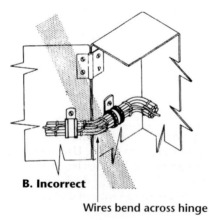

B. Incorrect

Wires bend across hinge

Figure 8-7-26. Support inside junction box.

Wires may be fed through short lengths of conduit by taping the end of the bundle together and pushing it through. Longer runs require a leader, as shown in Figure 8-7-24. The leader should fit loosely within the conduit. Soapstone talc may be used as a lubricant for passing wires through conduit.

Wires at the end of a conduit run should be supported by MS21919 cable clamps, as shown in Figure 8-7-25.

Wire Bundles in Junction Boxes

Use MS21919 cable clamps to support wires hinged across doors so the wires are twisted and not stretched by bending, as shown in Figure 8-7-26. Attach wire bundles to the walls of junction boxes to prevent chafing or abrasion against terminal studs or other items in the box.

Lacing and Tying

Wire groups and bundles are laced or tied to provide ease of installation, maintenance, and inspection. Tying bundles and wire groups is preferable over the use of plastic wire ties (cable straps), since the materials used for tying or lacing are less expensive, lighter, and take up less space.

Tying secures together a group or a bundle of wires with individual ties at regular intervals around the group or bundle. *Lacing* secures together a group or bundle installed inside enclosures by means of a continuous cord forming loops at regular intervals. Whenever possible, use flat, narrow tape for lacing and tying. Round cord may also be used, but it is not preferred because the cord has a tendency to cut into the wire insulation. Cotton, linen, nylon or glass fiber cord, or tape may be used according to the temperature requirements. Cotton or linen cord or tape must be prewaxed to make it moisture and fungus resistant. Nylon cord or tape may be waxed or unwaxed. Glass fiber cord or tape is usually not waxed. Use only flat braided waxed nylon tape to lace or tie coaxial cables or bundles containing coaxial cables, since round materials will cut the soft outer covering of many coaxial cables.

Use either vinyl or glass fiber pressure-sensitive tape, according to temperature requirements. Pressure-sensitive tape must only be used when permitted specifically. If the temperature is not expected to exceed 350°F, then molded nylon self-clinching cable straps may be used.

Observe the following precautions when lacing or tying wire groups or bundles:

- Lace or tie bundles tightly enough to prevent slipping but not so tightly the cord or tape cuts into or deforms the insulation. Be especially careful when lacing or tying

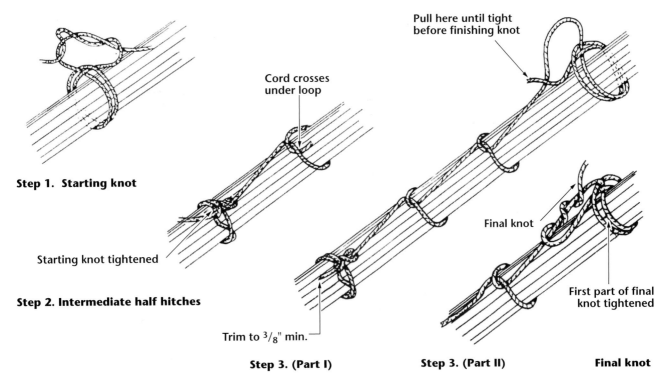

Pull here until tight before finishing knot

Cord crosses under loop

Step 1. Starting knot

Starting knot tightened

Step 2. Intermediate half hitches

Final knot

First part of final knot tightened

Trim to $3/8$" min.

Step 3. (Part I)   **Step 3. (Part II)**   **Final knot**

Figure 8-7-27. Single-cord lacing.

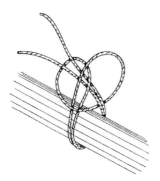

Step 1. Starting knot - bowline on a bight

Starting knot tightened

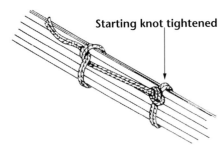

Step 2. Intermediate half hitches

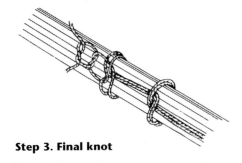

Step 3. Final knot

Figure 8-7-28. Double-cord lacing.

coaxial cable, which has a soft dielectric insulation between the inner and outer conductors. Pinching the coaxial cable will affect its electrical properties.

- Do not use ties on the part of a wire group or bundle located inside conduit.

- When tying wire bundles behind connectors, start the ties far enough from the connector to avoid splaying of the contacts.

- Complete the assembly of one connector, then lace or tie the group or bundle toward an end that has not been assembled.

Lacing

Continuous lacing may only be used on wire groups or bundles that are to be installed in panels or junction boxes. Use double cord lacing on groups or bundles larger than 1 inch in diameter. Use single or double cord lacing on bundles less than 1 inch in diameter.

Single-Cord Lacing. Refer to Figure 8-7-27.

1. Start the lacing at the thick end of the wire group or bundle with a knot consisting of a clove hitch with an extra loop.

2. At regular intervals along the wire group or bundle and at each point where a wire or wire group branches off, continue the lacing with half hitches.

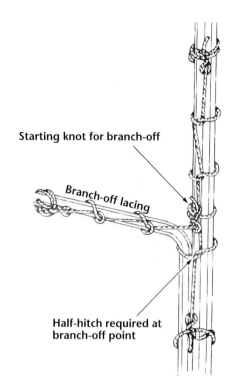

Starting knot for branch-off

Branch-off lacing

Half-hitch required at branch-off point

Figure 8-7-29. Lacing a branch-off.

3. End the lacing with a knot consisting of another clove hitch with an extra loop.

4. Trim the free ends of the lacing cord to 3/8-inch minimum.

Double-Cord Lacing. Refer to Figure 8-7-28.

1. Start the lacing at the thick end of the wire group or bundle with a bowline on a bight.

2. At regular intervals along the wire group or bundle and at each point where a wire or wire group branches off, continue the lacing with half hitches, holding both ends together.

3. End the lacing with a knot consisting of a half hitch, using one cord clockwise

and the other cord counter-clockwise and then tie the cord ends with a square knot.

4. Trim the free ends of the lacing cord to 3/8-inch minimum.

Lacing Branch Offs. Lace a wire group that branches off the main wire bundle as follows. Refer to Figure 8-7-29.

1. Begin the branch-off lacing with a starting knot located on the main bundle, just past the branch-off point. When single cord lacing, make this starting knot as described in the single-cord instructions, Step 1. When double-cord lacing is used, make it as described in the double-cord instructions, Step 1.

2. Continue lacing along the branch, using regularly spaced half hitches. Where double-cord lacing is used, both cords are held together.

3. End the lacing with the regular knot used in single- or double-cord lacing as described in the respective sections, Step 3.

4. Trim the free ends of the lacing cord to 3/8-inch minimum.

Tying

Tie all wire groups or bundles where supports are more than 12 inches apart. Space ties 12 inches apart or less. Refer to Figure 8-7-30.

1. Wrap cord around wire groups or bundles as shown.

2. Make a clove hitch, followed by a square knot with an extra loop.

3. Trim the free ends of the lacing cord to 3/8-inch minimum.

If pressure sensitive tape is required, install as follows. Refer to Figure 8-7-31.

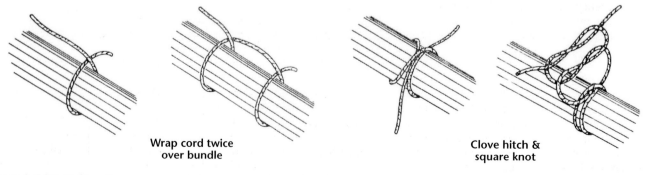

Wrap cord twice over bundle

Clove hitch & square knot

Figure 8-7-30. Making ties.

1. Wrap tape around wire groups or bundles three times with two-thirds overlap for each turn.

2. Heat seal the loose tape end with a heat gun.

Self-clinching cable straps are more commonly known as plastic-wire ties, or zip ties. They are adjustable, lightweight, flat, nylon straps with molded ribs or serrations on the inside surface to grip the wire. They may be used in place of individual cord ties for fast securing of wire groups or bundles. There are two types of straps used in aviation. The MS17821 is a plain cable strap, and the MS17822 is similar, but it has a flat surface for identification marking. Both types of straps are available in ten colors, as listed in Table 8-7-7.

Self-clinching cable straps should be installed with a hand tool, which can tighten the strap and, at the same time, cut it safely. Self-clinching cable strap part numbers, type, intended use, and tool numbers are listed in Table 8-7-8 . Figure 8-7-32 demonstrates how to install self-clinching cable straps.

Shear, Lock, and Seal Wire

Electric connectors, emergency devices, autopilot servos, and other electric and avionic equipment in aircraft are secured with safety wire, quite often, to prevent accidental loosening of bolts or screws.

Lock wire is a heavy, twisted, double-strand wire used to secure parts against inadvertent opening in all areas of high vibration, such as the engine compartment. Electric connectors are lock-wired in high-vibration areas, which are normally inaccessible for periodic maintenance and inspection.

Shear wire is a light, single-strand wire used to secure parts that may be subject to periodic disconnection, maintenance, and inspection or for parts that must be quickly removed.

Seal wire is thin, easily breakable wire used as a seal on fire extinguishers, oxygen regulators, emergency activation switches, and other devices that must be quickly released for use and to indicate whether these devices have been used.

In any of these cases, never reuse wire. Only use new wire. Use wire of the shortest length that allows the safety, shear, or seal wiring process to be completed. Moreover, secure the wire tightly so that there will be tension if the part begins to loosen, but do not tighten the wire to the point where it is susceptible to breakage under load or vibration.

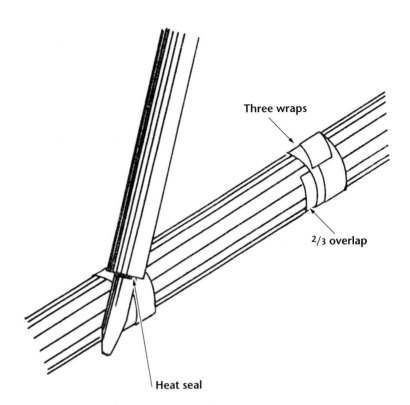

Figure 8-7-31. Securing with tape.

Color dash no.	Color
-0	Black
-1	Brown
-2	Red
-3	Orange
-4	Yellow
-5	Green
-6	Blue
-7	Purple
-8	Gray
-9	Natural

Table 8-7-7. Cable strap colors.

MS Part no.	Type	For bundle diameter (inches)	MS Tool no.
mS17821-1	Thin	1/16 - 1 3/4	MS17823
MS17821-2	Thin	1/16 - 4	MS17823
MS17821-3	Thick	3/16 - 3 3/4	MS17824
MS17822-1	Thin	3/8 - 1 3/4	MS17823

Table 8-7-8. Self-clinching plastic cable and installing tools.

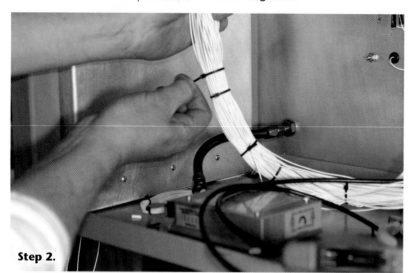

Step 2.

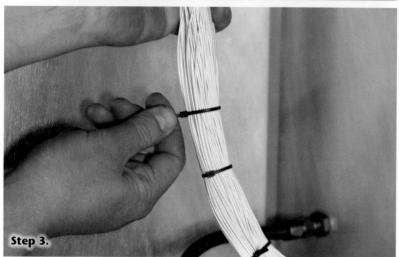

Step 3.

Step 5.

Figure 8-7-32. Installing a self-clinching cable strap.

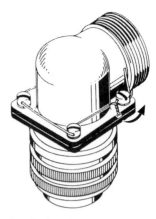

Bend pigtail around screw
to protect personnel

Figure 8-7-33. Single-wire method.

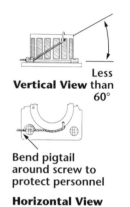

Less
Vertical View than
60°

Bend pigtail
around screw to
protect personnel

Horizontal View

Figure 8-7-34. Double-twist lock wiring.

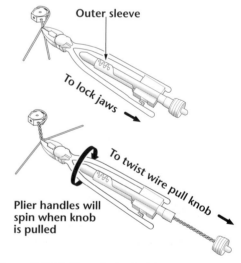

Outer sleeve

To lock jaws

To twist wire pull knob

Plier handles will
spin when knob
is pulled

Figure 8-7-35. Use of wire twister.

For single-twist wiring, use the method shown in Figure 8-7-33 in all conditions where shear and seal wire is required. The single-wire method may be used in areas that are hard to reach and for small screws in a closely spaced pattern.

For double-twist lock wiring, use the method illustrated in Figure 8-7-34. Use the double-twist method of lock wiring in areas of high vibration and for electrical connectors in inaccessible areas.

When wires are twisted by hand, use pliers for the final twists to apply tension and to secure the ends of the wire. Cut off the part of the wire gripped by the pliers to remove the rough edges.

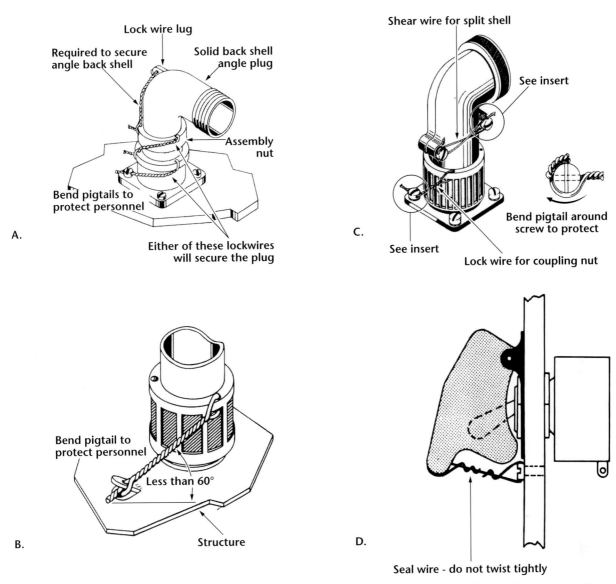

Figure 8-7-36. (A) Wiring AN type connector, (B) Lock wiring connector to structure, (C) Wiring split shell assembly screws, (D) Seal wiring switch guard.

In all cases, ensure the wire does not become kinked or nicked during twisting. If the wire is damaged, replace it with new wire.

Safety wire pliers may be used, as shown in Figure 8-7-35. This tool has jaws to hold the wire, diagonal cutting blades, and a handle with an integrated spinner. To use safety wire pliers:

- Grip the wire in the jaws of the safety wire pliers and slide the outer sleeve down with your thumb to lock the handles.
- Pull the spinner knob, which will spin the spiral rod, spin the handle, and twist the wire.
- Squeeze the handle to release the wire.

Figure 8-7-36 shows examples of lock, seal, and safety wiring connectors and switches.

Section 8
Circuit Protection

Aircraft circuits are protected by current limiters, fuses, and circuit breakers. All three of these devices open a circuit when too much current is being drawn.

Current limiters, shown in Figure 8-8-1, are a form of fuse that is used in circuits drawing large amounts of power. Current limiters open slowly, which allows them to carry an overload for a short period of time. Current limiters enclose the fusible link (enclosed link type) and are installed in a block-type fuse holder and are not replaceable by the flight crew during flight.

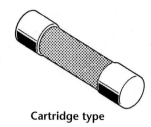

Cartridge type

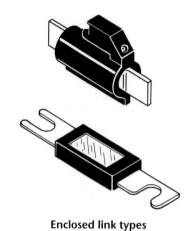

A.   **Enclosed link types**

2 7/16

11/32   11/32

B.   **Encloses the fusable link**

Figure 8-8-1. (A) Types of current limiters, (B) Diagram showing a fusible link enclosed in a link-type current limiter.

Fuses also protect circuits. The cartridge-type fuse is installed in either an extractor post-style fuse holder or in fuse clips, as shown in Figure 8-8-2. Table 8-8-1 shows MS part numbers and characteristics of several fuses and current limiters.

Observe the following precautions when replacing fuses.

- Do not use tools to remove or insert fuses.
- Make sure new fuses have the same electrical features as the fuses being replaced.
- Make sure the new fuse has the same physical dimensions as the fuse being replaced.
- Make sure the plating on all metal parts is clean and intact.
- Make sure the wire inside the replacement fuses exhibits continuity.
- Make sure the replacement fuse has no cracks or breaks.
- Do not force a fuse into a holder that does not readily accept it; first, check that the fuse is the correct size.

Most often, circuits are protected by circuit breakers. Push-pull breakers can be manually opened by pulling on the button or reset by pushing on the button. Push-to-reset breakers cannot be manually opened but can be reset by pushing the button. Toggle-type breakers resemble a switch and can be manually set or reset by moving the handle. A toggle-type breaker has an amperage value stamped into the handle, which will positively identify it as a circuit breaker. These three types of breakers are shown in Figure 8-8-3.

Extractor post type

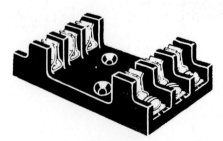

Block type

Figure 8-8-2. Typical fuse holders.

Enclosed link type			
MS Part number	Voltage rating	Current rating	Type
MS24124-5	115/200 VAC	5 amps	A
-10		10 amps	A
-20		20 amps	A
-30		30 amps	A
-40		40 amps	A
-50		50 amps	A
-60		60 amps	A
MS24125-5	115/200 VAC	5 amps	B
-10		10 amps	B
-20		20 amps	B
-30		30 amps	B
-40		40 amps	B
-50		50 amps	B
-60		60 amps	B

Table 8-8-1. Fuses used in aircraft electrical system.

Wire gauge	Circuit breaker amps	Fuse amps
20	7.5	5
18	10	10
16	15	20
14	20	15

Table 8-8-2. Typical circuit breaker and fuse ratings vs. wire size.

Circuit breakers have two types of design. The magnetic or electromagnetic type passes the current through a coil. Similar to a relay, when the current in the coil reaches the value design for the circuit breaker, then the electromagnetic field is strong enough to pull open the contacts.

The thermal-type breaker passes the current through a bimetallic strip. As the current increases, the strip heats up. When the current in the strip reaches the rated value of the circuit breaker, there is enough heat to bend the bimetallic strip away from its contact, opening the circuit.

Although circuit breakers come in the two main types described above, there are a multitude of physical shapes and sizes. Space is limited behind circuit breaker panels, so the technician must take great care to install a circuit breaker of the correct amperage value, shape, size, and contact arrangement as the rest of the circuit breakers.

Typical fuse and circuit breaker values compared to wire gauge is shown in Table 8-8-2. Aviation circuit breakers are required to be trip free. Trip free means they cannot be forcibly reset when the circuit current exceeds the circuit breaker value.

Section 9
Avionics Integration

Avionics are more complex than many mobile electronic systems because avionics are integrated into the aircraft. Simple systems have a low level of integration, while complex systems have a high level of integration.

At the simplest level, a communication system is integrated into the aircraft bus to receive power and will have connectors installed in the instrument panel for a microphone and headphones. At the most complex level, an avionics suite communicates, navigates, and flies the airplane, all under flight management system control.

An avionics technician must understand some of the standards and conventions that allow avionics systems to be integrated.

Audio Integration

In nearly all aircraft containing more than one audio-producing avionics system, the avionics is integrated through an audio system. If an aircraft has only one communication radio, then the integration is rather simple, as shown in Figure 8-9-1. The radio is tied to the bus, to a microphone jack, and to a headphones jack.

Aviation microphone jacks are 0.21 inches in diameter and have two contacts in addition to the grounding sleeve. Aviation microphone plugs have a grounding sleeve, a ring contact,

Toggle

Push to reset

Push-pull

Figure 8-8-3. Circuit breakers.

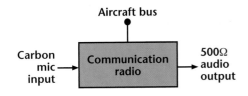

Figure 8-9-1. Single COM radio integration.

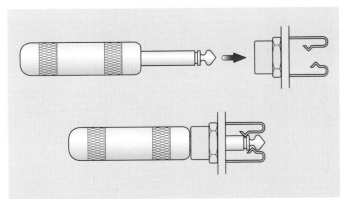

Figure 8-9-2. Aviation standard microphone plug and jack.

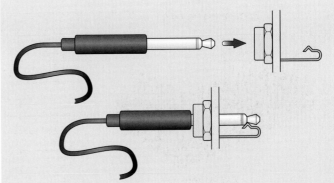

Figure 8-9-3. Aviation standard headphone plug and jack.

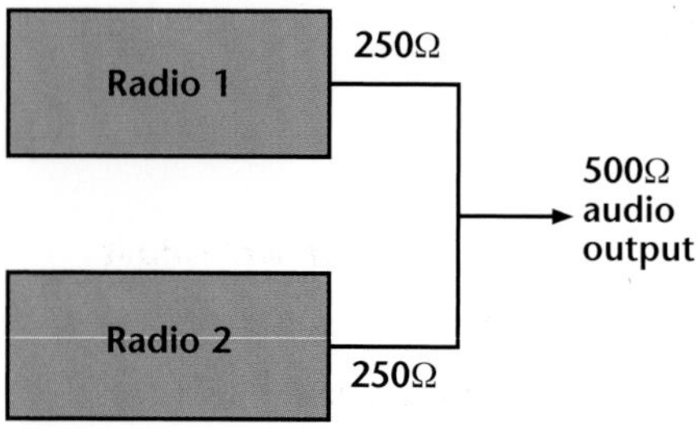

Figure 8-9-4. Radios in parallel.

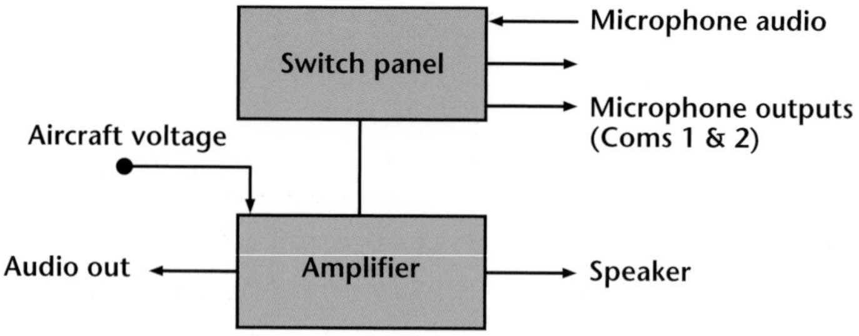

Figure 8-9-5. A generic audio system.

Figure 8-9-6. Garmin audio system with intercom combined with a marker receiver.

Courtesy of Garmin

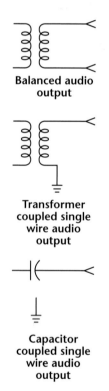

Balanced audio output

Transformer coupled single wire audio output

Capacitor coupled single wire audio output

Figure 8-9-7. Audio output configurations.

and a tip contact. Aviation standard microphone plug and jack drawings are shown in Figure 8-9-2. The tip contact on the microphone plug is connected to the transmit push-to-talk (PTT) switch in the microphone and is known as the mircrophone key, or keyline. When the pilot presses the PTT switch, the tip of the plug connects to the grounding sleeve. The radio senses this ground and begins transmitting. Aircraft may be equipped with five or more microphone jacks.

Typically, the microphone jack sleeve is grounded to the airframe. In some aircraft with intercom systems installed, the sleeve may be grounded through the intercom system.

Aviation headphones are designed for 500 Ω impedance and use 1/4-inch jacks and plugs with one contact and a grounding sleeve. Shown in Figure 8-9-3, in most systems the sleeve is grounded to the airframe at the jack. Aircraft may have five or more headphone jacks installed.

Installing a second audio producing system causes problems immediately. An electrical or electronic systems principle is that for maximum power transfer, the impedance of both devices must be the same. This principle holds for AC electrical systems, antenna systems, and audio systems. When two radios are connected in parallel to one 500 Ω headset, as shown in Figure 8-9-4, each device "sees" an impedance that is half of its own. Power transfer, seen here as volume, is reduced. The problem worsens as more radios are added in parallel. The output is reduced and distorted.

To prevent this problem, aircraft use audio systems. Shown in Figure 8-9-5, a typical audio system includes a switch panel mounted in the instrument panel, which allows the pilot to select the radio to which they would like to listen. Also included in the switch panel is a microphone selector switch. Most audio systems have an auto mode, which allows both the audio output and the microphone to be switched at the same time.

The switch panel steers the selected 500 Ω audio to an amplifier, which has an output to the headphone jack or jacks and to the cabin speaker or speakers. The amplifier is connected to the aircraft voltage bus. Some audio systems include volume control. Others have a built-in intercom system.

Many systems in small aircraft combine the two components into a single, panel-mounted unit, as shown in Figure 8-9-6.

Audio systems allow convenient and simple selection of audio outputs. In addition, audio systems allow impedances to remain appropriately matched so no reduction or distortion occurs.

Audio systems may be balanced or unbalanced. A balanced audio system provides the audio output from a transformer where neither lead is at ground potential. Unbalanced systems provide audio output on one wire that may be capacitively- or transformer-coupled and uses ground as the return path. When integrating systems of different design, consult the installation documentation for

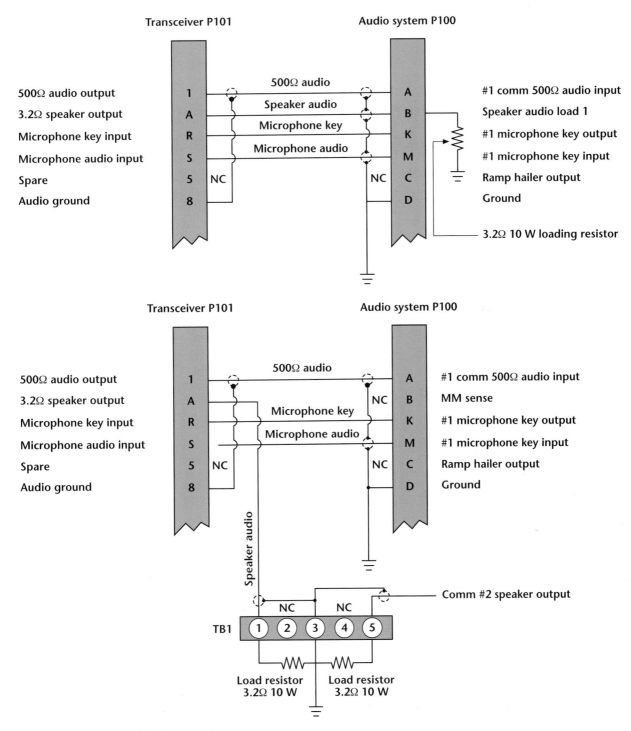

Figure 8-9-8. Two means of loading speaker outputs.

Speaker Output Loads

Some communication transceivers have a speaker amplifier included. If an audio system is to be used with this type of communication system, the speaker output must be loaded to prevent overheating and premature failure of the audio amplifier in the transceiver. Some audio systems include internal load resistors for use in such cases. The speaker output is connected to the appropriate pins in the audio system jack, which connect the speaker output to a load. In other cases, the installing agency must provide a resistor as part of the installation. In these cases, a terminal board is used to mount the load resistor, and the speaker output from the transceiver is connected to the resistor in the terminal board. Figure 8-9-8 illustrates two means of loading the transceiver speaker output.

compatibility. Audio output configurations are shown in Figure 8-9-7.

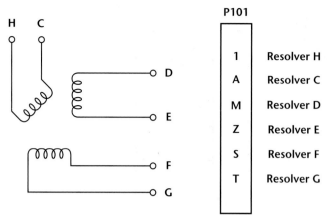

Figure 8-9-9. ARINC resolver standard schematic, nomenclature and partial connector labeling.

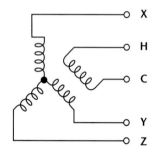

Figure 8-9-10. Schematic of a synchronous motor.

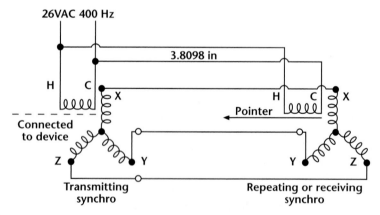

Figure 8-9-11. Transmitting and repeating synchronous motors.

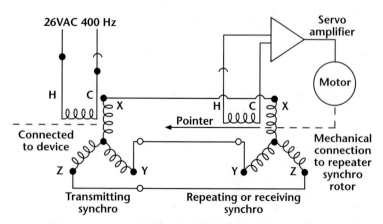

Figure 8-9-12. Transmitting and repeating synchronous motor system with servo amplifier.

Navigation Integration

Navigation systems integrate easily when each component is from the same manufacturer and series. When mixing navigation equipment from different manufacturers or series, however, the technician designing the system must check carefully to make sure that the equipment is compatible.

Most navigation receivers provide the composite navigation signal to the converter at 0.5 V RMS. However, some composite signals are as high as 3 V or as low as 0.3 V; and still others aren't defined and are set at whatever level allows the converter to produce standard navigation deviation.

In many navigation systems, the OBS resolver or resister is part of the indicator, while the rest of the navigation converter is part of either the panel-mounted receiver or a remote-mounted LRU. In either case, mixing manufacturers may present problems. When integrating these systems, the technician should look for standard nomenclature, as shown in Figure 8-9-9.

An ARINC standard resolver has a rotor winding and two stator windings, as shown in Figure 8-9-9. The rotor windings are labeled H and C for a resolver designed to operate at 30 Hz. Often, C is grounded. Stator No. 1 is labeled D and E, and stator No. 2 is labeled F and G. Resolvers may be labeled A and B in place of H and C, which indicates the resolver is designed to operate at 400 Hz.

Still other resolvers may be able to operate at either 400 Hz or 30 Hz, depending on how they are wired. Always consult the installation manuals and notes before attempting to integrate systems from different manufacturers.

Synchronous motors, or synchros, can be used in compass systems and autopilots. Like the resolver, the synchro has standard nomenclature. The schematic and labeling for a synchro is shown in Figure 8-9-10. Most synchros are designed to operate at 26 VAC 400 Hz, but the technician should always consult the installation manuals and notes before attempting to integrate systems from different manufacturers.

Like a resolver, the rotor of a synchronous motor is labeled H and C. Unlike a resolver, there are three stator windings, each spaced 120° from the other. When tied in parallel with another synchronous motor, as shown in Figure 8-9-11, both rotors are synchronized. In this way, an instrument can be used to drive a needle in another location.

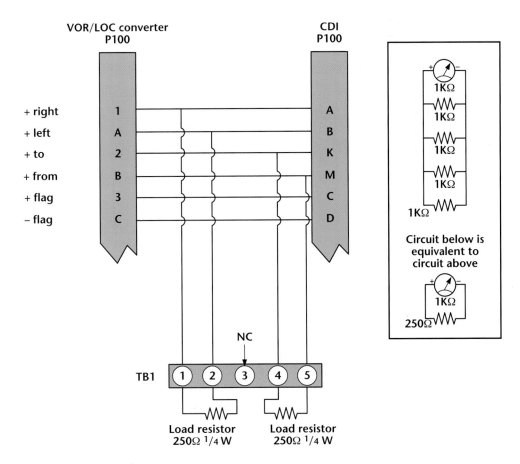

Figure 8-9-13. Loading the converter output.

Synchronous motors are used in RMIs, compass systems, HSIs, and autopilots. Unlike other motors, a synchronous motor is not always designed to produce horsepower or torque. Instead, it has just enough energy to move a pointer attached to the rotor. In some cases, the energy level is so small, engineers design amplifiers to increase the rotor signal to a level with which to drive a separate motor attached to the rotor, as shown in Figure 8-9-12.

In any synchronous motor system, if the rotors are not in alignment, magnetism from the stator applies torque to the rotor of the repeating synchro. If the rotor has mechanical resistance or if the magnetism is weak, then a signal will be present on the rotor H and C connection. This signal can be amplified by a servo amplifier, which drives a motor with sufficient torque to move the rotor. Once the rotor in the repeating synchro is aligned with the rotor in the transmitting synchro, the signal disappears, or nulls, and the rotor stops moving.

When integrating systems using synchronous motors, the technician must refer to the installation manuals to ensure the voltages and frequencies of both systems being integrated are the same.

Meter Loads

The standard impedance for a navigation deviation bar or flag is 1 kΩ. Often, converters are designed to drive multiple meter loads; some may drive up to five. If a converter output is designed to drive five loads but is only driving one, the installation manual may require that the output be loaded with resistors to simulate the loads of the other four meters. One method of loading is shown in Figure 8-9-13.

Navigation converters use various methods of driving CDI D-bars, and the technician must ensure compatibility between the CDI and the converter. Three different types are listed below.

- The six-wire system is shown in Figure 8-9-13. Each CDI element has two wires.

- The three-wire system ties *positive left* and *positive from* together. This common line is connected to a reference voltage. The *positive right* and *positive to* lines deviate higher or lower than the reference voltage. Often, the three-wire system uses a CDI with a combination from/to/off flag.

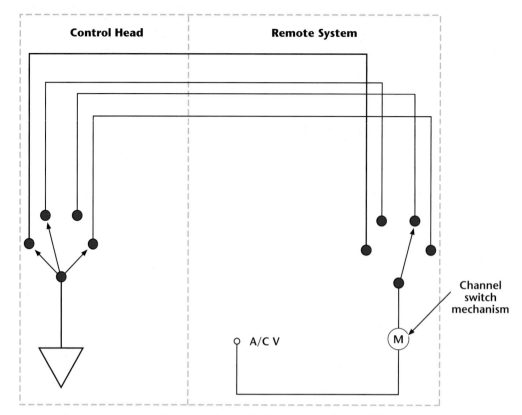

Actual systems used one wire for each MHz and one for each KHz

Figure 8-9-14. Open seeking line channeling.

- The four-wire system has two wires for each CDI element but has a CDI with a combination from/to/off flag.

Some HSI, PNI, or EFIS systems are equipped with a flag known as a *super flag*. A super flag has a meter movement that is activated by a voltage equal to the bus voltage. If the navigation indicator is using a super flag, then the converter must have a super flag output.

Autopilot Integration

Autopilots are heavily integrated into the airframe and avionics of any aircraft. So much so, an STC is required for an autopilot installation. Deviations from the STC are not allowed. Electronically and, depending on autopilot sophistication, it may be connected to the following systems.

- Attitude gyro or ADHRS system
- Directional gyro, HSI, or PNI
- Air data system
- Databus
- Navigation CDIs
- Turn and bank indicator (for rate information)

- Marker beacon system
- Static system
- Pitot system
- FMS

When integrating autopilots with navigation systems or flight management systems, be aware the word *steering* is a reference to a deviation output, which already takes into consideration course intercept information. For example, a VOR/LOC converter deviation output merely indicates whether the aircraft is to the left or right of the selected course. In contrast, a steering output takes heading into consideration, calculates an intercept angle, and indicates whether the aircraft is to the left or right of the ground track required to intercept the selected course.

Remote Frequency Control

There must be a method to control frequency remotely for remote mounted LRUs and for channeling information to be provided to glideslope receivers and DME transceivers. There are several remote frequency control systems. The earliest method of remote frequency control was to use a Teleflex cable connected to a dial on the radio control head and the tuning mechanism on the remote LRU. This method was known as a coffee grinder, because the number of turns necessary to achieve the desired frequency resembled the number of turns necessary to grind coffee beans. This system has been replaced in all but restored antique aircraft.

Parallel Channeling Methods

Early electronic remote frequency control involved a system called open seeking line. The open seeking line system featured a switch in the control head that connected all contacts to ground except one on the desired frequency or channel. The control head switch was connected in parallel with a similar switch in the remote LRU. The switch in the remote LRU had all contacts open except one, which would be connected to a drive motor, as shown in Figure 8-9-14. When the pilot changed channels, the motor would run, moving the switch mechanism until the line opened.

Due to the complexity, slowness, and heaviness of open seeking line channeling systems, they are rarely used today.

The 11-wire system is another method of electronic channeling featuring a switch in the control head connected by many wires to the remote LRU. In the case of NAV or COM channeling, this system requires 11 wires for the MHz frequencies and 11 more for the kHz frequencies. Each wire set would be selectively grounded in the control head to choose the desired frequency.

The 2 x 5, or two-out-of-five, channeling system is an improvement on the 11-wire system. In the 2 x 5 system, 11 wires control MHz and kHz. Five wires control MHz, another five control the 100 kHz frequencies, and one more wire is required to control the 50 kHz selection. This is an ARINC standard system, and it is still in use. The 2 x 5 system uses logic to determine frequency. A partial truth table is shown in Table 8-9-1.

A system using 2 x 5 channeling may be designed so the grounds forward bias diodes and transistors, which in turn place crystals into a local oscillator circuit or program a frequency synthesizer.

Slip Code channeling reduces the number of wires required for 2 x 5 by two. In this case, nine wires can control MHz and kHz. Four wires control the MHz and another four control the 100 kHz frequency. A fifth wire is required for the 50 kHz channels. The coding is similar to 2 x 5, and some think of slip code as a 2 x 5 system with one wire removed. Typically, slip code does not bias transistors or diodes

Frequency (MHz)	A	B	C	D	E
0.00	1	0	1	1	0
0.10	0	0	1	1	1
0.20	0	1	0	1	1

Table 8-9-1. Partial truth table for 2 x 5 channeling. 0 represents a ground and 1 represents an open.

Frequency (kHz)	K_0	K_1	K_2	K_3
0.00	0	0	1	1
0.10	0	0	0	1
0.20	0	0	0	0

Table 8-9-2. Partial truth table for slip code channeling.

Frequency (kHz)	A	B	C	D
0.00	0	0	0	0
0.10	0	0	0	1
0.20	0	0	1	0

Table 8-9-3. Partial truth table for shifted BCD.

directly. Instead, slip code is most often used to program synthesizers. A partial truth Table for slip code is shown in Table 8-9-2.

Another variation on slip code and 2 x 5 channeling is called *shifted BCD*. BCD stands for binary coded decimal. In this system, four wires are required for MHz, another four are required for 100 kHz, and a ninth wire is required for 50 kHz. Like slip code, shifted BCD does not bias diodes or transistors directly. Instead, the code is used to program frequency synthesizers. Table 8-9-3 shows a partial shifted BCD truth table.

There are many standards for serial channeling. The basic theory of serial channeling is that all the information is sent serially on one wire. As a practical matter, at least two wires are required, one wire for the information and a second as a ground return. In some systems, three wires are used. Although there are many proprietary serial channeling systems in aircraft, most aircraft today use a standard data bus for both channeling and other information transfer.

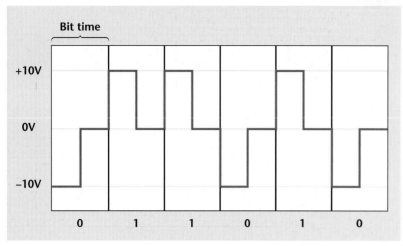

Figure 8-10-1. A portion of an ARINC 429 word showing bit time and voltage levels.

When planning an installation, the technician must ensure the control head is compatible with the LRU. The same brand of equipment may use more than one type of channeling standard. Furthermore, some LRUs can accept different channeling standards, depending on how they are wired.

Section 10

Data Bus

There are several forms of digital communication standards in use in aircraft. These standards that have been set forth by the General Aviation Manufacturer's Association (GAMA), ARINC and the military. A partial list of standards includes:

- RS-232
- RS-432
- ARINC 429
- ARINC 629
- MIL-STD-1553
- CSDB
- ASCB

Although these data systems can remotely channel a radio, their capabilities go way beyond channeling. This section describes four standards a few of the problems that can develop. A data bus can be used to send channeling, navigation, performance, and a host of other information, all on a pair of wires.

One measurement of data bus performance is speed. Speed is measured in bits per second (bps). Each of the systems described has a different bps speed. The higher the bps, the faster the data bus.

ARINC 429

ARINC 429 is a one-way, digital data bus. A single transiting LRU can send information to up to 20 receiving LRUs. The ARINC 429 system uses the digital information transfer system (DITS). The DITS uses a shielded, twisted pair of wires to carry the information from the transiting LRU to the receiving LRUs. If information needs to be transmitted in both directions, two buses are required.

ARINC 429 is a *return to zero system* (RTZ), which means 1s and 0s are defined by a voltage, and in between each digit, the voltage returns to 0 V. In RTZ +10.0 V defines a high, or 1 and -10.0 V defines a low, or 0, as shown in Figure 8-10-1.

There are two versions of the ARINC 429 system. The high-speed system runs at 100 kbps, and the low-speed system runs between 12 kbps and 14.5 kbps. In the high-speed system, a single bit lasts for 10 μS. In the low-speed system, a single bit lasts for between 69 μS and 80 μS.

The ARINC 429 system is considered *bipolar*, since the polarity of the two wires changes as lows and highs are sent. By returning to zero between each high and low, the units can be synchronized.

ARINC 429 data is sent in 32-bit words in four formats.

- Binary data (BNR)
- Binary coded decimal (BCD)

Label	SDI	English	Units	Range	SSM (BIN)	Data
206 (dec) 10000110 (bin)	00	Computed airspeed	Knots	1024	110	180 (dec) 010110100 (bin) 5 pad bits
Bit 32 - 01100010110100000000000001100001 - Bit 1						

Table 8-10-1. An ARINC word.

- Acknowledgement ISO alphabet maintenance (AIM)

- Discreet

Each word contains information in one of the four formats and other information including:

- a source-destination identifier (SDI)

- a label which describes how the data is to be decoded

- a sign-status matrix (SSM), which provides information about the word

- a parity bit for error detection

- and pad bits, which fill space unused by information

For binary and discreet formats, there is an 8-bit label, two SDI bits, 19 bits of data, two SSM bits, and one parity bit. In the BNR format, there is an 8-bit label, two SDI bits, 18 bits of data, three SSM bits, and a parity bit. In the AIM format, there is an 8-bit label, 21 data bits, two SSM bits, and a parity bit. Charts showing ARINC 429 words often start at the left with bit 32. Table 8-10-1 shows an example of ARINC 429 data.

ARINC 629

ARINC 629 is a 2 Mbps, bidirectional, current-based bus. The ARINC 629 system can use either a twisted pair or fiber optic line. The ARINC 629 system uses Manchester encoding and short spike voltages called doublets, which are used to induce current in the current mode couplers (CMC) clamped over the twisted pair or fiber optic line.

Manchester encoding divides time into windows. The first half of the window is the data half, the other half is the clock time. If the voltage in the data half of the window is 12 V, then the bit is 1. If the voltage in the data half of the window is 0 V, then the bit will be 0. The clock half always is the opposite of the data half, as shown in Figure 8-10-2. The two halves of the window form one unit of bit time, which for ARINC 629 is 100 μS.

A word, such as that shown in Table 8-10-1 is converted into ARINC 629 doublets for data transmission, as shown in Figure 8-10-3.

The hardware for ARINC 629, as shown in Figure 8-10-4, consists of a terminal controller (TC) attached to the LRU and a serial interface module (SIM). The SIM connects through a stub cable to a current mode coupler (CMC), which receives or transmits doublets from or to the twisted pair or fiber optic cable.

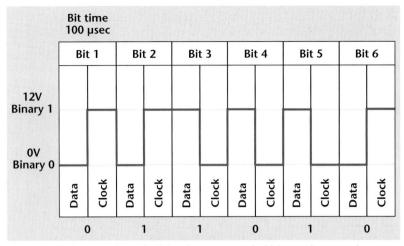

Figure 8-10-2. A portion of a Manchester encoded binary data word.

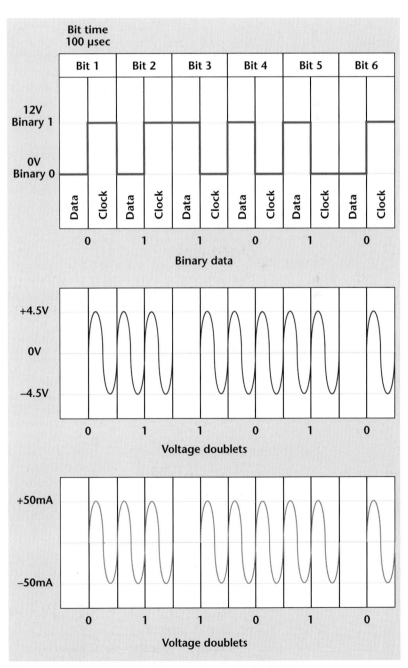

Figure 8-10-3. ARINC 629 voltage and current doublets.

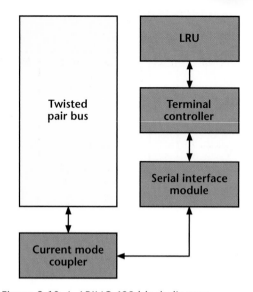

Figure 8-10-4. ARINC 629 block diagram.

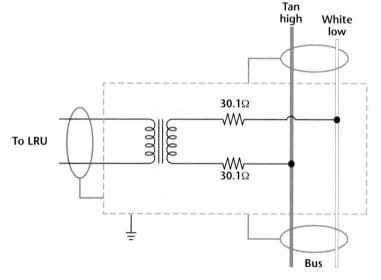

Figure 8-10-5. ASCB bus connection.

Other LRUs are connected to the data bus in the same way. The CMC shown in Figure 8-10-4 contains an inductive pickup. There is no direct electrical connection between the data bus cable and the CMC.

ARINC 629 operates like a party line or a common traffic advisory frequency. Only one LRU may transmit at a time, though several can listen. The messages transmitted are separated by timing signals to ensure proper sequencing of LRUs. In between messages there is a terminal gap (TG) and a synchronization gap (SG). Each time a message is sent, the TC starts a timing interval (TI) and does not send another message until the TI has expired, thus allowing other units to transmit.

Messages in ARINC 629 may contain up to 31 word strings. Each word string starts with a 12-bit label, followed by data of up to 16 bits with synchronization and parity bits in between.

ASCB

The *Avionics Standard Communication Bus* (ASCB) is used in corporate general aviation aircraft. The ASCB is a Manchester encoded, bidirectional bus operating at 0.667 MHz. ASCB uses +5 V for a logic one and 0 V for a logic 0. ASCB uses multiple bus controllers that request data. The bus itself is a 2-wire, 24-gauge shielded cable with limits on impedance and capacitance. The maximum length for an ASCB bus is 150 feet, with a maximum distance between LRUs of 36 inches.

The ASCB bus cable is terminated at each end with a 127 Ω resistance. The maximum capacitance allowed for the cable is 12 pF. LRUs are connected to the bus through transformer couplers, which induce or pick up current pulses on the bus. Bus wires are color coded white for low and tan for high. The connection between the bus and the transformer coupler is direct, with 30.1 Ω resistors connecting a transformer, as shown in Figure 8-10-5.

CSDB

The *Commercial Standard Digital Bus* (CSDB) is a General Aviation Manufacturer's Association (GAMA) standard and is also used in corporate general aviation aircraft. Like the ARINC 429 system, CSDB is a one-way bus, consisting of a twisted pair of 150 feet maximum length. The bus can operate at two speeds, 50 kbps or 12.5 kbps, and it can send data to 10 other LRUs. Bits are sent as a reversing polarity, as shown in Figure 8-10-6. Voltage levels range from 3 V to 5 V. Data on CSDB can be sent in three different formats, continuous repetition, non-continuous, and burst. CSDB data is sent in frames that are divided into blocks that are further divided into bytes consisting of a start bit, eight data bits, a parity bit, and a stop bit.

Databus Troubleshooting

Troubleshooting data buses can be accomplished with the use of a multimeter, oscilloscope, and a data bus analyzer. The multimeter is useful for testing continuity. The oscilloscope is useful for detecting distortion of the data, and the analyzer is important for encoding and decoding bus signals. A data bus analyzer can receive data transmissions and translate them into English. In addition, it can generate data bus messages. Table 8-10-2 lists common symptoms and possible causes.

Section 11

Load Analysis

When installing new equipment in an aircraft, a technician may be required to perform a load analysis. The general rule for load analysis is *continuous loads* on the generator or alternator may not exceed 80 percent of the generator or alternator capacity. This leaves 20 percent of generator or alternator capacity available to charge the battery. Continuous loads are those that last longer than two minutes. Any load with less than a two-minute duration is considered an *intermittent load*. The grand total of all loads, both continuous and intermittent, may be able to exceed 100 percent of generator or alternator capacity; however, this condition does not last more than two minutes, during which time the battery is able to supply the extra current.

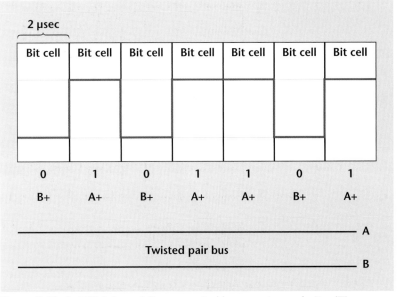

Figure 8-10-6. CSDB 1s and 0s are created by reversing polarity. (Time shown at high speed).

Section 12

Reduced Vertical Separation Minimums

Many aircraft are certified for flight in airspace using reduced vertical separation minimums (RVSM). The process of certifying these aircraft involves noting the errors in the flight data system within RVSM airspace, then using software to correct those errors.

Errors can be caused by loads on the static system, loads on the pitot system, ridges in paint, screws, and the shape of pitot tubes or static ports. Once certified, the aircraft has an RVSM critical area marked on the airframe.

No changes are allowed within that area. Furthermore, any damage in the RVSM critical area must be repaired before the aircraft can enter RVSM airspace.

If a technician performs any modification to the aircraft that impacts the static, pitot, or air data system, the aircraft must be checked to ensure that it still meets RVSM criteria. Technicians must be especially vigilant on RVSM certified aircraft, because there have been cases documented of external airframe modifications affecting altimeter accuracy, even though these modifications were outside of the RVSM critical area. A change in airflow over the airframe can cause changes in areas removed from the modification.

If installing equipment on an RVSM aircraft, work closely with the aircraft owner's director of maintenance.

Symptom	Known as	Possible reason	Notes
Loss of data parts	Drop outs	Loose connections	
Weak bus signal	Attenuation	Change of bus impedance	
Interference	Interference	Improper shielding	Other systems may not be shielded properly
Slow rise and fall times	Timing tolerance faults	Defective transmitter	

Table 8-10-2. Data bus symptoms and reasons.

Section 13

Paperwork

FAA Form 337

Installing avionics on an aircraft may trigger the requirement to submit an FAA Form 337: Major Repair and Alteration. An example is shown in Figure 8-13-1. Do not submit a 337 form unless it is determined that one is necessary. When filling out the form, complete blocks 1 and 2. When filling out block 4, remember that an alteration was made to an airframe. Often, students and novice technicians mistakenly fill out the appliance section of block 4. Leave the appliance section blank unless an LRU is modified, which is very unlikely.

In section 6 of Form 337, most avionics technicians include the name and address of the repair station under which they are performing the work. If the technician is an A & P mechanic, then he or she may fill out the form with his or her own name and address. In 6 B, mark the appropriate box. In 6 C, if the work was completed under the repair station certificate, put the repair station number there. If the work was completed by an A & P mechanic, then the individual's A&P certificate number should be written in.

Section 8 may not be large enough to describe the work completed. Be prepared to include drawings of the mechanical installation, the wiring diagram, and the weight and balance documentation by attaching additional documentation. If additional documents are attached, check the "Additional Sheets Are Attached" box at the bottom of Section 8.

At minimum in Section 8, the make, model, and serial number of all installed equipment must be noted. The technician must state by what authority the work was performed. In the example in Figure 8-13-1, the technician cited manufacturer's installation manuals, *FAA Advisory Circular 43.13-1A*, and *Advisory Circular 43.13-2A*. The technician also specified which paragraph numbers were used from the Advisory Circular.

State how the equipment was tested after it was installed to verify that it conforms to manufacturer's specifications and the federal aviation regulations. In this case, the technician cited the manufacturer's installation manuals, FAA Advisory Circular 30-138, paragraph 7, and FAR Part 43, Appendices E and F.

If flight manual supplements and instructions for continued airworthiness are required, state that they were included in the appropriate place. Finally, perform a load analysis to verify the electrical system does not exceed 80 percent of the useful load.

Instructions for Continued Airworthiness

If a new system is installed in an aircraft, then mechanics need instructions on how to inspect it. Technicians are required to supply the aircraft owner with instructions for continued airworthiness (ICA). Typically, installation manuals or STC manuals include an ICA for the technician to supply to the customer. If these instructions are not supplied, then at the next annual inspection or 100-hour inspection, there may not be any legal way for a mechanic to determine the airworthiness of the aircraft.

Flight Manual Supplements

If a new system is installed in an aircraft, then the pilot needs instructions on how to operate it. Technicians are required to supply the aircraft owner with a flight manual supplement (FMS).

Section 14

Antenna Installation

The installation of antennas on aircraft presents several challenges. The antenna must be structurally secure, free of obstructions, sealed against a harsh environment, and free from radio interference from other antennas. In some cases, meeting all of these requirements may be impossible on a small airframe. For example, avionics manufacturers design DME and ATC transponder systems with a suppression bus, which is used to disable one unit while the other is transmitting. In some cases, the suppression bus is the only way of preventing RF interference due to close antenna proximity.

Often avionics installation kits and manuals come with an antenna or with antenna specifications. Avionics installation technicians must use the supplied original equipment antenna or an antenna that meets the avionics specifications. Many antennas are passive. In other words, they are simply metal of the appropriate shape and act as a Marconi- or Hertzian-type radiator/receptor on the appropriate band of frequencies. Other antennas are active.

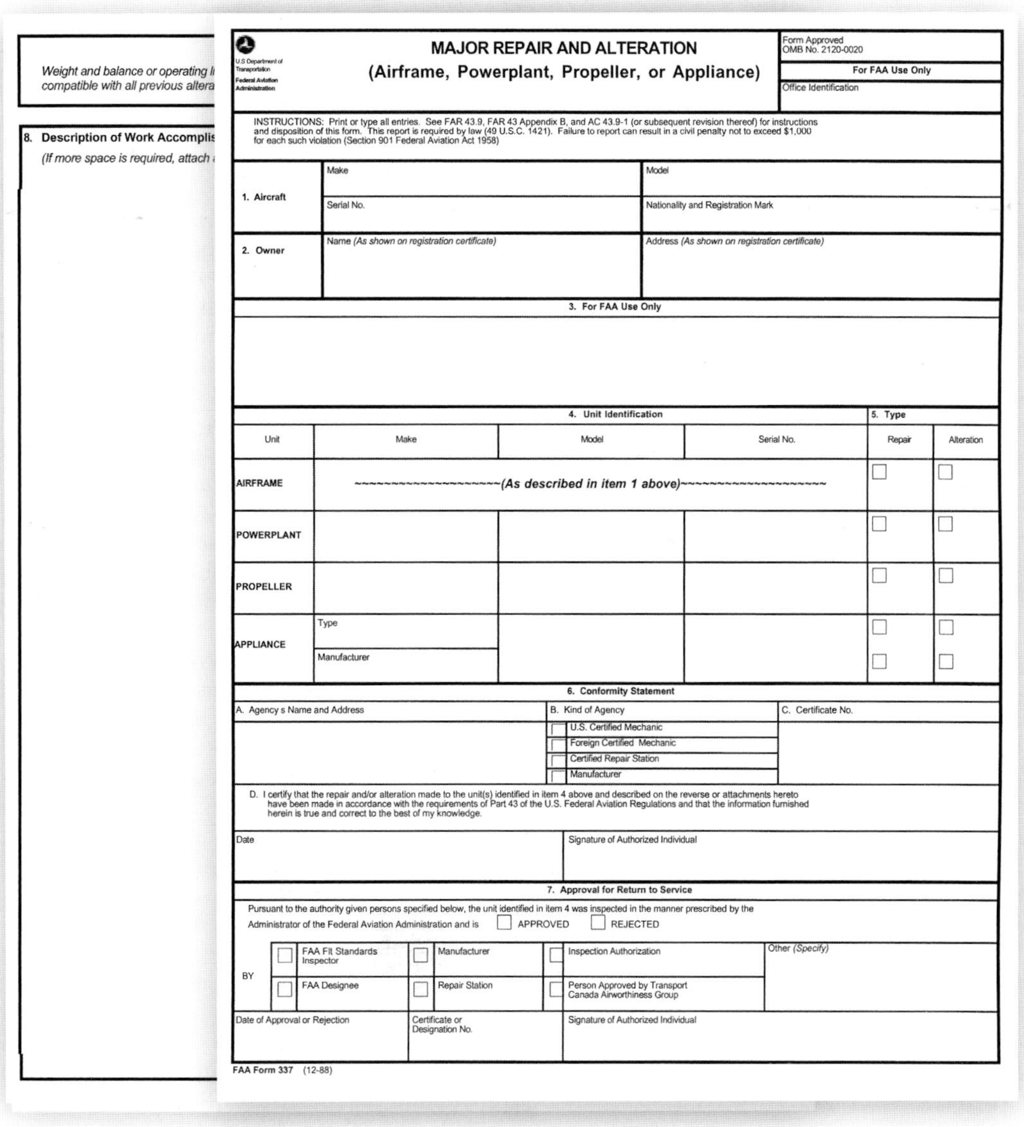

Weight and balance or operating li
compatible with all previous altera

8. Description of Work Accomplis
(If more space is required, attach a

U.S Department of Transportation
Federal Aviation Administration

MAJOR REPAIR AND ALTERATION
(Airframe, Powerplant, Propeller, or Appliance)

Form Approved
OMB No. 2120-0020

For FAA Use Only
Office Identification

INSTRUCTIONS: Print or type all entries. See FAR 43.9, FAR 43 Appendix B, and AC 43.9-1 (or subsequent revision thereof) for instructions and disposition of this form. This report is required by law (49 U.S.C. 1421). Failure to report can result in a civil penalty not to exceed $1,000 for each such violation (Section 901 Federal Aviation Act 1958)

1. Aircraft	Make	Model
	Serial No.	Nationality and Registration Mark
2. Owner	Name (As shown on registration certificate)	Address (As shown on registration certificate)

3. For FAA Use Only

4. Unit Identification				5. Type	
Unit	Make	Model	Serial No.	Repair	Alteration
AIRFRAME	~~~(As described in item 1 above)~~~			☐	☐
POWERPLANT				☐	☐
PROPELLER				☐	☐
APPLIANCE	Type			☐	☐
	Manufacturer			☐	☐

6. Conformity Statement

A. Agency s Name and Address	B. Kind of Agency	C. Certificate No.
	☐ U.S. Certified Mechanic ☐ Foreign Certified Mechanic ☐ Certified Repair Station ☐ Manufacturer	

D. I certify that the repair and/or alteration made to the unit(s) identified in item 4 above and described on the reverse or attachments hereto have been made in accordance with the requirements of Part 43 of the U.S. Federal Aviation Regulations and that the information furnished herein is true and correct to the best of my knowledge.

Date	Signature of Authorized Individual

7. Approval for Return to Service

Pursuant to the authority given persons specified below, the unit identified in item 4 was inspected in the manner prescribed by the Administrator of the Federal Aviation Administration and is ☐ APPROVED ☐ REJECTED

BY	☐ FAA Flt Standards Inspector	☐ Manufacturer	☐ Inspection Authorization	Other (Specify)
	☐ FAA Designee	☐ Repair Station	☐ Person Approved by Transport Canada Airworthiness Group	

Date of Approval or Rejection	Certificate or Designation No.	Signature of Authorized Individual

FAA Form 337 (12-88)

Figure 8-13-1. FAA Form 337.

Active antennas require a power supply and have built-in amplifiers or filters.

Antenna Specification Sheet

To ensure proper use and installation, aviation antenna manufacturers provide antenna specification sheets. The antenna specification sheet may cover more than one antenna, and it contains all pertinent information regarding the antenna. Technicians can expect to find the following information on an antenna specification sheet:

- Electrical characteristics including frequencies, polarization, DC and AC impedance, polarization, radiation pattern, transmitter power capability, and expected VSWR
- Mechanical characteristics including material, weight, height, shape, dimensions, and connector requirements
- Environmental limitations including temperature, altitude, and airspeed
- Federal specifications including Technical Standard Order information

Technicians may consult the antenna specification sheet to determine whether or not the antenna is appropriate for the system in use and also for troubleshooting purposes. In order to achieve an airworthy antenna installation, the following must be taken into consideration:

- Obstructions
- Spacing

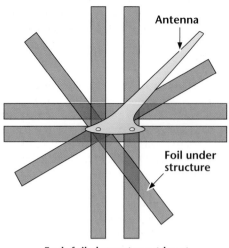

Figure 8-14-1. Counterpoise constructed for a fabric aircraft.

- Noise reception
- Vibration
- Flutter
- Static system interference

Antenna Obstructions and Spacing

In general, antennas must be placed in accordance with manufacturer's instructions and also where signal reception or transmission will not be obstructed. The location must not allow the antenna to be susceptible to interference from other antennas. If no guidance is provided by the equipment manufacturer, the general rule of thumb for antenna separation

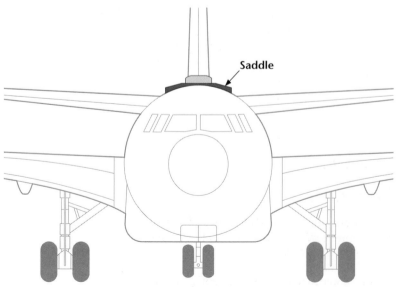

Figure 8-14-2. Antenna mounted with saddle.

is a minimum of 3 feet between VHF communication antennas. Separation between VHF communication and GNSS antennas should be at least 42 inches. Separation between DME antennas or between DME and ATC transponder antennas should be at least 6 feet.

VHF communication antennas must be located so there is a minimum of structure between the antenna and the ground-based radio station. If the aircraft has sufficient ground clearance, then the communication antenna may be located on the bottom of the fuselage. Since VHF communication antennas are of the Marconi type as described in Chapter 2, the base of the antenna must be electrically connected to the airframe in order to get a sufficient counterpoise. All antennas should be mounted as far as practical from sources of radio frequency noise, such as inverting power supplies and ignition systems.

For the most part, all antenna installations result in a compromise. For example, an electrically perfect HF antenna may range from approximately 8 feet to approximately 80 feet. The required counterpoise for such an antenna might be larger than the aircraft itself. As discussed in Chapter 2, the counterpoise is grounded to an area that balances the Marconi quarter wave antenna. In flight the airframe acts as ground. At frequencies in the HF range, the area required for a counterpoise is quite large. Most HF systems include an antenna coupler to electrically match an antenna that is too short. In other cases, usually military applications, a trailing wire antenna may be utilized. A trailing wire antenna has one end connected to the transceiver and the other end deployed out of the tail of the aircraft. The trailing wire antenna must be retracted during landing, takeoff, and ground operations.

Antennas should be located so that airflow is not obstructed to airframe areas requiring airflow. Furthermore, the antennas should not be located where heat from engine exhaust or vent fumes can damage the antennas. Since antennas may accumulate ice, attention must be paid to the airframe aft of the antenna. The antenna must not be located where departing ice could damage static ports, sensors, or flight controls. Antennas should be placed in a location where they cannot be misused as a hand or foot hold.

Surface Preparation

In order for antennas to operate properly as Marconi type or, in the case of VHF navigation, a balanced loop type antenna, the base of the antenna structure must have a very low impedance connection to the airframe. Antenna manufacturers may supply conductive gaskets to aid in this electrical connection. Before mounting, the surface between the antenna and the structure must be free of paint, primer, and corrosion. The technician should use an etching solution to ensure the aluminum surface is free from corrosion.

Composite and fabric-covered aircraft present an additional challenge since the aircraft surface material is not an electrical conductor. When installing an antenna on this type of airframe, the technician may need to build a counterpoise by bonding several lengths of metal foil on the inside surface of the structure, as shown in Figure 8-14-1.

In some composite aircraft, a layer of conductive material may be part of the outside structure. If this is the case, then the technician must ensure the base of the antenna makes contact with this conductive material. If not, then an aluminum grounding plate may be used as a counterpoise.

Structural Preparation

To prevent unacceptable vibration or flutter, the antenna must have an adequate mechanical installation. In most cases, the antenna manufacturer provides an adequate reinforcing plate, known as a *doubler plate*. If a doubler plate is not provided by the manufacturer, then its design and construction must be supervised and approved by a designated engineering representative (DER). The technician may have to calculate dynamic load because of aerodynamic drag and provide this information to the DER.

The approximate dynamic load can be determined by the following formula, in which:

D=drag load:

$D=0.000327\ AV2$

A=Frontal Area in ft^2

V=VNE in MPH

Antenna Specifications:

Frontal Area = 0.140 ft^2

VNE = 260 MPH

$D=0.000327\ X\ 0.140\ X\ 2602$

$D=0.000327\ X\ 0.140\ X\ 67,600$

$D=3.094728\ lbs$

The technician should be mindful of the fact a backing plate does not provide additional structural load support if it is not attached to the load carrying structure, such as a stringer or former.

Due to the stiffness of composite material, a tactile or visual inspection is not adequate to determine whether the material is of the appropriate strength for an antenna installation. When working with a composite aircraft, the manufacturer must be consulted regarding any modification to the aircraft skin.

Antennas should be mounted on a flat surface, whenever possible. Gaskets can compensate for a small amount of curvature, but if the curvature is too great, a mounting saddle should be used between the antenna and the aircraft structure, as shown in Figure 8-14-2.

Mounting and Sealing of Antennas

Many antenna installations use countersunk or panhead stainless steel mounting screws of sizes No. 8-32 or No. 10-32 in lengths that will vary depending on the situation. The technician should use stainless steel nuts with flat washers and lock washers or flat washers and locking nuts to properly secure the antenna. Torque values for No. 8-32 screws cannot exceed 20 in.lbs. Torque values for No. 10-32 screws cannot exceed 23 in.lbs.

Once the antenna is mounted, the gaps between the antenna, base plate, gasket, or skin should be filled with RTV silicone sealant to prevent moisture from getting trapped between the antenna and the aircraft skin. Some WAAS enabled GPS systems are extremely sensitive to the amount of sealant surrounding the base of the antenna. The antenna must be able to receive signals at a very low elevation angle. Even a small amount of sealant can block reception. Always become thoroughly familiar with the installation requirements of any antenna system.

Section 15

Summary

Installations and integrations must be carefully planned, taking into consideration, space, load, and operability.

Avionics come in many different configurations and are attached to the airframe in a variety of ways. Panel mounted LRUs may mount with mounting pawls, screws, or Dzus fasteners. Prior to installation the proper wire must be selected and prepared by stripping. Wires may be single, shielded, or shielded pairs, among others. Many MIL specifications cover wiring for aircraft, and all wires are stranded. Do not confuse coaxial cable with shielded wire. Wire may be cut with diagonal cutters, a circular saw with a cable cutting blade, cable shear, or even a hack saw. Wires should be identified by printing a set of numbers on the insulation, or with sleeves.

Once the wire is selected and cut, it should be stripped using strippers with dies cut so they won't damage the wire strands. Aluminum wire of all sizes and other wires No. 12 and smaller must not have any strands nicked or broken. Shielded cable must be properly terminated by attaching a ground lead or by dead ending. The ground lead may be attached with a crimped ferrule, by twisting the shield onto a ground jumper wire, or with a special heat shrink tube with solder and a jumper integrated within.

AN and MS connectors are available in a variety of sizes and types, including miniatures. Light duty connectors are also available in a wide variety of sizes and types; however, light duty connectors may not be used in areas critical to the safety of flight. Connectors include a plug, receptacle, contacts, inserts, and a method of strain relief. AN-MS connectors are available in six different classes. The class selected by the technician depends on the duty the connector is to perform. The part number of AN-MS connectors identifies the type, class, size, insert arrangement, contact style, and insert rotation. Contacts may be of solder or crimp type; however, fireproof connectors cannot have solder type contacts.

Solder-type connectors rely on the technician's skill to properly make the connection. A quality soldering job relies on wetting action, which is the combining of the two metals—wire and contact—into one continuous metal alloy. Wetting action cannot take place on a corroded surface. Rosin helps to remove small amounts of corrosion. Heat control is critical in soldering operations. Most solders have a plastic zone between complete liquidity, and solid. If the wire moves while the temperature of the solder is in the plastic zone, then a defective solder joint will result. A good solder joint is free from pits or cracks and has a smooth, shiny, and symmetrical appearance.

To properly attach wires to crimp-type connectors, the technician must use the appropriate crimping tool. Furthermore, the wire must be stripped to the appropriate length. Various tools may be necessary to install or remove the contacts in a crimp-type connector.

RF connectors come in a variety of shapes and sizes. The most common are BNC and TNC connectors. RF connectors may be of the solder and clamp type or of the crimp type. Special care must be taken not to pinch or otherwise damage the coaxial cable while installing an RF connector. Always perform a continuity test on the connector, after it has been installed.

Bonding and grounding of various parts of the airframe protects personnel and equipment from lightning. Furthermore, it reduces electrical noise, which could cause malfunctions. The technician must use the appropriate hardware for bonding and grounding to avoid corrosion and ensure a good electrical connection. Once the bonding or grounding operation is completed, the connection must be checked with a special Ohmmeter.

Electrical power is supplied from bus bars. The technician must select hardware and terminals carefully to ensure a strong mechanical connection that will also be electrically sound and avoid corrosion.

Wire bundles may be installed in conduit. Conduit must be properly supported and free from stress. Furthermore, it must be mounted where it will not be used as a hand or foothold. The low point in the conduit must be able to drain off condensation. Wire bundles inside conduit should not take up more than 80 percent of the available space. Soapstone talc can act as an aid to feeding wires through conduit.

Wire outside of conduit is considered open wiring and may be in groups or bundles. A bundle may contain two or more groups of wires. Unprotected wiring is not supplied power through a fuse or circuit breaker. All other wiring is protected. Wire groups and bundles should be neatly straightened and then laced or tied as appropriate. Technicians may use single- or double-cord lacing if the wire bundle is within a panel or junction box. Otherwise, bundles must be tied.

Open wiring must be supported, protected from fluids, and protected from chafing. Enough slack should be provided to allow servicing. MS21919 clamps are appropriate for bundle support, but they must be properly installed to avoid undue stress to the mounting hardware.

Connectors and hardware may be lock, shear, or seal wired. Wire twisting safety wire pliers act as an aid to double twist lock wiring. Lock or shear wiring must be installed so loosening of the hardware will tighten the wire. Seal wire must remain loose enough to be broken in an emergency.

Three types of devices protect wiring. They include fuses, current limiters, and circuit breakers. Current limiters may take overloads for short periods of time, and are installed in high current circuits. Fuses and circuit breakers come in a variety of types, and the technician must select the appropriate fuse or breaker based on size, shape, and amperage value.

All avionics are integrated to some degree. Standards exist for audio systems and navigation systems. Technicians must ensure compatibility when integrating various systems. There are several parallel channeling standards and several serial channeling standards, including data buses.

Data bus systems may be voltage or current based, and they may be one-way or bidirectional. Although only ARINC 429, ARINC 629, ASCB, and CSDB were discussed in this textbook, there are many others.

When installing a system on an RVSM-certified aircraft, special attention must be given to find out if the new system will affect the RVSM error budget and correction system.

Antennas must be installed in a structurally secure manner and in a way that they do not interfere with other antennas and in a location where they can receive the necessary signals.

If an installation is considered a major alteration, then an FAA Form 337 must be filled out and sent to the FAA for approval. Most installations require a flight manual supplement and instructions for continued airworthiness.

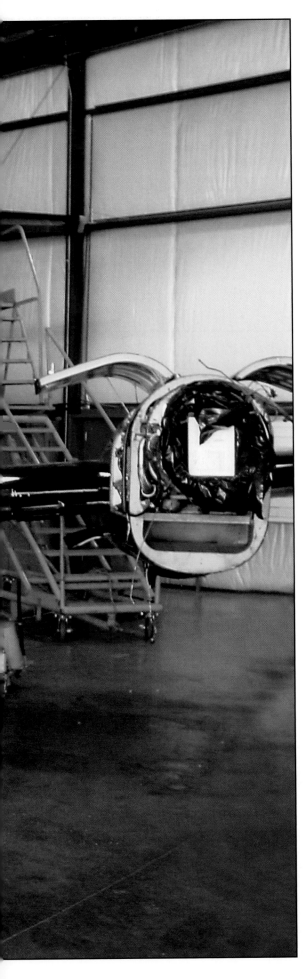

9

Aircraft Weight and Balance

Section 1

The Importance of Weight and Balance

The subject of weight and balance has been a concern of aircraft designers and manufacturers since the earliest aircraft were flown. If the aircraft is too heavy or the weight is not properly distributed, the aircraft may not fly, or if the aircraft does fly, its flight characteristics may be adversely affected.

In theory, all of the weight of the aircraft is concentrated at one point, which is referred to as the center of gravity (CG). In order for the aircraft to perform properly, a relationship between the weight forces and the aerodynamic forces must be established to ensure safe operation.

Problems

Problems concerning the weight and balance of an aircraft fall into three categories: over maximum weight, too much weight forward, too much weight aft. Any of these conditions will have an adverse effect on the aircraft's flight characteristics.

If the aircraft is overloaded, the following conditions will occur:

- More runway is needed.
- A lower climb angle and high speed is required.
- Structural safety factors are reduced.
- Stalling speeds are increased.
- More engine power is required.

Left. The equipment necessary for weighing the aircraft will vary with the type of aircraft being weighed.

If the aircraft has too much weight forward, the following conditions will occur:

- The aircraft will have a tendency to dive.
- Stability is decreased.
- Adverse spin characteristics.
- More engine power is required.

If the aircraft has too much weight aft, the following conditions will occur:

- Flying speed is decreased.
- Stall characteristics occur more readily.
- Stability is decreased.
- Adverse spin characteristics.
- More engine power is required.

Any of these conditions can result in the loss of the aircraft and loss of life. For these reasons, it is very important that the aircraft technician and the pilot have a thorough understanding of weight and balance.

Empty Weight Determination

The empty weight and the corresponding CG of all civil aircraft must be determined at the time of certification. The manufacturer can weigh the aircraft or compute the weight and balance report. A manufacturer is permitted to weigh one aircraft out of each ten produced. The remaining nine aircraft are issued a computed weight and balance report based on the averaged figures of aircraft that are actually weighed. The condition of the aircraft at the time of determining empty weight must be one that is well defined so that loading requirements can be easily computed.

Need for Reweighing

Aircraft have a tendency to gain weight because of the accumulation of dirt, greases, etc., in areas not readily accessible for washing and cleaning. The weight gained in any given period of time will depend on the function of the aircraft, its hours in flight, atmospheric conditions, and the type landing field from which it is operating. For this reason, periodic aircraft weighings are desirable and, in the case of air carrier and air taxi aircraft, are required by Federal Aviation Regulations (FARs). An aircraft may also need to be reweighed if the aircraft's weight and balance records are lost, destroyed, or if there is reason to believe they are inaccurate.

Privately owned and operated aircraft are not required by regulation to be weighed periodically. They are usually weighed when originally certificated, or after making major repairs or alterations that can affect the weight and balance. Even though the aircraft need not be weighed, it must be mathematically loaded so that the maximum weight and CG limits are not exceeded during operation.

Air carrier and air taxi aircraft (scheduled and nonscheduled) carrying passengers or cargo are subject to certain rules that require owners to show that the aircraft is properly loaded and will not exceed the authorized weight and balance limitations during operation.

Section 2

Principles of Weight and Balance

Weight and Balance Theory

The theory of weight and balance is extremely simple. It is that of the familiar lever that is in equilibrium, or balance, when it rests on the fulcrum in a level position. The influence of weight is directly dependent upon its distance from the fulcrum. To balance the lever, the weight must be distributed so that the turning effect is the same on one side of the fulcrum as on the other. In general, a lighter weight far out on the lever has the same effect as a heavy weight near the fulcrum.

The distance of any object from the fulcrum is called the lever arm. The lever arm multiplied by the weight of the object is its turning effect about the fulcrum. This turning effect is known as the moment. (Figure 9-2-1.) In this figure, note that although the two weights are different, they balance because of the difference in the distance of the arms of the fulcrum.

An aircraft is balanced if it would remain level when suspended from an imaginary point. This point is the location of its ideal CG. To obtain this balance is simply a matter of placing loads so that the average arm of the loaded aircraft falls within the CG range. The exact location of the range is specified for each type of airplane.

Because fuel and other items are consumed, passengers and crew may move about, and for various other reasons, an aircraft cannot remain in perfect balance during flight. For this reason, a safe range of CG travel is established by the manufacturer.

Mathematical proof. Weight and balance control consists of mathematical proof of the correct

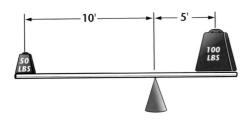

Figure 9-2-1. Balance may change by changing weights or the fulcrum points.

weight, balance, and loading within specified limits. These limits are set forth in the specifications for a particular aircraft. The removal or addition of equipment changes the aircraft empty weight and the CG. The useful load is affected accordingly. The effects that these changes produce on the balance of an aircraft must be investigated to determine the effect on the flight characteristics of the aircraft.

Weight and balance data. Weight and balance data can be obtained from the following sources:

- The Aircraft Specifications or Type Certificate Data Sheet
- The aircraft operating limitations
- The aircraft flight manual
- The aircraft weight and balance report

When weight and balance records have been lost and cannot be duplicated from any source, the aircraft must be reweighed. A new set of weight and balance records must be computed and compiled.

Terms Used in Weight and Balance

Before any study of weight and balance can begin, the following terms must be fully understood:

Datum. The datum is an imaginary vertical plane from which all horizontal measurements for balance purposes are taken with the aircraft in level flight attitude. It is a plane at right angles to the longitudinal axis of the aircraft. For each aircraft make and model, all locations of equipment, tanks, baggage compartments, seats, engines, propellers, etc., are listed in the Aircraft Specification or Type Certificate Data Sheets (TCDS) as being so many inches from the datum.

There is no fixed rule for the location of the datum. In some cases, it is located on the nose of the aircraft or some point on the aircraft structure itself. In most cases, it is located a certain distance forward of the nose section of

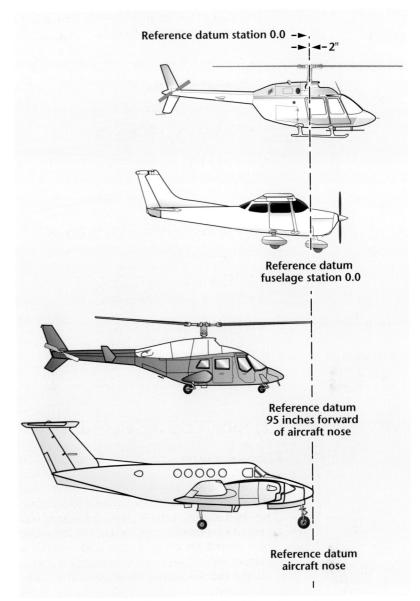

Figure 9-2-2. Reference datums chosen by different manufacturers.

the aircraft. The manufacturer has the choice of locating the datum where it is most convenient for measurement, locating equipment, and weight-and-balance computation.

The datum location is indicated on most aircraft specifications. On some of the older aircraft, where the datum is not indicated, any convenient datum may be selected. However, once the datum is selected, it must be properly identified so that anyone who reads the figures will have no doubt about the exact datum location. Figure 9-2-2 shows some datum locations used by manufacturers.

Arm. The arm is the horizontal distance that an item of equipment is located from the datum. The arm's distance is always given or measured in inches and, except for a location that might be exactly on the datum (0), it is preceded by the algebraic sign for plus (+) or minus (–).

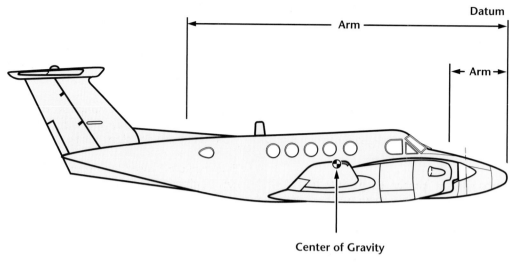

Figure 9-2-3. Reference datum line.

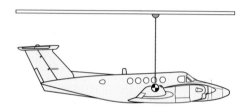

Figure 9-2-4. An airplane suspended from its center of gravity.

The plus (+) sign indicates a distance aft of the datum and the minus (–) sign indicates a distance forward of the datum.

If the manufacturer chooses a datum that is at the most forward location on an aircraft (or some distance forward of the aircraft), all the arms will be plus (+), or aft, of the datum, and few, if any, arms will be minus (–), or forward, of the datum (Figure 9-2-3).

The arm of each item is usually included in parentheses immediately after the item's name or weight in the specifications for the aircraft, (e.g., seat [+23]). When such information is not given, it must be obtained by actual measurement.

The following terminology is used in the practical application of weight and balance control, and should be thoroughly studied.

Aircraft leveling. Reference points are provided for leveling the aircraft on the ground. They are designated by the manufacturer and are indicated in the pertinent Aircraft Specifications or TCDS. The most common leveling procedure is to place a spirit level at designated points on the aircraft structure. Some aircraft have special leveling scales built into the airframe structure. The scale is used with a plumb bob to level the aircraft longitudinally and laterally.

Balance point. The balance point is the point at which the nose-heavy moments and the tail-heavy moments are of equal magnitude. This point may also be known as the center of gravity (CG) (Figure 9-2-4).

Ballast. Ballast is any weight added to the aircraft used to bring the CG within a desirable range. This weight may be permanent or it may be temporary. Ballast is often in the form of lead and should be marked as such. Permanent ballast is often used on helicopters and is placed in the nose or the tail to minimize the weight. Temporary ballast is usually used for a specific loading problem to obtain the desired CG.

Center of gravity. The CG of an aircraft is a point about which the nose-heavy and tail-heavy moments are exactly equal in magnitude. An aircraft suspended from this point would have no tendency to rotate in either a nose-up or nose-down attitude. It is the point about which the weight of an airplane or any object is concentrated. The CG location is measured from the datum.

Empty weight. The empty weight of an aircraft includes all operating equipment that has a fixed location and is actually installed in the aircraft. It includes the weight of the airframe, powerplant, required equipment, optional or special equipment, fixed ballast, hydraulic fluid, and residual fuel and oil.

Residual fuel and oil are the fluids that will not normally drain out because they are trapped in the fuel lines, oil lines, and tanks.

Aircraft type certified under FAR Part 23 after March 1, 1978, require that all operating fluids be included in the empty weight including full oil. Information regarding fluids that will be included in the empty weight or are residual will be given in the Aircraft Specifications or TCDS for the specific aircraft.

Basic weight. Basic weight is a weight determined by the manufacturer. It typically consists of weighing every tenth aircraft prior to adding any optional equipment. The optional equipment is then added mathematically. Do not confuse the basic weight with the empty weight.

Empty-weight center of gravity (EWCG). The EWCG is the CG of an aircraft in its empty weight condition. It is an essential part of the weight and balance record of the aircraft. It has no usefulness in itself, but serves as a basis for other computations and not as an indication of what the loaded CG will be. The EWCG is computed at the time of weighing, using formulas established for tailwheel- and nosewheel-type aircraft.

Empty-weight center of gravity (EWCG) range. The EWCG range is an allowable variation of travel within the CG limits. When the EWCG of the aircraft falls within this range, it is impossible to exceed the EWCG limits using standard specification loading arrangements. Not all aircraft have this range indicated on the Aircraft Specifications or TCDS. Where it is indicated, the range is valid only as long as the aircraft is loaded according to the standard specification. The installation of items not listed in the specification will not permit use of this range.

Full oil. Full oil is the quantity of oil shown as oil capacity in the Aircraft Specifications or TCDS. When weighing an aircraft, the oil tank should contain either the number of gallons of oil specified or be drained. When an aircraft with full oil tanks is weighed, the weight of the oil must be subtracted from the recorded readings to arrive at the actual empty weight. The weight and balance report must show whether weights include full oil or if the oil tanks were drained.

Lateral center-of-gravity formula. This formula is used most often on helicopter applications where the lateral CG is computed as well as the longitudinal CG.

$$CG = \frac{(AL \times C) + (BR \times D)}{W}$$

Where:
W = Weight of aircraft
AL = Butt Measurement Left
BR = Butt Measurement Right
C = Weight of Main Scale Left
D = Weight of Main Scale Right

Left Butt Line is Negative
Right Butt Line is Positive

Longitudinal center-of-gravity formulas. Two different types of formulas are used in the computation of the longitudinal CG.

The first of these is the simplest. However, it may be subject to errors due to the fact that the plus (+) or minus (-) sign may be confused.

This formula is used almost exclusively when new equipment is added to the aircraft.

$$CG = \frac{Total\,moment}{Total\,weight}$$

Other formulas used for longitudinal center of gravity are often used for the original weighing of the aircraft and are contained in AC 43.13-1B.

$$CG = D - \left(\frac{F \times L}{W}\right) = \begin{array}{l}\text{Nosewheel with datum}\\ \text{forward of the main wheels}\end{array}$$

$$CG = -\left(D + \frac{F \times L}{W}\right) = \begin{array}{l}\text{Nosewheel with datum aft of}\\ \text{the main wheels}\end{array}$$

$$CG = D + \left(\frac{R \times L}{W}\right) = \begin{array}{l}\text{Tailwheel with datum}\\ \text{forward of the main wheels}\end{array}$$

$$CG = -D + \left(\frac{R \times L}{W}\right) = \begin{array}{l}\text{Tailwheel with datum aft of}\\ \text{the main wheels}\end{array}$$

Where:
W = Weight of aircraft
D = Distance from datum to the main wheel weighing point
L = Distance from the main wheel weighing point to the nosewheel or tailwheel weighing point
F = Weight at the nosewheel weighing point
R = Weight at the tailwheel weighing point

Straight line variation between points. Straight line variation between points is a term often used to describe a weight and balance shift within the envelope. It means that a shift forward of the actual CG has the same effect as an equal shift aft of the actual CG (i.e., the variation is in equal percentages and varies in a straight line).

Maximum weight. The maximum weight is the maximum authorized weight of the aircraft and its contents and is indicated in the specifications. For many aircraft, there are variations to the maximum allowable weight, depending on the purpose and conditions under which the aircraft is to be flown.

For example, a certain aircraft may be allowed a maximum gross weight of 2,750 pounds when flown in the normal category, but when flown in the utility category, the same maximum allowable gross weight would be 2,175 pounds.

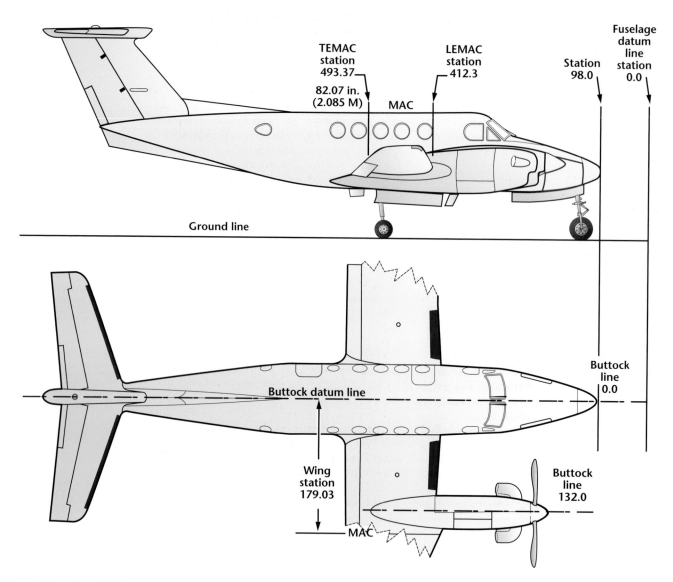

Figure 9-2-5. The MAC for a taper-winged aircraft.

Many transport category aircraft have other maximum weights, which include maximum landing weight, maximum ramp weight, and maximum takeoff weight. Their definitions are:

- Maximum landing weight is the maximum weight that the aircraft can land. This is usually less than the maximum takeoff weight due to the structural loads placed on the aircraft during landing.

- Maximum ramp weight is usually greater than the maximum takeoff weight. The weight difference between ramp weight and takeoff weight is fuel burned during taxi to the runway.

- Maximum takeoff weight is the maximum weight at which the aircraft can start its takeoff on the runway.

Mean Aerodynamic Chord (MAC). The MAC is the mean average chord of the wing.

An airfoil section is a cross section of a wing from leading edge to trailing edge. A chord is usually defined as an imaginary straight line drawn parallel to the airfoil through the leading and trailing edges of the section. The MAC of a constant-chord wing would be the same as the actual chord of the wing. Any departure from a rectangular wing planform will affect the length of the MAC and the resulting distance from the MAC leading edge to the aircraft's wing leading edge. Figure 9-2-5 shows the MAC for a taper-winged aircraft.

The aircraft CG is usually placed at the maximum forward position of the center of pressure on the MAC to obtain the desired stability. Because of the relationship between the CG location and the moments produced by aerodynamic forces, the greatest of which is lift, the CG location is generally expressed with respect to the wing. This is done by specifying CG in percent of the wing's MAC.

The leading or trailing edge of the wing is used along with the reference datum line to determine MAC. The leading edge of the MAC is usually referred to as the LEMAC and the trailing edge is referred to as the TEMAC.

The location of the MAC, in relation to the datum, is given in the Aircraft Specifications or Type Certificate Data Sheets, the weight and balance report, or the aircraft flight manual.

Minimum fuel. The term minimum fuel should not be interpreted to mean the minimum amount of fuel required to fly an aircraft. Minimum fuel, as it applies to weight and balance, is the amount of fuel that must be shown on the weight and balance report when the airplane is loaded for an extreme-condition check.

The minimum fuel load for a small aircraft with a reciprocating engine for balance purposes is based on engine horsepower. It is calculated in the maximum except takeoff (METO) horsepower and is the figure used when the fuel load must be reduced to obtain the most critical loading on the CG limit being investigated. Either of two formulas may be used:

Minimum fuel = 1/12 gallons per horsepower
hp × 1/12 × 6 lb
1,200 × 1/12 × 6 = 1,200 × 1/2 = 600 lb fuel

Minimum fuel = 1/2 lb per engine horsepower
hp × 1/2 = minimum fuel
1,200 × 1/2 = 600 lb fuel

This will be the minimum pounds of fuel required for the forward or rearward weight check.

For turbine-engine-powered aircraft, the minimum fuel load is specified by the aircraft manufacturer.

The fuel tank location in relation to the CG limit affected by the computation determines the use of minimum fuel. For example, when a forward weight check is performed, if the fuel tanks are located forward of the forward CG limit, they are assumed to be full. If the minimum fuel required for a particular aircraft exceeds the capacity of the tanks located forward of the forward CG limit, the excess fuel must be loaded in the tanks that are aft of the forward CG limit. When a rearward weight check is conducted, the fuel loading conditions are opposite to those used for the forward check.

Moment. A moment is the product of a weight multiplied by its arm.

The moment of an item about the datum is obtained by multiplying the weight of the item by its horizontal distance from the datum.

Likewise, the moment of an item about the CG can be computed by multiplying its weight by the horizontal distance from the CG.

A 20-pound weight located 30 inches from the datum would have a moment of 20 × 30 or 600 lb-in. Whether the value of 600 lb.-in. is preceded by a plus (+) or minus (–) sign depends on the relationship of the arm to the datum.

Moment index. The moment index is the moment reduced by 10,000, 1,000, or 100 for ease in balance calculations, and it is often shown as MOM/1000 or MOM × 100.

Operating CG range. The operating CG range is the distance between the forward and rearward CG limits indicated in the pertinent Aircraft Specification or TCDS.

Determined at the time of design and manufacture, these limits are the extreme loaded CG positions allowable within the applicable regulations controlling the design of the aircraft. They are shown in either percent of MAC or inches from the datum of the aircraft.

The loaded aircraft CG location must remain within these limits at all times. Accordingly, detailed instructions for determining load distribution are provided on placards, loading charts, and load adjusters.

Standard weights. Standard weights used in weight and balance computations are as follows:

Aviation gasoline .... 6.0 pounds per gallon
Turbine fuel .... 6.7 pounds per gallon
Oil .... 7.5 pounds per gallon
Water .... 8.35 pounds per gallon
Crew and passengers ...... 170 pounds per person

Additional FAR Part 135 Standard Weights are:

Adults .... 160 (summer) per person
Adults .... 165 (winter) per person
Children .... 80 pounds per person
Crew other than
flight attendants .... 170 pounds per person
Female flight attendants . 130 pounds per person
Male flight attendants ..... 150 pounds per person
Check-in baggage .... 23.5 pounds per item
Carry-on baggage .... 10 pounds per item

Station. A station is any longitudinal location on the aircraft measured from the datum or a lateral wing point measured from butt line 0. Stations are normally measured in inches, with the least measurement usually 0.50 inches. It is not, however, unusual to find measurements as low as 0.05 inches.

Tare weight. Tare includes the weight of all extra items on the weighing scale platform that are not a part of the item being weighed, such as jacks, blocks, and chocks. The weight of these items, when included in the scale reading, is deducted to obtain the actual weight of the aircraft.

Unusable fuel. The unusable fuel is the fuel left in the fuel system, which cannot be consumed by the engine. This amount is usually given in the Aircraft Specifications or Type Certificate Data Sheets.

Undrainable oil. Undrainable oil is the oil that remains trapped in the oil system when the oil is drained.

Useful load. The useful load of an aircraft is determined by subtracting the empty weight from the maximum allowable gross weight. For aircraft certificated in both the normal and utility categories, there may be two useful loads listed in the aircraft weight and balance records.

An aircraft with an empty weight of 900 pounds will have a useful load of 850 pounds, if the normal category maximum weight is listed as 1,750 pounds. When the aircraft is operated in the utility category, the maximum gross weight may be reduced to 1,500 pounds, with a corresponding decrease in the useful load to 600 pounds. Some aircraft have the same useful load regardless of the category in which they are certificated.

The useful load consists of full oil, fuel, passengers, baggage, pilot, copilot, and crewmembers. A reduction in the weight of an item, where possible, may be necessary to remain within the maximum weight allowed for the category in which an aircraft is operating. Determining the distribution of these weights is called a weight check.

For aircraft type certified under FAR Part 23 after March 1, 1978, oil is not included in the useful load. Full oil is considered part of the empty weight of the aircraft.

Weighing points. In weighing an aircraft, the point on the scale at which the weight is concentrated is called the weighing point.

When weighing light- to medium-weight aircraft, the wheels are usually placed on the scales. This means that the weighing point is, in effect, the same location obtained by extending a vertical line through the centerline of the axle and onto the scale.

Other structural locations capable of supporting the aircraft, such as jack pads on the main spar, may also be used if the aircraft weight is resting on the jack pads. The weighing points should be clearly indicated in the weight and balance report.

Zero fuel weight. The zero fuel weight is the maximum allowable weight of a loaded aircraft without fuel. Included in the zero fuel weight is the weight of cargo, passengers, and crew. All weights in excess of the zero fuel weight must consist of usable fuel.

Section 3
Aircraft Weighing Procedures

Preparation for Weighing

Before any weighing can begin, it is necessary to become familiar with the pertinent data available concerning the weight and balance of the particular aircraft. This information will be found in the FAA documentation and the manufacturer's manuals and would include:

- Aircraft Specifications
- Type Certificate Data Sheet
- Manufacturer's maintenance manual (MM)

The Type Certificate Data Sheet and the Aircraft Specifications contain basically the same information. However, the Aircraft Specifications have more detail concerning optional approved equipment and their arms and weight. This information is now furnished by the manufacturer on aircraft that have a Type Certificate Data Sheet. In both documents, the following pertinent information can be found:

- CG range
- Empty weight CG range
- Leveling means
- Maximum weight
- Seats and location
- Baggage capacity
- Fuel capacity
- Datum location

Figure 9-3-1 is an excerpt of a typical type certificate data sheet. Much of the information necessary to perform the weighing and computations are self-explanatory. However, a few do need some explanations.

Looking at the top block of the Type Certificate Data Sheet, several aircraft are included in the same data sheet. Even though there is a large number of aircraft, it is not unusual that multiple variations of the same aircraft are manufactured

DEPARTMENT OF TRANSPORTATION
FEDERAL AVIATION ADMINISTRATION

	3A19
	Revision 35
	CESSNA
150	150J
150A	150K
150B	A150K
150C	150L
150D	A150L
150E	150M
150F	A150M
150G	152
150H	A152
	August 15, 1980

TYPE CERTIFICATE DATA SHEET NO. 3A19

This data sheet which is part of Type Certificate No. 3A19 prescribes conditions and limitations under which the product for which the type of certificate was issued meets the airworthiness requirements of the Federal Aviation Regulations.

Type Certificate Holder

Cessna Aircraft Company
Pawnee Division
Wichita, Kansas 67201

IX - Model 152,2 PCLM (Utility Category) Approved March 16, 1977

Engine	Lycoming 0-235-L2C
Fuel	100LL/100 min. grade aviation gasoline
Engine Limits	For all operations 2550 rpm. (110 hp.)
C.G. Range	(+32.65) to (+36.5) 1670 lb. (+31.0) to (+36.5) at 1350 lb. or less Straight line variation between points given.
Empty Wt. C.G. Range	None
Leveling Means	Jig located nut plates and screws at Stations (+94.63) and (+132.94) on left side of tailcone
*Maximum Weight	1670 lb. 1675 lb. ramp weight (S/N 15282032 and on)
No. of Seats	2 at (+39); (for child's optional jump seat, refer to Equipment List)
Maximum Baggage	120 lb. (Reference Weight and balance data)
Fuel Capacity	26 gal. (24.5 gal usable two 13 gal. tanks in wings at +42.0) See NOTE 1 for data on usable fuel.
Oil Capacity	6qt. (-14.7; unusable 2 qt.) See NOTE 1 for data on undrainable oil

Data Pertinent to All Models

Datum	Fuselage station 0.0 front face of firewall

Note 1.   Current weight and balance report together with list of equipment included in certificated empty weight and loading instructions when neccessary must be provide for each aircraft at time of original certification.

Serial Nos. 15077006 through 15079405 and A1500610 through A1500734.
The certificated empty weight and corresponding center of gravity location must include unusable fuel of 21 lb. at (+40) and full oil of 11.3 lb. at (-13.5) for landplane.

Serial Nos. 15279406 through 1520735 and A1520735 and on.
The certificated empty weight and corresponding center of gravity location must include unusable fuel of 9 lb. at (+40) and full oil of 11.3 lb. at (-14.7) for landplane.

Figure 9-3-1. Typical Type Certificate Data Sheet.

under the same Aircraft Specification or data sheet.

When several models are covered on one data sheet, the pertinent information for a particular model is listed in one area, as shown in Figure 9-3-1. The information includes the facts such as the CG range and empty CG range. On some aircraft, no empty CG range is given. This is due to the use of a loading graph by the pilot to determine if the aircraft is loaded properly. In this case, the only CG range given is the loaded CG range. However, not all aircraft make use of a loading graph like the one described.

Additional information needed for weighing the aircraft includes the leveling means. During the actual weighing process, the aircraft must be level. The maximum weight may include a ramp weight, which is heavier than the maximum weight. This additional weight would be lost prior to takeoff due to fuel consumed during engine runup and taxiing.

Both the fuel and oil capacity refer to Note 1. These give different specifications for different serial numbered aircraft. It might be noted that the later serial numbered aircraft include full oil in the empty weight.

Some data is pertinent to all models covered by the data sheet. One of these items is the datum, which is located at the firewall of the aircraft. Other information, such as the location of seats, may have value in a loading investigation. Information such as loading charts and equipment will be found in the operator's manual for the aircraft.

Weighing an aircraft is a very important and exacting phase of aircraft maintenance and must be carried out with accuracy. Thoughtful preparation saves time and prevents mistakes.

Preparation of the aircraft. The first step in preparing the aircraft for weighing is to thoroughly clean the aircraft. The dirt, which is spread over a large area, can add to the total weight of the aircraft.

Drain the fuel system until the quantity indication reads zero or empty with the aircraft in a level attitude. If any fuel is left in the tanks the aircraft will weigh more, and all later calculations for useful load and balance will be affected. Only trapped or unusable fuel (residual fuel) is considered part of the aircraft's empty weight. Fuel tank caps should be on the tanks or placed as close as possible to their correct locations, so that the weight distribution will be correct.

In special cases, the aircraft may be weighed with the fuel tanks full, provided a means of determining the exact weight of the fuel is available. Consult the aircraft manufacturer's instructions to determine whether a particular model aircraft would be weighed with full fuel or with the fuel drained.

Before draining oil from the aircraft, the Aircraft Specifications should be checked to determine if the tanks should be full or empty. If the engine oil is not included, drain all engine oil from the oil tanks. The system should be drained with all drain valves open. Under these conditions, the amount of oil remaining in the oil tank, lines, and engine is termed residual oil and is included in the empty weight. If impractical to drain, the oil tanks should be completely filled and the weight of the oil computed.

The position of items such as spoilers, slats, flaps, and helicopter rotor systems is an important factor when weighing an aircraft. Always refer to the manufacturer's instructions for the proper position of these items.

Unless otherwise noted in the Aircraft Specifications or manufacturer's instructions, hydraulic reservoirs and systems should be filled, drinking and washing water reservoirs and lavatory tanks should be drained, and constant-speed-drive oil tanks should be filled.

Inspect the aircraft to see that all items included in the certificated empty weight are installed in the proper location. Remove items that are not regularly carried in flight. Also look in the baggage compartments to make sure they are empty.

Replace all inspection plates, all stressed panels, oil and fuel tank caps, junction box covers, cowling, doors, emergency exits, and other parts that have been removed. All doors, windows, and sliding canopies should be in their normal flight position.

The aircraft should be in the hangar with the doors closed to minimize the air gusts that might destabilize the scales.

After the scales have been properly calibrated to zero, the aircraft must then be placed on them. If the aircraft is weighed on the wheels, ramps are usually used to roll the aircraft on to the scales. For heavier aircraft, it may be necessary to jack the aircraft and slide the scale under the wheel. On most large aircraft, the jack points are used with electronic scales. In these cases, the load cell is placed between the jack and the jackpoint as shown in Figure 9-3-2.

All aircraft have leveling points or lugs, and care must be taken to level the aircraft, especially along the longitudinal axis. With light, fixed-wing airplanes, the lateral level is not as critical as it is with heavier airplanes. However,

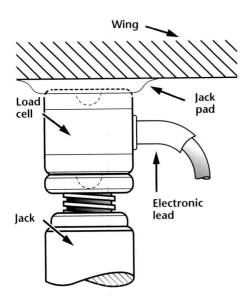

Figure 9-3-2. Load cell placement.

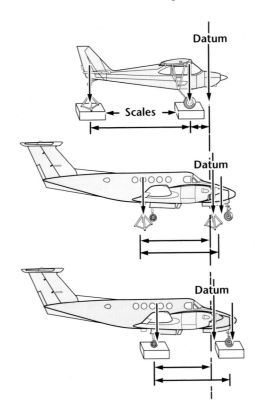

Figure 9-3-3. Jacking configurations.

a reasonable effort should be made to level the light airplanes around the lateral axis. Accuracy in leveling all aircraft longitudinally cannot be overemphasized.

Equipment. The equipment necessary for weighing the aircraft will vary with the type of aircraft to be weighed. Some aircraft are weighed at the wheels while others are weighed from jackpoints. Tailwheel aircraft will require additional equipment to raise the tail to the level position (Figure 9-3-3).

The preparation for weighing the aircraft should begin with a review of the manufacturer's MM and the Aircraft Specifications for the particular aircraft and gathering the necessary equipment as required.

Scales may be either mechanical or electronic. In either case they should be in good mechanical order and recalibrated as required. Electronic scales are available today that simplify the weighing procedure for light aircraft (Figure 9-3-4).

If the aircraft is to be weighed using the wheels as weighing points, chocks will be necessary. The chocks are used to hold the aircraft on the scales and are considered as part of the tare weight. The parking brakes should never be used for this purpose because they may place a side load on the scales.

When jackpoints are used for weighing, appropriate jacks will be necessary for all jackpoints because the aircraft must be leveled and weighed from these points.

To level the aircraft, either a spirit level or a plumb bob will be necessary depending upon the leveling means provided by the manufacturer.

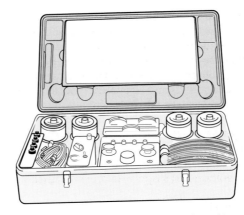

Figure 9-3-4. Aircraft electronic weighing kit.

Additional equipment will include a straight edge, measuring tape, chalk line, and plumb bob to obtain actual wheel or jackpoint measurements as required.

Appropriate data must always be available. This will include specifications and manufacturer maintenance information concerning weight and balance.

Recording the data. The distance from the datum to the main weighing point centerline, and the distance from the main weighing point centerline to the tail (or nose) weighing point centerline must be known to determine the CG relative to the main weighing point and the datum.

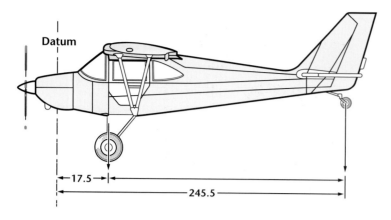

Figure 9-3-5. A typical tail wheel conventional aircraft.

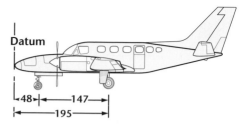

Figure 9-3-6. Typical nose wheel (tricycle) aircraft.

An example of main weighing point to datum and main weighing point to tail weighing point is shown in Figure 9-3-5. Refer to Figure 9-3-6 for an example of main weighing point to datum and main weighing point to nosewheel measurements.

These distances may be calculated using information from the Aircraft Specifications or Type Certificate Data Sheets. However, it will often be necessary to determine them by actual measurement.

After the aircraft has been placed on the scales (Figure 9-3-6) and leveled, hang plumb bobs from the datum, the main weighing point, and the tail or nose weighing point so that the points of the plumb bobs touch the floor. Make a chalk mark on the floor at the points of contact. If desired, a chalk line may be drawn connecting the chalk marks. This will make a clear pattern of the weighing point distances and their relation to the datum.

Weighing points should be clearly indicated on the aircraft weighting form. Record the weights indicated on each of the scales and make the necessary measurements while the aircraft is still level. After all weights and measurements are obtained and recorded, the aircraft may be removed from the scales. Weigh the tare and deduct its weight from the scale reading at each respective weighing point where tare is involved.

Locating the Balance Point

Balance computations. Once the scale weights and measurements are obtained from the actual weighing process, two items can be computed. One is the empty weight of the aircraft and the other is the empty weight CG. Without these two figures, the proper loading of the aircraft cannot be determined.

Since the weighing procedure varies to some degree, a total of three different aircraft will be calculated. They will include one light aircraft, one small transport aircraft, and later in the chapter, one helicopter. The first of these aircraft will be a light training aircraft.

Problem 1. This aircraft is a simple, single engine, nosewheel aircraft that can easily be weighed using a scale as shown in Figure 9-3-7.

The information obtained from the Type Certificate Data Sheet includes:

Datum......................... Front face of firewall
Maximum weight .... 1,670 lbs
CG Range.................... (+32.65) to (+36.50) at
1,670 lbs
(+31.00) to (+36.50) at
1,350 lbs or less
Leveling means .... Stations (+94.63) and
(+132.94) of the left side of
the tail cone
Oil capacity................. Use full oil for the empty
CG calculation
Maximum baggage .... 120 lb.
Seats .... 2 at (+39)
Fuel capacity.............. 26 gal (24.50 gal usable);
Two 13 gal tanks at
(+42.00)

1. Clean the aircraft and remove all loose articles. Drain the fuel and check the oil level for full. The serial number is 15285979, therefore, according to the Type Certification Data Sheet, full oil is included in the empty weight. It might also be noted that 1.5 gallons of fuel is considered unusable and will be included in the empty weight by computation.

2. Place the aircraft in a closed hangar and retract the flaps.

3. Check the scale adjustments for zero and place the aircraft on the scales. Use chocks under the wheels. Use no brakes.

4. Place a spirit level on the tailcone leveling points and deflate the nose strut to obtain level.

5. Record the scale readings and subtract the tare (Table 9-3-1).

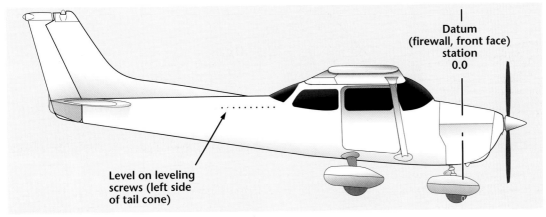

Figure 9-3-7. Typical lightweight training aircraft.

6. Using a plumb bob and a steel tape, measure the horizontal distances from the nosewheel to the main wheels and the datum to the nosewheel. The distances are (+46.75) and (–10.9), respectively.

7. Using the formula from page 9-5 for nosewheel aircraft, compute the empty CG:

$$CG = D - \left(\frac{F \times L}{W}\right)$$

D = 46.75
F = 355
L = 57.65
W = 1,143

$$46.75 - \frac{355 \times 57.65}{1,143} = 28.85$$

8. Using the formula for moment, compute the moment.

CG × Weight = Moment
29.85 × 1,143 = 32,975.55

In order to obtain the basic empty weight, unusable fuel, which is 9 lb at (+40), must be added (Table 9-3-2).

Problem 2. A commuter aircraft is flown by several regional carriers and carries 30 passengers. Although it is much larger than the trainer, the weighing and computations are much the same (Figure 9-3-8).

Datum................................ 98 inches forward of
the nose
Leveling means .... Bubble level on seat
track
Mean Aerodynamic Chord.. 82.07 inches, LEMAC
412.3
Empty weight .... Must include total
engine and gear box
oil; 75 lb at (+363);
hydraulic oil 25 lb at
(+218); unusable fuel
110 lb at (+440)

Maximum weights:
Ramp 27,300
Takeoff............................... 27,000 (27,275 with
1083 mod)
Landing.............................. 26,500
Max zero fuel weight 25,000
Minimum crew 2

1. Clean the aircraft and remove all loose articles. Drain the fuel, galley water, and baggage compartments.

2. Service the engine oil, gear box oil, hydraulic system, and other standard systems.

3. Place the aircraft in a closed hangar.

4. Check the scales for zero and place the load cells between the jacks and the jackpoints and raise the aircraft (Figure 9-3-9).

5. Level the aircraft both laterally and longitudinally.

6. Record the reading.

NOTE: No use of tare is required because of use of electronic scales).

	Gross	Tare	Net
Left main	406	2	404
Right main	406	2	404
Nosewheel	355	0	355

Table 9-3-1. Typical weight record.

	Weight	Arm	Moment
As weighed	1,143	29.85	34,118.5
Fuel	+9	40.0	360
Basic empty weight	1,152		
Total moment		29.92	34,478.5

Table 9-3-2. Typical weight and balance sheet.

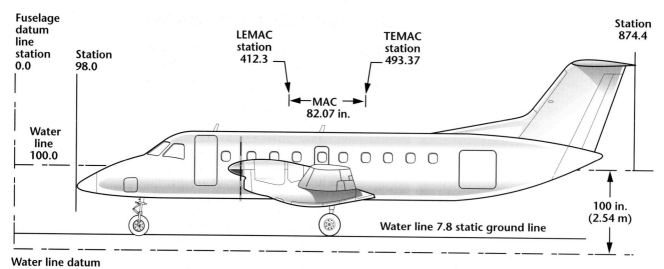

Figure 9-3-8. Typical commuter aircraft.

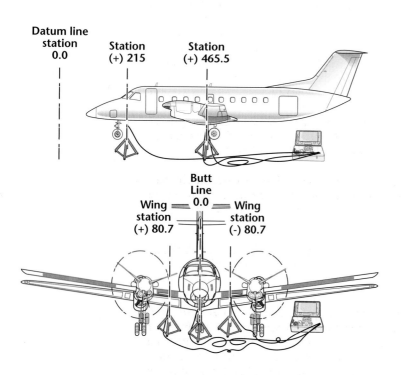

Figure 9-3-9. Weighing a commuter aircraft using an electronic weighing kit.

Left main jackpoint..............7,614
Right main jackpoint............7,564
Nose jackpoint.....................2,724

17,902

7. The jackpoint measurements are:

Nose jackpoint..................... 215 inches

Wing jackpoint............ ..... 465.5 inches

8. Using the formula for nosewheel aircraft with the datum forward of the main wheels, compute the CG.

$$CG = D - \left(\frac{F \times L}{W} \right)$$

$$= 465.50 - \frac{2,724 \times 250.50}{17,902}$$

$$= 465.50 - \frac{682,362}{17,902}$$

$$= 465.50 - 38.11$$

$$= 427.40$$

9. Since 110 lb of unusable fuel at station 440 must be included in the empty weight and CG, this should be added at this time using the total moment/total weight formula.

NOTE: The moments can be divided by 100 to reduce the size of the number for the loading chart (Table 9-3-3).

17,902	427.40	7,651,314		76,513
110	440.00	48,400	or	484
18,012		7,699,714		76,997

NOTE: The moments can be divided by 100 to reduce the size of the number for loading chart, i.e.,

7,699,714 ÷ 100	=	76,997
76,997 ÷ 18,012	=	4.274,
then 4274 × 100	=	427.50
CG	=	427.50

The new empty weight figures are:
18,012 = Empty Weight   CG = 427.50

10. Because this aircraft has tapered wings the graphs used for weight and balance express the CG in percent of MAC (Figure 9-3-8). For this reason, it will be necessary to convert the CG from inches to percent of MAC. To do so, we must know the station of CG (427.5), the MAC (82.07) and LEMAC (412.3) and use the formula:

$$\%\text{MAC} = \frac{\text{STA} - \text{LEMAC}}{\text{MAC}} \times 100$$
$$= \frac{427.5 - 412.3}{82.07} \times 100$$
$$\text{CG} = 18.5\% \text{ of MAC}$$

11. For some of the loading charts used with larger aircraft, weights and moments are used only to determine if the aircraft is within limits.

Center-of-Gravity Range

Empty CG range. Once the empty center-of-gravity (CG) has been established, as has been done in the previous problems, this information is used by the flight crew in loading the aircraft within the CG range. It should be noted that some aircraft have an empty CG range and some aircraft have a loaded CG range.

The empty CG range is normally associated with older light aircraft. When the choice to use empty CG range has been made by the manufacturer, as long as the aircraft is flown within its limitations and all standard loading is within the CG range, no further computations are required. Unfortunately, very few aircraft have an empty weight CG.

To utilize the empty weight and the empty CG, two typical systems are used. The flight crew is furnished with either a graph or a chart to determine the loaded CG. The use of these methods will be covered in the loading section of this chapter. When no chart or graph is furnished by the manufacturer, it will be necessary to investigate the extreme CG conditions in order to include the most forward and most aft conditions. These checks could require ballast for either convenience or necessity. The helicopter, which is described in the section on helicopter weight and balance, is such an aircraft.

Loaded CG range. The loaded CG range, (often referred to as the operating CG range), is the established forward and aft CG limits for a particular model of aircraft operated in a certain manner within its established weights. For example, an aircraft that may be operated in two different categories will have different limitations in the normal and utility categories. Since the flight maneuvers for the two categories are different, the maximum weight and the CG range are less in the utility category than in the normal category.

It is also quite typical for aircraft to have loaded CG ranges that vary with the weight of the aircraft. Typically, the aircraft used in the empty CG problems had the CG range change as the aircraft approached the maximum weight.

Shifting the Center-of-Gravity)

Ballast. The use of ballast on aircraft is quite limited because no one likes to carry additional weight in the aircraft when it is not necessary. The two types of ballast that may be used are temporary and permanent ballast.

Temporary ballast is normally used when an unusual flight condition occurs, or if some item is removed from the aircraft that could change the CG to an adverse condition. Normally such problems can be handled by loading the aircraft in a different configuration, such as restricting the use of certain passenger seats, placing all cargo in one compartment, or limiting the fuel load. If temporary ballast is used, it must be marked as such so that it is not removed by mistake.

Permanent ballast is used when the CG location will cause problems for normal loading of the aircraft. Under these circumstances, the ballast is marked permanent ballast and secured to the structure of the aircraft. When permanent ballast is required, the least amount of weight should be used. For this reason, the nose and the tail are typical locations for ballast as long as the structure can hold the weight required. Some manufacturers have specific locations for ballast as shown in Figure 9-3-10.

Calculations. Regardless of whether the ballast is temporary or permanent, it must be determined by the use of the formula:

$$\text{Ballast} = \frac{\text{Derived Weight} \times (\text{Required CG} - \text{Derived CG})}{\text{Ballast Arm} - \text{Required CG}}$$

Shifting weight. The CG is the distance of the exact point of balance of an aircraft from the established reference datum line. In other words, the CG is the arm of the aircraft. One way of shifting the CG without adding additional weight in the form of ballast is to move or shift weight, such as passengers, cargo, or equipment within the aircraft. By shifting weight within the aircraft, the CG is changed based on the amount of weight moved and the distance that it is moved.

Calculation. To determine how much weight is to be shifted or how far to shift a known weight, the following formula may be used:

$$\frac{\text{WS}}{\text{TW}} = \frac{\text{CG}}{\text{D}}$$

Where:
WS = Weight to be shifted
TW = Total weight
CG = Required change in CG
D = Distance weight is to be shifted

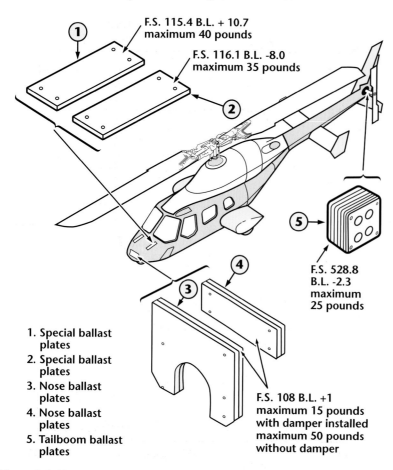

F.S. 115.4 B.L. + 10.7
maximum 40 pounds

F.S. 116.1 B.L. -8.0
maximum 35 pounds

F.S. 528.8
B.L. -2.3
maximum
25 pounds

1. Special ballast
   plates
2. Special ballast
   plates
3. Nose ballast
   plates
4. Nose ballast
   plates
5. Tailboom ballast
   plates

F.S. 108 B.L. +1
maximum 15 pounds
with damper installed
maximum 50 pounds
without damper

Figure 9-3-10. Typical example of ballast installation.

	Longitudinal			Lateral	
	Weight	Arm	Moment	Arm	Moment
Empty weight	5,065.00	256.30	1,298,159	0.50	2,532.50
Pilot/copilot	340.00	168.20	+57,188	+1.00	+340.00
Passengers facing aft	340.00	211.20	+71,808	0.00	0.00
Oil and engine	28.60	270.00	+7,722	0.00	0.00
	5,773.60	248.50	1,434,877	0.40	2,192.50
	Total weight	CG	Total moment	Lateral CG	Lateral moment

Table 9-3-3. Most forward CG chart.

	Longitudinal			Lateral	
	Weight	Arm	Moment	Arm	Moment
Empty weight	5,065.00	256.30	1,298,159	0.50	2,532.50
Pilot	170.00	168.20	+28,594	+16.00	+2,720.00
Passengers 3 aft seat	510.00	257.00	+131,070	0.00	0.00
Fuel	1,264.80	264.30	+334,287	0.00	0.00
Oil and engine	28.60	270.00	+7,722	0.00	0.00
	7,038.40	255.70	1,799,832	0.02	187.50

Table 9-3-4. Most rear CG chart.

Determine the weight to be shifted using the following formula:

$$WS = \frac{TW \times CG}{D}$$

Determine the distance that a given weight is to be shifted using the following formula:

$$D = \frac{TW \times CG}{WS}$$

Adverse Center of Gravity

The empty weight of an aircraft includes the aircraft and its required equipment, unusable fuel, and, when applicable, transmission and gear box oil and fixed ballast. It is this weight, arm, and moment that is used for loading the aircraft. If no loading charts have been established for an aircraft, it is necessary to investigate the most adverse forward and aft loading, as well as the maximum weight loading. The investigation of these extreme conditions is based on the empty CG of the aircraft.

The forward condition is investigated by simply loading the aircraft in such a manner that all useful load forward of the loaded CG range is at maximum weight, and all minimum weights necessary for flight are used aft of the forward limit.

The rearward condition is investigated in a similar manner. All useful load aft of the rearward loaded CG range is at maximum weight, and all minimum weights necessary for flight are used forward of the aft limit.

Fuel computations for adverse loading checks. For computation purposes, the standard weights defined in Section 2 of this chapter are used.

Minimum fuel will be used when the fuel tank lies behind the forward limit when calculating the most forward center of gravity, and ahead of the aft limit when figuring the most rearward CG.

For fuel computations during this investigation, the following rules apply:

- If the tank is ahead of the forward limit, full fuel is calculated at the standard weight.

- If the fuel tank is behind the most rearward CG, then the fuel tank should be full when the most rearward CG is calculated.

- For reciprocating-engine aircraft, minimum fuel is figured at the rate of one-twelfth of a gallon for each horsepower at maximum except takeoff (METO). To figure pounds of fuel, the formula, METO divided by 2, is used.

- On turbine-powered aircraft, minimum fuel is established by the manufacturer because specific fuel consumption varies so greatly.

Most forward CG investigation. To investigate the most forward CG limit of a given aircraft, the weight and arms after the installation are given in Table 9-3-3.

When plotted on the graphs in Figures 9-3-11 and 9-3-12, it can be seen that the aircraft is within CG limits at 248.5.

Most aft CG investigation. Rearward adverse loading requires a different set of circumstances than forward adverse loading. Note the absence of a copilot, additional fuel, and the number and location of the passengers as compared to the example of forward adverse loading. (Table 9-3-4).

As can be seen by the graphs in Figures 9-3-11 and 9-3-12, the aircraft is within limits at 255.7 with a weight of 7,038.4 pounds.

Maximum weight investigation. Checking the maximum weight of an aircraft is a simple matter of adding the empty weight of the aircraft to the weight of the crew, passengers, baggage, cargo, fuel, additional equipment not included in the empty weight, and, when required, ballast and engine oil.

Empty weight	5,065.00
Pilot/copilot	340.00
Passengers (2)	340.00
Passengers (3)	510.00
Oil engine	28.60
Fuel	1,264.80
Baggage	500.00
Total Weight	8,048.40

The computed maximum weight, when compared to the graph in Figure 9-3-11 is well within the allowable maximum weight of this aircraft. Note that the maximum allowable weight, as shown by the graph, is 8,250 pounds.

Weight and Balance Changes After Alteration

When equipment to be added is on the approved equipment list, it typically will have a weight and arm given in the list and all computations will be completed on paper. If the item is not approved on the list, actual weights and arms will have to be physically measured and weighed. If the alterations are extensive, it is best to reweigh the aircraft and construct a new equipment list.

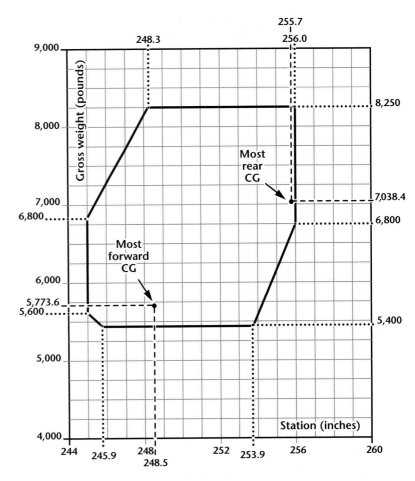

Figure 9-3-11. Longitudinal CG range graph.

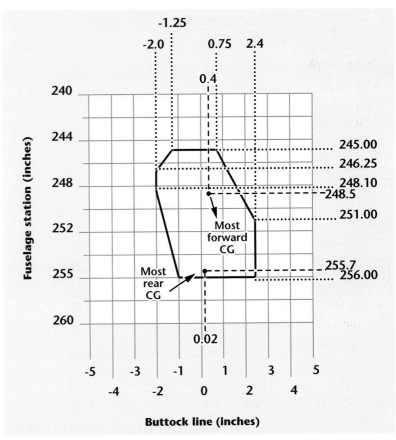

Figure 9-3-12. Lateral CG range graph.

For demonstration purposes some additional equipment will be added to the light training aircraft used previously. The equipment added will be a child's seat installation in the baggage compartment. It is approved equipment and is taken from the equipment list contained in the aircraft information/owner's manual (Table 9-3-5).

Addition of equipment. The present empty weight is 1,152.20 and the CG is 29.90. The moment is 34,450.78.

The child seat weighs 10.50 pounds with an arm of 66.50 inches. To calculate the change in the aircraft the Total Moment over Total Weight formula will be used (Table 9-3-6).

The new weight is 1,162.70, the new CG is 30.20, and the new moment is 35,149.03.

Removal of equipment. Sometimes it may be necessary to delete equipment rather than add equipment. Basically the same method is used, but special attention must be given to the signs of the numbers. The weight will become a negative number changing the moment as well. If the seat were now to be removed, the following computations would be used: (Table 9-3-7).

The new weight is 1,152.5, the CG is 29.9, and the moment is 34,450.78.

Once the new weight and balance has been established, the old one should be marked superseded and dated. This will prevent the old papers from being used by mistake.

Item no.	Equipment list description	Wt. lbs.	Arm. Ins
D-4	Recorder, engine hour meter	0.6	5.2
D-5	Outside air temperature indicator	0.1	22.0
D-6	Tachometer installation, engine – recording tach indicator	1.0	12.5
D-7	Indicator, turn coordinator (24 volt only)	0.8	17.0
D-8	Indicator, turn coordinator (10-30 volt)	1.8	17.2
D-9	Indicator, vertical speed	1.0	17.2
	E. Cabin accommodations	1.0	18.0
E-1	Seat, pilot individual sliding	11.1	45.2
E-2	Seat, vertically adjustable, pilot	17.0	45.2
E-3	Seat, copilot individual sliding	11.1	45.2
E-4	Seat vertically adjustable, copilot	17.0	45.2
E-5	Child seat installation, auxiliary	10.5	66.5

Table 9-3-5. Typical installed equipment list.

	Weight	Arm	Moment
Aircraft	1,152.20	29.90	34,450.78
Seat	10.50	66.50	698.25
New total	1,162.70	30.20	35,149.03

Table 9-3-6. Adding weight.

	Weight	Arm	Moment
Aircraft	1,162.70	30.20	35,149.03
Removed seat	-10.50	66.50	-698.25
New total	1,152.20	29.90	34,450.78

Table 9-3-7. Removing weight.

Appendix A

National Telecommunications and Information Administration (NTIA) Frequency Allocation Charts

* Legend on page A-7

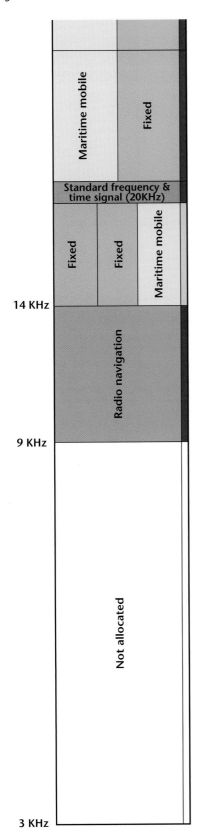

Figure 1A. Very low frequency (VLF) band 0 kHz to 30kHz.

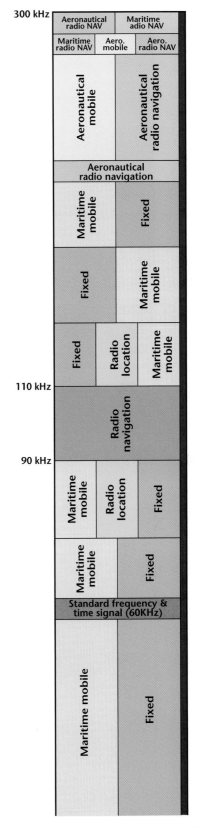

Figure 1B. Low frequency (LF) band 30 kHz to 300kHz.

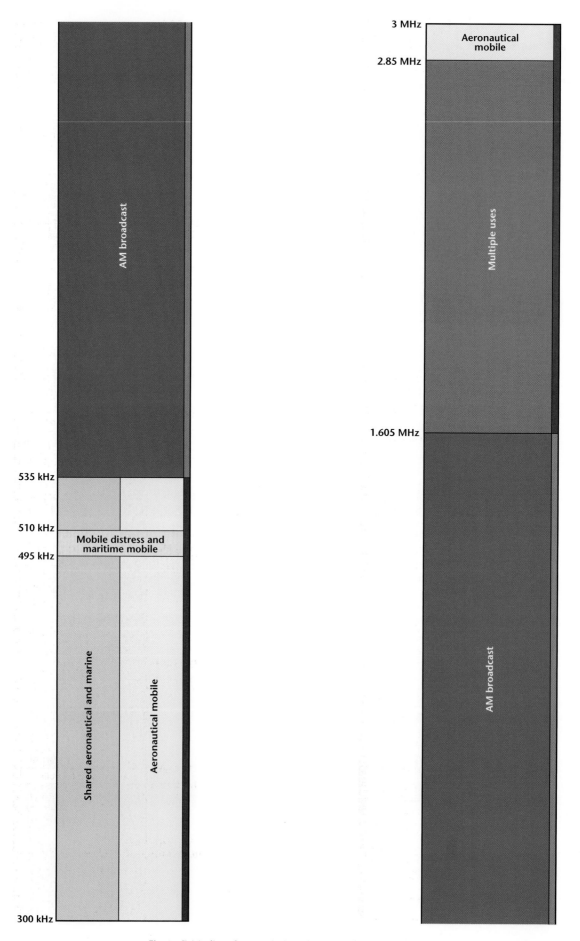

Figure 2. Medium frequency (MF) band 300 kHz to 3 MHz.

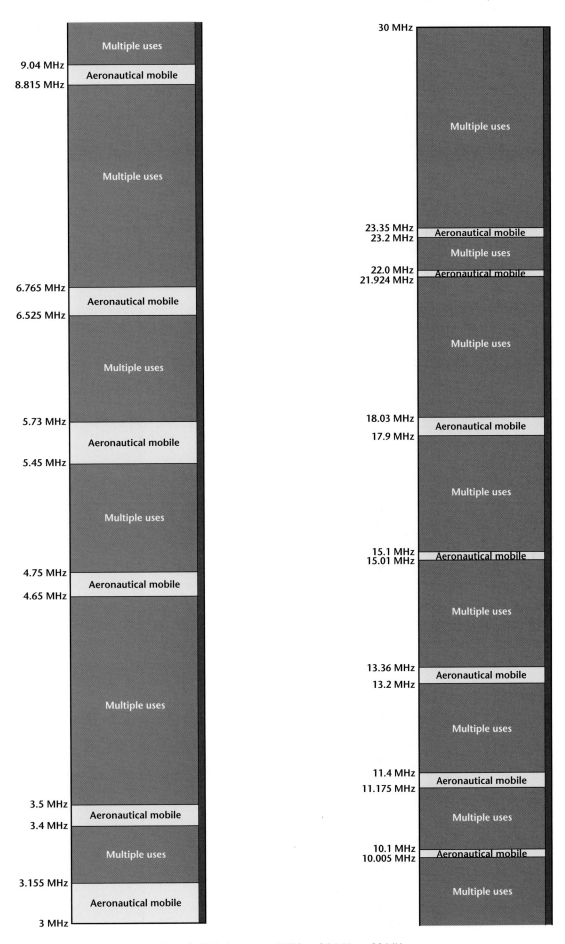

Figure 3. High frequency (HF) band 3 MHz to 30 MHz.

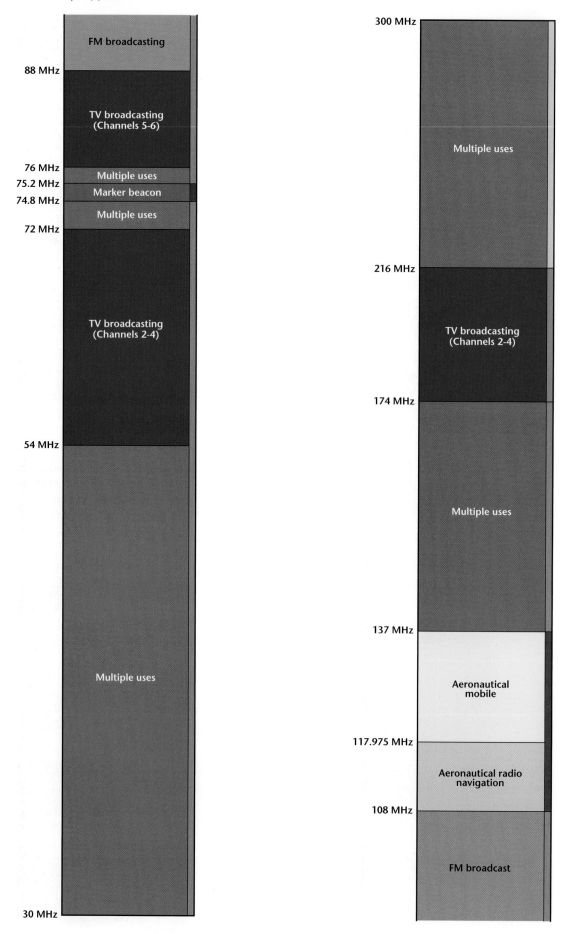

Figure 4. Very high frequency (VHF) band 30 MHz to 300 MHz.

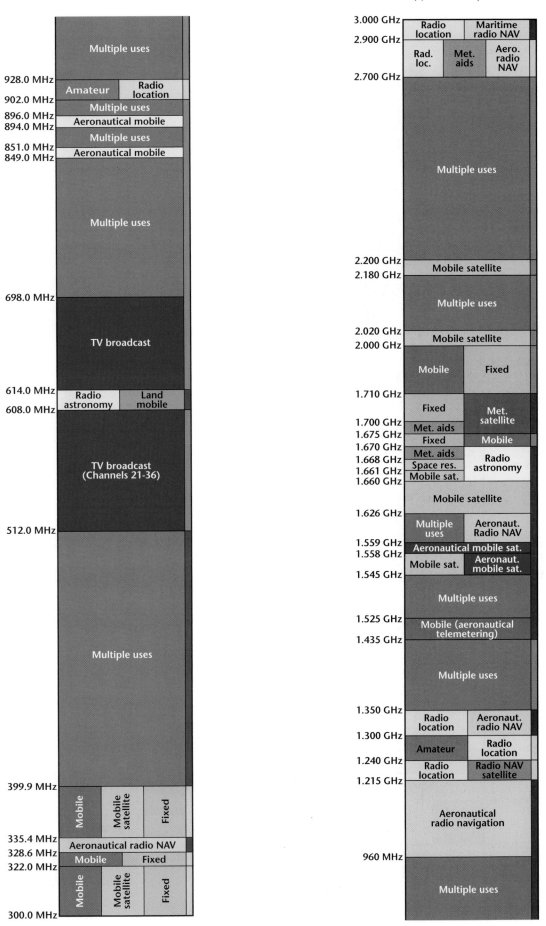

Figure 5. Ultra high frequency (UHF) band 300 MHz to 3 GHz.

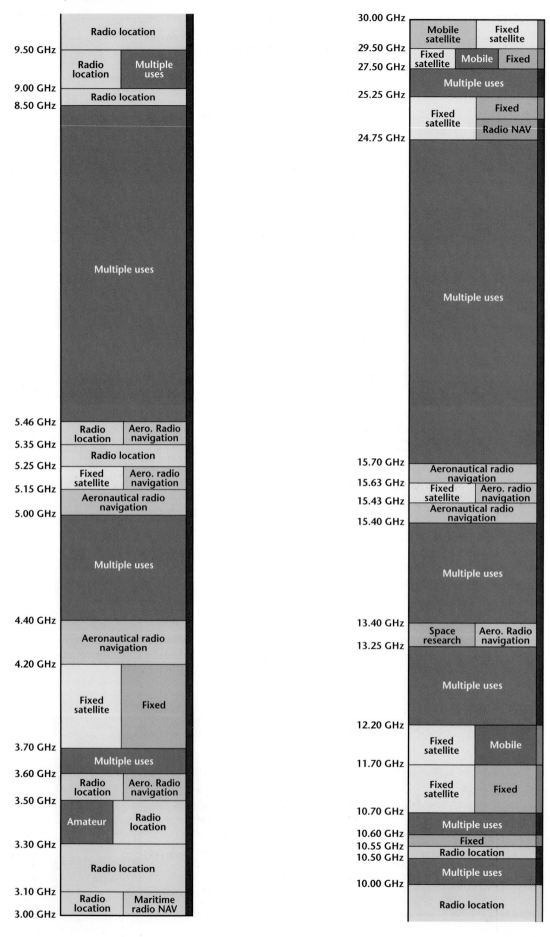

Figure 6. Super high frequency (SHF) band 3 GHz to 30 GHz.

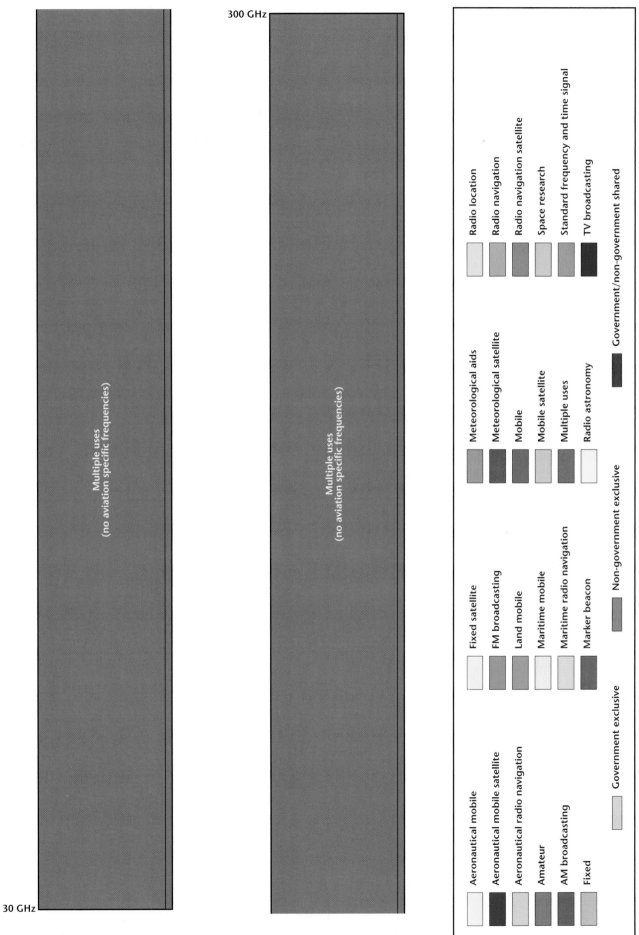

300 GHz

Multiple uses
(no aviation specific frequencies)

Multiple uses
(no aviation specific frequencies)

30 GHz

Figure 7. Extremely high frequency (EHF) band 30 GHz to 300 GHz.

Aeronautical mobile
Aeronautical mobile satellite
Aeronautical radio navigation
Amateur
AM broadcasting
Fixed

Government exclusive

Fixed satellite
FM broadcasting
Land mobile
Maritime mobile
Maritime radio navigation
Marker beacon

Non-government exclusive

Meteorological aids
Meteorological satellite
Mobile
Mobile satellite
Multiple uses
Radio astronomy

Radio location
Radio navigation
Radio navigation satellite
Space research
Standard frequency and time signal
TV broadcasting

Government/non-government shared

Appendix B

Air Transport Association ATA 100 Codes

Sys/ Chap	Subsys/ Section	Title
00		**Introduction**
01		**Operations information**
05		**Periodic inspections**
	-00	General
	-10	Time limits
	-20	Scheduled maintenance checks
	-50	Unscheduled maintenance checks
06		**Dimensions and areas**
07		**Lifting and shoring**
	-00	General
	-10	Jacking
	-20	Shoring
08		**Leveling and weighing**
	-00	General
	-10	Weighing & balancing
	-20	Leveling
09		**Towing and taxiing**
	-00	General
	-10	Towing
	-20	Taxiing
10		**Parking, mooring, storage and return to service**
	-00	General
	-10	Parking & storage
	-20	Mooring
	-30	Return to service
11		**Placards and markings**
	-00	General
	-10	Exterior color schemes & markings
	-20	Exterior placards & markings
	-30	Interior placards
12		**Servicing routine maintenance**
	-00	General
	-10	Replenishing
	-20	Scheduled servicing
	-30	Unscheduled servicing
18		**Vibration and noise analysis (helicopter only)**
	-00	General
	-10	Vibration analysis
	-20	Noise analysis

Sys/ Chap	Subsys/ Section	Title
		Group definition – airframe systems
20		**Standard practices - airframe**
21		**Air conditioning**
	-00	General
	-10	Compression
	-20	Distribution
	-30	Pressurization control
	-40	Heating
	-50	Cooling
	-60	Temperature control
	-70	Moisture or air contaminant control
	-97	Wiring discrepancies
22		**Auto flight**
	-00	General
	-10	Autopilot
	-20	Speed - attitude correction
	-30	Auto throttle
	-40	System monitor
	-50	Aerodynamic load alleviating
	-97	Wiring discrepancies
23		**Communications**
	-00	General
	-10	Speech communications
	-15	SATCOM
	-20	Data transmission & automatic calling
	-30	Passenger address, entertainment, and comfort
	-40	Interphone
	-50	Audio integrating
	-60	Static discharging
	-70	Audio and video monitoring
	-80	Integrated automatic tuning
	-97	Wiring discrepancies
24		**Electrical power**
	-00	General
	-10	Generator drive
	-20	Ac generation
	-30	Dc generation
	-40	External power
	-50	Ac electrical load distribution
	-60	Dc electrical load distribution
	-70	Primary and secondary power
	-97	Wiring discrepancies

Sys/Chap	Subsys/Section	Title
25		**Equipment and furnishings**
	-00	General
	-10	Flight compartment
	-20	Passenger compartment
	-30	Buffet or galley
	-40	Lavatories
	-50	Cargo compartments
	-60	Emergency
	-70	Accessory compartments
	-80	Insulation
	-97	Wiring discrepancies
26		**Fire protection**
	-00	General
	-10	Detection
	-20	Extinguishing
	-30	Explosion suppression
	-97	Wiring discrepancies
27		**Flight controls**
	-00	General
	-10	Aileron and tab
	-20	Rudder and tab
	-30	Elevator and tab
	-40	Horizontal stabilizer or stabilator
	-50	Flaps
	-60	Spoiler, drag devices and variable aerodynamic fairings
	-70	Gust lock and damper
	-80	Lift augmenting
	-97	Wiring discrepancies
28		**Fuel**
	-00	General
	-10	Storage
	-20	Distribution - drain valves
	-30	Dump
	-40	Indicating
29		**Hydraulic power**
	-00	General
	-10	Main
	-20	Auxiliary
	-30	Indicating
	-97	Wiring discrepancies
30		**Ice and rain protection**
	-00	General
	-10	Airfoil
	-20	Air intakes
	-30	Pitot and static
	-40	Windows, windshields & doors
	-50	Antennas and radomes
	-60	Propellers or rotors

Sys/Chap	Subsys/Section	Title
	-70	Water lines
	-80	Detection
	-97	Wiring discrepancies
31		**Indicating and recording systems**
	-00	General
	-10	Instrument & control panels
	-20	Independent instruments
	-30	Recorders
	-40	Central computers
	-50	Central warning systems
	-60	Central display systems
	-70	Automatic data reporting systems
	-97	Wiring discrepancies
32		**Landing gear**
	-00	General
	-10	Main gear and doors
	-20	Nose gear, tail gear, and doors
	-30	Extension and retraction
	-40	Wheels and brakes
	-50	Steering
	-60	Position and warning
	-70	Supplementary gear
	-97	Wiring discrepancies
33		**Lights**
	-00	General
	-10	Flight compartment
	-20	Passenger compartment
	-30	Cargo and service compartments
	-40	Exterior lighting
	-50	Emergency lighting
	-97	Wiring discrepancies
34		**Navigation**
	-00	General
	-10	Flight environment data
	-20	Attitude and direction
	-30	Landing and taxiing aids
	-40	Independent position determining
	-50	Dependent position determining
	-60	Flight management computing
	-97	Wiring discrepancies
35		**Oxygen**
	-00	General
	-10	Crew
	-20	Passenger
	-30	Portable
	-97	Wiring discrepancies
36		**Pneumatic**
	-00	General
	-10	Distribution

Sys/ Chap	Subsys/ Section	Title
	-20	Indicating
	-97	Wiring discrepancies
37		**Vacuum**
	-00	General
	-10	Distribution
	-20	Indicating
	-97	Wiring discrepancies
38		**Water or waste**
	-00	General
	-10	Potable
	-20	Wash
	-30	Waste disposal
	-40	Air supply
39		**Electrical electronic panels and multipurpose computers**
	-00	General
	-10	Instrument and control panels
	-20	Electrical and electronic equipment racks
	-30	Electrical and electronic junction boxes
	-40	Multipurpose electronic components
	-50	Integrated circuits
	-60	Printed circuit card assemblies
41		**Water ballast**
	-00	General
	-10	Storage
	-20	Dump
	-30	Indication
42		**Integrated modular avionics**
	-00	General
	-20	Core system
	-30	Network components
44		**Cabin systems**
	-00	General
	-10	Cabin core system
	-20	In flight entertainment system
	-30	External communication system
	-40	Cabin mass memory system
	-50	Cabin monitoring system
	-60	Miscellaneous cabin system
	-97	Wiring discrepancies
45		**Central maintenance system (CMS)**
	-00	General
	-05	CMS / aircraft general
	-19	CMS / aircraft general
	-20	CMS / airframe systems
	-44	CMS / airframe systems
	-45	Central maintenance system
	-50	CMS / structures
	-59	CMS / structures

Sys/ Chap	Subsys/ Section	Title
	-60	CMS / Propellers
	-69	CMS / Propellers
	-70	CMS / Power plant
	-89	CMS / Power plant
	-97	Wiring discrepancies
46		**Information systems**
	-00	General
	-10	Airplane general information systems
	-20	Flight deck information systems
	-30	Maintenance information systems
	-40	Passenger cabin information systems
	-50	Miscellaneous information systems
47		**Inert gas system**
	-00	General
	-10	Generation and storage
	-20	Distribution
	-30	Control
	-40	Indicating
49		**Airborne auxiliary power**
	-00	General
	-10	Power plant
	-20	Engine
	-30	Engine fuel and control
	-40	Ignition and starting
	-50	Air
	-60	Engine controls
	-70	Indicating
	-80	Exhaust
	-90	Oil
50		**Cargo & accessory compartments**
	-00	General
	-10	Cargo compartments
	-20	Cargo loading systems
	-30	Cargo related systems
	-40	Unassigned
	-50	Accessory compartments
	-60	Insulation
	-97	Wiring discrepancies
Group definition – structures		
51		**Standard practices & structures general**
	-00	General
	-10	Investigation, cleanup & aerodynamic smoothness
	-20	Processes
	-30	Materials
	-40	Fasteners
	-50	Support of airplane for repair & alignment check procedures
	-60	Control-surface balancing

Sys/ Chap	Subsys/ Section	Title
	-70	Repairs
	-80	Electrical bonding
52		**Doors**
	-00	General
	-10	Passenger and crew
	-20	Emergency exit
	-30	Cargo
	-40	Service
	-50	Fixed interior
	-60	Entrance stairs
	-70	Monitoring & operation
	-80	Landing gear
53		**Fuselage**
	-00	General (10 through 90 fuselage sections)
	-10	Main frame
	-20	Auxiliary structure
	-30	Plates-skin
	-40	Attach fittings
	-50	Aerodynamic fairings
54		**Nacelles / pylons**
	-00	General
	-10	Nacelle
	-20	Nacelle
	-30	Nacelle
	-40	Nacelle
	-50	Pylon
	-60	Pylon
	-70	Pylon
	-80	Pylon
55		**Stabilizers**
	-00	General
	-10	Horizontal stabilizer / stabilator or canard
	-20	Elevator
	-30	Vertical stabilizer
	-40	Rudder
56		**Windows**
	-00	General
	-10	Flight compartment
	-20	Passenger compartment
	-30	Door
	-40	Inspection and observation
57		**Wings**
	-00	General
	-10	Center wing
	-20	Outer wing
	-30	Wing tip
	-40	Leading edge and leading edge devices
	-50	Trailing edge and trailing edge devices

Sys/ Chap	Subsys/ Section	Title
	-60	Ailerons and elevons
	-70	Spoilers
	-90	Wing folding system
	**Group definition – propeller/rotor**	
60		**Standard practices - propeller / rotor**
61		**Propellers / propulsion**
	-00	General
	-10	Propeller assembly
	-20	Controlling
	-30	Braking
	-40	Indicating
	-50	Propulsor duct
	-97	Wiring discrepancies
62		**Rotors**
	-00	General
	-10	Rotor blades
	-20	Rotor head(s)
	-30	Rotor shaft(s) / swashplate assembly(ies)
	-40	Indicating
63		**Rotor drive(s)**
	-00	General
	-10	Engine / gearbox couplings
	-20	Gearbox(es)
	-30	Mounts, attachments
	-40	Indicating
64		**Tail rotor**
	-00	General
	-10	Rotor blades
	-20	Rotor head
	-30	[Unassigned]
	-40	Indicating
65		**Tail rotor drive**
	-00	General
	-10	Shafts
	-20	Gearboxes
	-40	Indicating
66		**Folding blades & tail pylon**
	-00	General
	-10	Rotor blades
	-20	Tail pylon
	-30	Controls & indicating
67		**Rotors flight control**
	-00	General
	-10	Rotor control
	-20	Anti-torque rotor control (yaw control)
	-30	Servo-control system

Sys/Chap	Subsys/Section	Title
	-97	Wiring discrepancies
Group definition – power plant		
70		**Standard practices engine**
71		**Power plant general**
	-00	General
	-10	Cowling
	-20	Mounts
	-30	Fire seals
	-40	Attach fittings
	-50	Electrical harness
	-60	Air intakes
	-70	Engine drains
72		**Engine turbine/turboprop, ducted fan/unducted fan**
	-00	General
	-10	(Turboprop and/or front mounted driven propulsor)
	-20	Air inlet section
	-30	Compressor section
	-40	Combustion section
	-50	Turbine section
	-60	Accessory drives
	-70	By-pass section
	-80	Propulsor section (rear mounted)
73		**Engine fuel & control**
	-00	General
	-10	Distribution
	-20	Controlling
	-30	Indicating
	-97	Wiring discrepancies
74		**Ignition**
	-00	General
	-10	Electrical power supply
	-20	Distribution
	-30	Switching
	-97	Wiring discrepancies
75		**Air**
	-00	General
	-10	Engine anti-icing
	-20	Cooling
	-30	Compressor control
	-40	Indicating
76		**Engine controls**
	-00	General
	-10	Power control
	-20	Emergency shutdown
	-97	Wiring discrepancies
77		**Engine indicating**
	-00	General

Sys/Chap	Subsys/Section	Title
	-10	Power
	-20	Temperature
	-30	Analyzers
	-40	Integrated engine instrument systems
	-97	Wiring discrepancies
78		**Exhaust**
	-00	General
	-10	Collector - nozzle
	-20	Noise suppressor
	-30	Thrust reverser
	-40	Supplemental air
	-97	Wiring discrepancies
79		**Oil**
	-00	General
	-10	Storage
	-20	Distribution
	-30	Indicating
	-97	Wiring discrepancies
80		**Starting**
	-00	General
	-10	Cranking
81		**Turbines**
	-00	General
	-10	Power recovery
	-20	Turbo-supercharger
82		**Water injection**
	-00	General
	-10	Storage
	-20	Distribution
	-30	Dumping & purging
	-40	Indicating
83		**Accessory gear boxes**
	-00	General
	-10	Drive shaft section
	-20	Gear box section
84		**Propulsion augmentation**
	-00	General
	-10	Jet assist takeoff
91		**Charts**
115		**Flight simulator systems**
116		**Flight simulator cuing systems**

Appendix C

General Aviation Manufacturer's Association
GAMA Specification 2 Chapter Codes

Sys/ Chap	Subsys/ Section	Title
4		**Airworthiness limitations**
5		**Time limits & maintenance checks**
	00	General
	10	Time limits
	20	Scheduled maintenance checks
	50	Unscheduled maintenance checks
6		**Dimensions and areas**
7		**Lifting and shoring**
	00	General
	10	Jacking
	20	Shoring
8		**Leveling and weighing**
9		**Towing and taxiing**
	00	General
	10	Towing
	20	Taxiing
10		**Parking and mooring**
	00	General
	10	Parking
	20	Mooring
11		**Required placards**
	00	General
	10	Exterior color schemes and markings
	20	Exterior placards and markings
	30	Interior placards and markings
20		**Standard practices - airframe**
21		**Environmental systems**
	00	General
	10	Pressurization
	20	Distribution
	30	Pressurization control
	40	Heating
	50	Cooling
	60	Temperature control
	70	Moisture or air contaminant control
22		**Auto flight**
	00	General
	10	Autopilot
	20	Speed - attitude correction
	30	Auto throttle
	40	System monitor
23		**Communications**
	00	General
	10	Speech communications
	20	Data transmission & automatic calling

Sys/ Chap	Subsys/ Section	Title
	30	Passenger address and entertainment
	40	Interphone
	50	Audio integrating
	60	Static discharging
	70	Voice recorders
24		**Electrical power**
	00	General
	10	Generator drive
	20	AC generation
	30	DC generation
	40	External power
	50	Electrical load distribution
25		**Equipment and furnishings**
	00	General
	10	Flight compartment
	20	Passenger compartment
	30	Buffet or galley
	40	Lavatories
	50	Cargo compartments
	60	Emergency
	70	Accessory compartments
26		**Fire protection**
	00	General
	10	Detection
	20	Extinguishing
	30	Explosion suppression
27		**Flight controls**
	00	General
	10	Aileron and tab
	20	Rudder and tab
	30	Elevator and tab
	40	Horizontal stabilizer
	50	Flaps
	60	Spoiler, drag devices and variable aerodynamic fairings
	70	Gust lock and damper
	80	Lift augmenting
28		**Fuel**
	00	General
	10	Storage
	20	Distribution
	30	Dump
	40	Indicating
29		**Hydraulic power**
	00	General

Sys/Chap	Subsys/Section	Title
	10	Main
	20	Auxiliary
	30	Indicating
30		**Ice and rain protection**
	00	General
	10	Airfoil
	20	Air intakes
	30	Pitot and static
	40	Windows and windshields
	50	Antennas and radomes
	60	Propellers
	70	Water lines
	80	Detection
31		**Indicating & recording systems**
	00	General
	10	Panels
	20	Independent instruments
	30	Recorders
	40	Computers
32		**Landing gear**
	00	General
	10	Main gear and doors
	20	Nose gear and doors
	30	Extension and retraction
	40	Wheels and brakes
	50	Steering
	60	Position and warning
	70	Supplementary gear
33		**Lights**
	00	General
	10	Flight compartments
	20	Passenger compartment
	30	Cargo and service compartments
	40	Exterior
	50	Emergency lighting
34		**Navigation**
	00	General
	10	Flight environment data and pitot static
	20	Attitude and direction
	30	Landing and taxiing aids
	40	Independent position determining
	50	Dependent position determining
	60	Position computing
35		**Oxygen**
	00	General
	10	Crew
	20	Passenger
36		**Pneumatic**
	00	General
	10	Distribution
	20	Indicating

Sys/Chap	Subsys/Section	Title
37		**Vacuum**
	00	General
	10	Distribution
	20	Indicating
38		**Water or waste**
	00	General
	10	Potable
	20	Wash
	30	Waste disposal
	40	Air supply
39		**Electric/electronic panels and multipurpose computers**
	00	General
	10	Instrument & control panels
	20	Electrical & electronic equipment racks
	30	Electrical & electronic junction boxes
	40	Multipurpose electrical and electronic parts
	50	Integrated circuits
	60	Printed circuit card assemblies
49		**Airborne auxiliary power**
	00	General
	10	Power plant
	20	Engine
	30	Engine fuel & control
	40	Ignition / starting
	50	Air
	60	Engine controls
	70	Indicating
	80	Exhaust
	90	Oil
51		**Structures**
	00	General
52		**Doors**
	00	General
	10	Passenger / crew
	20	Emergency exit
	30	Cargo
	40	Service
	50	Fixed interior
	60	Entrance stairs or step
	70	Door warning
	80	Landing gear
53		**Fuselage**
	00	General
	10	Main frame
	20	Auxiliary structure
	30	Plates / skin
	40	Attach fittings
	50	Aerodynamic fairings
54		**Nacelles**
	00	General

Sys/Chap	Subsys/Section	Title
	10	Main frame
	20	Auxiliary structure
	30	Plates / skin
	40	Attach fittings
	50	Fillets / fairings
55		**Stabilizers**
	00	General
	10	Horizontal stabilizer
	20	Elevator / elevon
	30	Vertical stabilizer
	40	Rudder
	50	Attach fittings
	60	Auxiliary stabilizers
56		**Windows**
	00	General
	10	Flight compartment
	20	Cabin
	30	Door
	40	Inspection & observation
57		**Wings**
	00	General
	10	Main frame
	20	Auxiliary structure
	30	Plates / skin
	40	Attach fittings
	50	Flight surfaces
60		**Standard practices – propeller**
61		**Propellers**
	00	General
	10	Propeller assembly
	20	Controlling
	30	Braking
	40	Indicating
70		**Standard practices engine**
71		**Power plant**
	00	General
	10	Cowling
	20	Mounts
	30	Fire seals
	40	Attach fittings
	50	Electrical harness
	60	Air intakes
	70	Engine drains
72		**Engine turbine/turboprop**
	00	General
	10	Reduction gear and shaft section (turbo-prop)
	20	Air inlet section
	30	Compression section
	40	Combustion section
	50	Turbine section
	60	Accessory drives
	70	By-pass section
72		**Engine reciprocating**
	00	General
	10	Front section
	20	Cylinder section
	30	Power section
	40	Supercharger section
	50	Lubrication
73		**Engine fuel systems**
	00	General
	10	Distribution
	20	Controlling
	30	Indicating
75		**Air**
	00	General
	10	Engine anti-icing
	20	Accessory cooling
	30	Compressor control
	40	Indicating
76		**Engine controls**
	00	General
	10	Power control
	20	Emergency shutdown
77		**Engine indicating**
	00	General
	10	Power
	20	Temperature
	30	Analyzers
79		**Oil**
	00	General
	10	Storage
	20	Distribution
	30	Indicating
80		**Starting**
	00	General
	10	Cranking
81		**Turbines**
	00	General
	10	Power recovery
	20	Turbo-supercharger
83		**Accessory gear boxes**
	00	General
	10	Drive shaft section
	20	Gear box section
91		**Charts & wiring diagrams**
95		**Special purpose equipment**

Appendix D

FAA Joint Aircraft System Component Code Table

JASC/ Code	SUBJASC/ Code	Title
11		**Placards and markings**
	1100	Placards and markings
12		**Servicing**
	1210	Fuel servicing
	1220	Oil servicing
	1230	Hydraulic fluid servicing
	1240	Coolant servicing
14		**Hardware**
	1400	Miscellaneous hardware
	1410	Hoses and tubes
	1420	Electrical connectors
	1430	Fasteners
	1497	Miscellaneous wiring
18		**Helicopter vibration**
	1800	Helicopter vib/noise analysis
	1810	Helicopter vibration analysis
	1820	Helicopter noise analysis
	1897	Helicopter vibration system wiring
21		**Air conditioning**
	2100	Air conditioning system
	2110	Cabin compressor system
	2120	Air distribution system
	2121	Air distribution fan
	2130	Cabin pressure control system
	2131	Cabin pressure controller
	2132	Cabin pressure indicator
	2133	Pressure regulator/outflow valve
	2134	Cabin pressure sensor
	2140	Heating system
	2150	Cabin cooling system
	2160	Cabin temperature control system
	2161	Cabin temperature controller
	2162	Cabin temperature indicator
	2163	Cabin temperature sensor
	2170	Humidity control system
	2197	Air conditioning system wiring
22		**Auto flight**
	2200	Auto flight system
	2210	Autopilot system
	2211	Autopilot computer
	2212	Altitude controller

JASC/ Code	SUBJASC/ Code	Title
	2213	Flight controller
	2214	Autopilot trim indicator
	2215	Autopilot main servo
	2216	Autopilot trim servo
	2220	Speed-attitude correct. System
	2230	Auto throttle system
	2250	Aerodynamic load alleviating
	2297	Autoflight system wiring
23		**Communications**
	2300	Communications system
	2310	HF communication system
	2311	UHF communication system
	2312	VHF communication system
	2320	Data transmission auto call
	2330	Entertainment system
	2340	Interphone/passenger PA system
	2350	Audio integrating system
	2360	Static discharge system
	2370	Audio/video monitoring
	2397	Communication system wiring
24		**Electrical power**
	2400	Electrical power system
	2410	Alternator-generator drive
	2420	AC generation system
	2421	AC generator-alternator
	2422	AC inverter
	2423	Phase adapter
	2424	AC regulator
	2425	AC indicating system
	2430	DC generating system
	2431	Battery overheat warn. System
	2432	Battery/charger system
	2433	DC rectifier/converter
	2434	DC generator-alternator
	2435	Starter-generator
	2436	DC regulator
	2437	DC indicating system
	2440	External power system
	2450	AC power distribution system
	2460	DC power/distribution system
	2497	Electrical power system wiring

JASC/ Code	SUBJASC/ Code	Title
25		**Equipment/furnishings**
	2500	Cabin equipment/furnishings
	2510	Flight compartment equipment
	2520	Passenger compartment equipment
	2530	Buffet/galleys
	2540	Lavatories
	2550	Cargo compartments
	2551	Agricultural spray system
	2560	Emergency equipment
	2561	Life jacket
	2562	Emergency locator beacon
	2563	Parachute
	2564	Life raft
	2565	Escape slide
	2570	Accessory compartment
	2571	Battery box structure
	2572	Electronic shelf section
	2597	Equip/furnishing system wiring
26		**Fire protection**
	2600	Fire protection system
	2610	Detection system
	2611	Smoke detection
	2612	Fire detection
	2613	Overheat detection
	2620	Extinguishing system
	2621	Fire bottle, fixed
	2622	Fire bottle, portable
	2697	Fire protection system wiring
27		**Flight controls**
	2700	Flight control system
	2701	Control column section
	2710	Aileron control system
	2711	Aileron tab control system
	2720	Rudder control system
	2721	Rudder tab control system
	2722	Rudder actuator
	2730	Elevator control system
	2731	Elevator tab control system
	2740	Stabilizer control system
	2741	Stabilizer position indicating
	2742	Stabilizer actuator
	2750	TE flap control system
	2751	TE flap position ind. System
	2752	TE flap actuator
	2760	Drag control system
	2761	Drag control actuator

JASC/ Code	SUBJASC/ Code	Title
	2770	Gust lock/damper system
	2780	Le slat control system
	2781	Le slat position ind. System
	2782	Le slat actuator
	2797	Flight control system wiring
28		**Fuel**
	2800	Aircraft fuel system
	2810	Fuel storage
	2820	Aircraft fuel distrib. System
	2821	Aircraft fuel filter/strainer
	2822	Fuel boost pump
	2823	Fuel selector/shut-off valve
	2824	Fuel transfer valve
	2830	Fuel dump system
	2840	Aircraft fuel indicating system
	2841	Fuel quantity indicator
	2842	Fuel quantity sensor
	2843	Fuel temperature indicator
	2844	Fuel pressure indicator
	2897	Fuel system wiring
29		**Hydraulic power**
	2900	Hydraulic power system
	2910	Hydraulic system, main
	2911	Hydraulic power accumulator, main
	2912	Hydraulic filter, main
	2913	Hydraulic pump, (ELECT/ENG), main
	2914	Hydraulic handpump, main
	2915	Hydraulic pressure relief VLV, main
	2916	Hydraulic reservoir, main
	2917	Hydraulic pressure regulator, main
	2920	Hydraulic system, auxiliary
	2921	Hydraulic accumulator, auxiliary
	2922	Hydraulic filter, auxiliary
	2923	Hydraulic pump, auxiliary
	2925	Hydraulic pressure relief, auxiliary
	2926	Hydraulic reservoir, auxiliary
	2927	Hydraulic pressure regulator, aux.
	2930	Hydraulic indicating system
	2931	Hydraulic pressure indicator
	2932	Hydraulic pressure sensor
	2933	Hydraulic quantity indicator
	2934	Hydraulic quantity sensor
	2997	Hydraulic power system wiring
30		**Ice and rain protection**
	3000	Ice/rain protection system
	3010	Airfoil anti/de-ice system

JASC/ Code	SUBJASC/ Code	Title
	3020	Air intake anti/de-ice system
	3030	Pitot/static anti-ice system
	3040	Windshield/door rain/ice removal
	3050	Antenna/radome anti-ice/de-ice system
	3060	Prop/rotor anti-ice/de-ice system
	3070	Water line anti-ice system
	3080	Ice detection
	3097	Ice/rain protection system wiring
31		**Instruments**
	3100	Indicating/recording system
	3110	Instrument panel
	3120	Independent instruments (clock, etc.)
	3130	Data recorders (flt/maint)
	3140	Central computers (EICAS)
	3150	Central warning
	3160	Central display
	3170	Automatic data
	3197	Instrument system wiring
32		**Landing gear**
	3200	Landing gear system
	3201	Landing gear/wheel fairing
	3210	Main landing gear
	3211	Main landing gear attach section
	3212	Emergency flotation section
	3213	Main landing gear strut/axle/truck
	3220	Nose/tail landing gear
	3221	Nose/tail landing gear attach section
	3222	Nose/tail landing gear strut/axle
	3230	Landing gear retract/extend system
	3231	Landing gear door retract section
	3232	Landing gear door actuator
	3233	Landing gear actuator
	3234	Landing gear selector
	3240	Landing gear brake system
	3241	Brake anti-skid section
	3242	Brake
	3243	Master cylinder/brake valve
	3244	Tire
	3245	Tire tube
	3246	Wheel/ski/float
	3250	Landing gear steering system
	3251	Steering unit
	3252	Shimmy damper
	3260	Landing gear position and warning
	3270	Auxiliary gear (tail skid)
	3297	Landing gear system wiring

JASC/ Code	SUBJASC/ Code	Title
33		**Lights**
	3300	Lighting system
	3310	Flight compartment lighting
	3320	Passenger compartment lighting
	3330	Cargo compartment lighting
	3340	Exterior lighting
	3350	Emergency lighting
	3397	Light system wiring
34		**Navigation**
	3400	Navigation system
	3410	Flight environment data
	3411	Pitot/static system
	3412	Outside air temp. ind./sensor
	3413	Rate of climb indicator
	3414	Airspeed/mach indicator
	3415	High speed warning
	3416	Altimeter, barometric/encoder
	3417	Air data computer
	3418	Stall warning system
	3420	Attitude and direction data system
	3421	Attitude gyro and ind. system
	3422	Directional gyro and ind. system
	3423	Magnetic compass
	3424	Turn and bank/rate of turn indicator
	3425	Integrated flt. Director system
	3430	Landing and taxi aids
	3431	Localizer/VOR system
	3432	Glide slope system
	3433	Microwave landing system
	3434	Marker beacon system
	3435	Heads up display system
	3436	Wind shear detection system
	3440	Independent pos. determining system
	3441	Inertial guidance system
	3442	Weather radar system
	3443	Doppler system
	3444	Ground proximity system
	3445	Air collision avoidance system (TCAS)
	3446	Non radar weather system
	3450	Dependent position determining system
	3451	DME/TACAN system
	3452	ATC transponder system
	3453	LORAN system
	3454	VOR system
	3455	ADF system
	3456	Omega navigation system

JASC/Code	SUBJASC/Code	Title
	3457	Global positioning system
	3460	Flt manage. Computing hardware sys
	3461	Flt manage. Computing software sys
	3497	Navigation system wiring
35		**Oxygen**
	3500	Oxygen system
	3510	Crew oxygen system
	3520	Passenger oxygen system
	3530	Portable oxygen system
	3597	Oxygen system wiring
36		**Pneumatic**
	3600	Pneumatic system
	3610	Pneumatic distribution system
	3620	Pneumatic indicating system
	3697	Pneumatic system wiring
37		**Vacuum**
	3700	Vacuum system
	3710	Vacuum distribution system
	3720	Vacuum indicating system
	3797	Vacuum system wiring
38		**Water/waste**
	3800	Water and waste system
	3810	Potable water system
	3820	Wash water system
	3830	Waste disposal system
	3840	Air supply (water press. system)
	3897	Water/waste system wiring
45		**Central maint. system**
	4500	Central maint. computer
	4597	Central maint. system wiring
49		**Airborne auxiliary power**
	4900	Airborne APU system
	4910	APU cowling/containment
	4920	APU core engine
	4930	APU engine fuel and control
	4940	APU start/ignition system
	4950	APU bleed air system
	4960	APU controls
	4970	APU indicating system
	4980	APU exhaust system
	4990	APU oil system
	4997	APU system wiring
51		**Standard practices/structures**
	5100	Standard practices/structures
	5101	Aircraft structures
	5102	Balloon reports

JASC/Code	SUBJASC/Code	Title
52		**Doors**
	5200	Doors
	5210	Passenger/crew doors
	5220	Emergency exits
	5230	Cargo/baggage doors
	5240	Service doors
	5241	Galley doors
	5242	E/E compartment doors
	5243	Hydraulic compartment doors
	5244	Accessory compartment doors
	5245	Air conditioning compart. Doors
	5246	Fluid service doors
	5247	APU doors
	5248	Tail cone doors
	5250	Fixed inner doors
	5260	Entrance stairs
	5270	Door warning system
	5280	Landing gear doors
	5297	Door system wiring
53		**Fuselage**
	5300	Fuselage structure (general)
	5301	Aerial tow equipment
	5302	Rotorcraft tail boom
	5310	Fuselage main, structure
	5311	Fuselage main, frame
	5312	Fuselage main, bulkhead
	5313	Fuselage main, longeron/stringer
	5314	Fuselage main, keel
	5315	Fuselage main, floor beam
	5320	Fuselage miscellaneous structure
	5321	Fuselage floor panel
	5322	Fuselage internal mount structure
	5323	Fuselage internal stairs
	5324	Fuselage fixed partitions
	5330	Fuselage main, plate/skin
	5340	Fuselage main, attach fittings
	5341	Fuselage, wing attach fittings
	5342	Fuselage, stabilizer attach fittings
	5343	Landing gear attach fittings
	5344	Fuselage door hinges
	5345	Fuselage equipment attach fittings
	5346	Powerplant attach fittings
	5347	Seat/cargo attach fittings
	5350	Aerodynamic fairings
	5397	Fuselage wiring

JASC/ Code	SUBJASC/ Code	Title
54		**Nacelles/pylons**
	5400	Nacelle/pylon structure
	5410	Nacelle/pylon, main frame
	5411	Nacelle/pylon, frame/spar/rib
	5412	Nacelle/pylon, bulkhead/firewall
	5413	Nacelle/pylon, longeron/stringer
	5414	Nacelle/pylon, plate skin
	5415	Nacelle/pylon, attach fittings
	5420	Nacelle/pylon miscellaneous struct.
	5497	Nacelle/pylon system wiring
55		**Stabilizers**
	5500	Empennage structure
	5510	Horizontal stabilizer structure
	5511	Horizontal stabilizer, spar/rib
	5512	Horizontal stabilizer, plate/skin
	5513	Horizontal stabilizer, tab structure
	5514	Horizontal stab miscellaneous structure
	5520	Elevator structure
	5521	Elevator, spar/rib structure
	5522	Elevator, plates/skin structure
	5523	Elevator, tab structure
	5524	Elevator miscellaneous structure
	5530	Vertical stabilizer structure
	5531	Vertical stabilizer, spar/rib struct.
	5532	Vertical stabilizer, plates/skin
	5533	Ventral structure
	5534	Vert. stab. miscellaneous structure
	5540	Rudder structure
	5541	Rudder, spar/rib
	5542	Rudder, plate/skin
	5543	Rudder, tab structure
	5544	Rudder miscellaneous structure
	5550	Empennage flt. cont., Attach fitting
	5551	Horizontal stabilizer, attach fitting
	5552	Elevator/tab, attach fittings
	5553	Vert. stab., attach fittings
	5554	Rudder/tab, attach fittings
	5597	Stabilizer system wiring
56		**Windows**
	5600	Window/windshield system
	5610	Flight compartment windows
	5620	Passenger compartment windows
	5630	Door windows
	5640	Inspection windows
	5697	Window system wiring

JASC/ Code	SUBJASC/ Code	Title
57		**Wings**
	5700	Wing structure
	5710	Wing, main frame structure
	5711	Wing spar
	5712	Wing, rib/bulkhead
	5713	Wing, longeron/stringer
	5714	Wing, center box
	5720	Wing miscellaneous structure
	5730	Wing, plates/skins
	5740	Wing, attach fittings
	5741	Wing, fuselage attach fittings
	5742	Wing, nac/pylon attach fittings
	5743	Wing, landing gear attach fittings
	5744	Wing, cont. Surface attach fittings
	5750	Wing, control surfaces
	5751	Ailerons
	5752	Aileron tab structure
	5753	Trailing edge flaps
	5754	Leading edge devices
	5755	Spoilers
	5797	Wing system wiring
61		**Propellers/propulsors**
	6100	Propeller system
	6110	Propeller assembly
	6111	Propeller blade section
	6112	Propeller de-ice boot section
	6113	Propeller spinner section
	6114	Propeller hub section
	6120	Propeller controlling system
	6121	Propeller synchronizer section
	6122	Propeller governor
	6123	Propeller feathering/reversing
	6130	Propeller braking
	6140	Propeller indicating system
	6197	Propeller/propulsors system wiring
62		**Main rotor**
	6200	Main rotor system
	6210	Main rotor blades
	6220	Main rotor head
	6230	Main rotor mast/swashplate
	6240	Main rotor indicating system
	6297	Main rotor system wiring
63		**Main rotor drive**
	6300	Main rotor drive system
	6310	Engine/transmission coupling
	6320	Main rotor gearbox

JASC/ Code	SUBJASC/ Code	Title
	6321	Main rotor brake
	6322	Rotorcraft cooling fan system
	6330	Main rotor transmission mount
	6340	Rotor drive indicating system
	6397	Main rotor drive system wiring
64		**Tail rotor**
	6400	Tail rotor system
	6410	Tail rotor blades
	6420	Tail rotor head
	6440	Tail rotor indicating system
	6497	Tail rotor system wiring
65		**Tail rotor drive**
	6500	Tail rotor drive system
	6510	Tail rotor drive shaft
	6520	Tail rotor gearbox
	6540	Tail rotor drive indicating system
	6597	Tail rotor drive system wiring
67		**Rotors flight control**
	6700	Rotorcraft flight control
	6710	Main rotor control
	6711	Tilt rotor flight control
	6720	Tail rotor control system
	6730	Rotorcraft servo system
	6797	Rotors flight control system wiring
71		**Powerplant**
	7100	Powerplant system
	7110	Engine cowling system
	7111	Engine cowl flaps
	7112	Engine air baffle section
	7120	Engine mount section
	7130	Engine fireseals
	7160	Engine air intake system
	7170	Engine drains
	7197	Powerplant system wiring
72		**Turbine/turboprop engine**
	7200	Engine (turbine/turboprop)
	7210	Turbine engine reduction gear
	7220	Turbine engine air inlet section
	7230	Turbine engine compressor section
	7240	Turbine engine combustion section
	7250	Turbine section
	7260	Turbine engine accessory drive
	7261	Turbine engine oil system
	7270	Turbine engine bypass section
	7297	Turbine engine system wiring

JASC/ Code	SUBJASC/ Code	Title
73		**Engine fuel and control**
	7300	Engine fuel and control
	7310	Engine fuel distribution
	7311	Engine fuel/oil cooler
	7312	Fuel heater
	7313	Fuel injector nozzle
	7314	Engine fuel pump
	7320	Fuel controlling system
	7321	Fuel control/turbine engines
	7322	Fuel control/reciprocating engines
	7323	Turbine governor
	7324	Fuel divider
	7330	Engine fuel indicating system
	7331	Fuel flow indicating
	7332	Fuel pressure indicating
	7333	Fuel flow sensor
	7334	Fuel pressure sensor
	7397	Engine fuel system wiring
74		**Ignition**
	7400	Ignition system
	7410	Ignition power supply
	7411	Low tension coil
	7412	Exciter
	7413	Induction vibrator
	7414	Magneto/distributor
	7420	Ignition harness (distribution)
	7421	Spark plug/igniter
	7430	Ignition/starter switching
	7497	Ignition system wiring
75		**Air**
	7500	Engine bleed air system
	7510	Engine anti-icing system
	7520	Engine cooling system
	7530	Compressor bleed control
	7531	Compressor bleed governor
	7532	Compressor bleed valve
	7540	Bleed air indicating system
	7597	Engine bleed air system wiring
76		**Engine controls**
	7600	Engine controls
	7601	Engine synchronizing
	7602	Mixture control
	7603	Power lever
	7620	Engine emergency shutdown system
	7697	Engine control system wiring

JASC/ Code	SUBJASC/ Code	Title
77		**Engine Indicating**
	7700	Engine Indicating System
	7710	Power Indicating System
	7711	Engine Pressure Ratio (EPR)
	7712	Engine BMEP/Torque Indicating
	7713	Manifold Pressure (MP) Indicating
	7714	Engine Rpm Indicating System
	7720	Engine Temp. Indicating System
	7721	Cylinder Head Temp (CHT) Indicating
	7722	ENG. EGT/TIT Indicating System
	7730	Engine Ignition Analyzer System
	7731	Engine Ignition Analyzer
	7732	Engine Vibration Analyzer
	7740	Engine Integrated Instrument System
	7797	Engine Indicating System Wiring
78		**Engine Exhaust**
	7800	Engine Exhaust System
	7810	Engine Collector/Tailpipe/Nozzle
	7820	Engine Noise Suppressor
	7830	Thrust Reverser
	7897	Engine Exhaust System Wiring
79		**Engine Oil**
	7900	Engine Oil System (Airframe)
	7910	Engine Oil Storage (Airframe)
	7920	Engine Oil Distribution (Airframe)
	7921	Engine Oil Cooler
	7922	Engine Oil Temp. Regulator
	7923	Engine Oil Shutoff Valve
	7930	Engine Oil Indicating System
	7931	Engine Oil Pressure
	7932	Engine Oil Quantity
	7933	Engine Oil Temperature
	7997	Engine Oil System Wiring
80		**Starting**
	8000	Engine Starting System
	8010	Engine Cranking
	8011	Engine Starter
	8012	Engine Start Valves/Controls
	8097	Engine Starting System Wiring
81		**Turbocharging**
	8100	Exhaust Turbine System (Recip)
	8110	Power Recovery Turbine (Recip)
	8120	Exhaust Turbocharger
	8197	Turbocharging System Wiring
82		**Water Injection**
	8200	Water Injection System

JASC/ Code	SUBJASC/ Code	Title
	8297	Water injection system wiring
83		**Accessory gearboxes**
	8300	Accessory gearboxes
	8397	Accessory gearbox system wiring
85		**Reciprocating engine**
	8500	Engine (reciprocating)
	8510	Reciprocating engine front section
	8520	Reciprocating engine power section
	8530	Reciprocating engine cylinder section
	8540	Reciprocating engine rear section
	8550	Reciprocating engine oil system
	8560	Reciprocating engine supercharger
	8570	Reciprocating engine liquid cooling
	8597	Reciprocating engine system wiring

Appendix E

List of Common Acronyms Used in this Text

ACARS - Aircraft Communication Addressing and Reporting System

AD - Airworthiness Directive

ADF - Automatic Direction Finder

ADHRS - Air Data Heading Reference System

ADIRS - Air Data Inertial Reference System

ADIRU - Air Data Inertial Reference Unit

ADM - Air Data Module

ADR - Air Data Reference

ADS-C - Automated Dependent Surveillance System

AFMS - Aircraft Flight Manual Supplement

AGC - Automatic Gain Control

AGL - Above Ground Level

AGRAS - Automatic Ground Receiver Access System

AHRS - Attitude Heading Reference System

AIM - Acknowledgement ISO Alphabet Maintenance

AM - Amplitude Modulated

AOA - Angle of Attack

AOR-E - Inmarsat Satellite Atlantic Ocean Region – East

AOR-W - Inmarsat Satellite Atlantic Ocean Region – West

ARINC - Aeronautical Radio Incorporated

ASCB - Avionics Standard Communication Bus

ASI - Standby Airspeed Indicator

BCD - Binary Coded Decimal

BFO - Beat Frequency Oscillator

BNR - Binary Data

BPS - Bits per second

C/A Code - Course Acquisition Code

CAS - Calibrated Airspeed

CAVU - Clear, visibility unlimited

CDU - Control Display Unit

CMC - Current Mode Coupler

CSDB - Commercial Standard Digital Bus

DAS - Designated Alteration Station

DDM - Difference in Depth Modulation

DER - Designated Engineering Representative

DG - Directional Gyro

DITS - Digital Information Transfer System

DME - Distance Measuring Equipment

DOA - Delegation Option Authorization Holder

DTMF - Dual tone Modulating Frequencies

EFIS - Electronic Flight Instrumentation System

EHF - Extremely High Frequency

EHSI - Electronic Horizontal Situation Indicator

ETE - Estimated Time En Route

ETOPS - Extended Operation and Extended Twin Engine Operation

FDE - Fault Detection Exclusion

FMS - Flight Management System and Flight Management Supplement

FOG - Fiber Optic Gyroscope

GAMA - General Aviation Manufacturers' Association

GBAS - Ground-Based Augmentation System

GDOP - Geometric Dilution of Precision

GNSS - Global Navigation Satellite System

GPS - Global Positioning System

HF - High Frequency

HIRF - High Intensity Radiated Fields

HSI - Horizontal Situation Indicator

IAS - Indicated Airspeed

IF - Intermediate Frequency

ILS - Instrument Landing System

ILSDME - ILS site with DME capabilities

INS - Inertial Navigation System

IOR - Inmarsat Satellite Indian Ocean Region

IRS - Inertial Reference System

IRSCDU - IRS Control Display Unit

IRU - Inertial Reference System

ITU - International Telecommunications Union

LAAS - Local Area Augmentation System

LEO - Low Earth Orbit

LF - Low Frequency

LO - Local Oscillator

LOC - Localizer

LOP - Lines of Position

LVDT - Linear Voltage Differential Transducer

MCDU - Multifunction Control Display Unit

MEMS - Microelectro-Mechanical Systems

MF - Medium Frequency

MIDO - Manufacturing Inspection District Office

MSL - Main Sea Level

NDB - Non-directional Beacon

NPN - Negative Positive Negative

OBS - Omnibearing Selector

OOOI - Out of Gate, Off Ground, On Ground, and In Gate

PNI - Pictorial Navigation Indicator (also known as Horizontal Situation Indicator)

PNP - Positive Negative Positive

POR - Inmarsat Satellite Pacific Ocean Region

PRN - Pseudo Random Noise

PRR - Pulse Repetition Rate

PTT - Push-To-Talk

R-NAV - Area Navigation

RAIM - Receiver Autonomous Integrity Monitoring

RF - Radio Frequency

RNR - Required Navigation Performance

RRTNM - Radar Round Trip Nautical Mile

RTZ - Return to Zero System

RVSM - Reduced Vertical Separation Minimums

SATCOM - Satellite Communication

SAW - Surface Acoustic Wave

SBD - Short Burst Data

SDI - Source Destination Identifier

SDU - Satellite Data Unit

SELCAL - Selective Calling

SG - Synchronization Gap

SHF - Super High Frequency

SIM - Serial Interface Module

SMO - Stabilized Master Oscillator

SMS - Short Message Service

SSM - Sign Status Matrix

STC - Supplemental Type Certificate

SV - Space Vehicle

TACAN - Tactical Navigation

TC - Terminal Controller

TD - Time Delay

TG - Terminal Gap

TI - Timing Interval

TR - Transmit/Receive

UHF - Ultra High Frequency

VCO - Voltage Controlled Oscillator

VFR - Visual Flight Rules

VHF - Very High Frequency

VHF COM - Aeronautical VHF Communication Systems

VLF - Very Low Frequency

VOR - VHF Omnirange

VORDME - VOR site with DME capabilities

WAAS - Wide Area Augmentation System

WARC 89 - World Administrative Radio Conference

WILCO - Will Comply

WRC - World Radio Communications Conference

Glossary

Aeronautical Fixed Service - A radio communication service between specified fixed points provided primarily for the safety of air navigation and for the regular, efficient and economical operation of air transport.

Aeronautical Fixed Station - A station in the aeronautical fixed service.

Aeronautical Mobile Off-Route Service - An aeronautical mobile service intended for communications, including those relating to flight coordination, primarily outside national or international civil air routes.

Aeronautical Mobile Route (R) Service - An aeronautical mobile service reserved for communications relating to safety and regularity of flight, primarily along national or international civil air routes.

Aeronautical Mobile Satellite Off-Route (OR) Service - An aeronautical mobile satellite service intended for communications, including those relating to flight coordination, primarily outside national and international civil air routes.

Aeronautical Mobile Satellite Route Service - An aeronautical mobile-satellite service reserved for communications relating to safety and regularity of flights, primarily along national or international civil air routes.

Aeronautical Mobile Satellite Service - A mobile-satellite service in which mobile earth stations are located onboard aircraft; survival craft stations and emergency position-indicating radio beacon stations may also participate in this service.

Aeronautical Mobile Service - A mobile service between aeronautical stations and aircraft stations, or between aircraft stations, in which survival craft stations may participate; emergency position-indicating radio beacon stations may also participate in this service on designated distress and emergency frequencies.

Aeronautical Radio Navigation Satellite Service - A radio navigation satellite service in which earth stations are located onboard aircraft.

Aeronautical Radio Navigation Service - A radio-navigation service intended for the benefit and for the safe operation of aircraft.

Aeronautical Station - A land station in the aeronautical mobile service.

NOTE: In certain instances, an aeronautical station may be located, for example, onboard a ship or on a platform at sea.

Aircraft Earth Station - A mobile earth station in the aeronautical mobile-satellite service located onboard an aircraft.

Aircraft Station - A mobile station in the aeronautical mobile service, other than a survival craft station, located onboard an aircraft.

Assigned Frequency Band - The frequency band within which the emission of a station is authorized; the width of the band equals the necessary bandwidth plus twice the absolute value of the frequency tolerance. Where space stations are concerned, the assigned frequency band includes twice the maximum Doppler shift that may occur in relation to any point of the earth's surface.

Assignment (of a radio frequency or radio frequency channel) - Authorization given by an administration for a radio station to use a radio frequency or radio frequency channel under specified conditions (RR).

Base Earth Station - An earth station in the fixed-satellite service or, in some cases, in the land mobile-satellite service, located at a specified fixed point or within a specified area on land to provide a feeder link for the land mobile-satellite service.

Base Station - A land station in the land mobile service.

Broadcasting Satellite Service - A radio communication service in which signals transmitted or retransmitted by space stations are intended for direct reception by the general public.

Carrier Power (of a radio transmitter) - The average power supplied to the antenna transmission line by a transmitter during one radio frequency cycle taken under the condition of no modulation.

Characteristic Frequency - A frequency which can be easily identified and measured in a given emission.

Class of Emission - The set of characteristics of an emission designated by earth stations, beyond which the level of permissible interference will not be exceeded and coordination is therefore not required.

Comité Consultatif International des Radio Communications (CCIR) - French International Radio Consultative Committee.

> **AUTHOR'S NOTE:** *This term is used, but not defined in CFR 47, Part 2.*

Conterminous United States - The contiguous 48 states and the District of Columbia (FCC).

Coordinated Universal Time (UTC) - Time scale, based on the second (SI), as defined in Recommendation ITU–R TF.460–6.

Differential Global Positioning System (DGPS) Station - A differential RNSS station for specific augmentation of GPS.

Differential Radio Navigation Satellite Service (Differential RNSS) Station - A station used for the transmission of differential correction data and related information (such as ionospheric data and RNSS satellite integrity information) as an augmentation to an RNSS system for the purpose of improved navigation accuracy.

Direct Sequence Systems - A spread spectrum system in which the carrier has been modulated by a high speed spreading code and an information data stream. The high speed code sequence dominates the modulating function and is the direct cause of the wide spreading of the transmitted signal.

Duplex Operation - Operating method in which transmission is possible simultaneously in both directions of a telecommunication channel.

Effective Radiated Power (ERP) - The product of the power supplied to the antenna and its gain relative to a half-wave dipole in a given direction.

Emergency Position-Indicating Radio Beacon Station - A station in the mobile service whose emissions are intended to facilitate search and rescue operations.

Emission - Radiation produced, or the production of radiation, by a radio transmitting station.

Facsimile - A form of telegraphy for the transmission of fixed images, with or without half-tones, with a view to their reproduction in a permanent form.

Frequency Tolerance - The maximum permissible departure by the center frequency of the frequency band occupied by an emission from the assigned frequency, or by the characteristic frequency of an emission from the reference frequency.

Full Carrier Single-Sideband Emission - A single-sideband emission without suppression of the carrier.

Gain of an Antenna - The ratio, usually expressed in decibels, of the power required at the input of a loss-free reference antenna to the power supplied to the input of the given antenna. In a given direction, this produces the same field strength or the same power flux density at the same distance. When not specified otherwise, the gain refers to the direction of maximum radiation. The gain may be considered for a specified polarization.

NOTE: *Depending on the choice of the reference antenna, a distinction is made between:*

1. *Absolute or isotropic gain (Gi), when the reference antenna is an isotropic antenna isolated in space*

2. *Gain relative to a half-wave dipole (Gd), when the reference antenna is a half-wave dipole isolated in space whose equatorial plane contains the given direction*

3. *Gain relative to a short vertical antenna (Gv), when the reference antenna is a linear conductor, much shorter than one quarter of the wavelength, normal to the surface of a perfectly conducting plane, which contains the given direction.*

Geostationary Satellite - A geosynchronous satellite whose circular and direct orbit lies in the plane of the earth's equator and which thus remains fixed relative to the earth; by extension, a geosynchronous satellite which remains approximately fixed relative to the Earth.

Geostationary Satellite Orbit - The orbit in which a satellite must be placed to be a geostationary satellite.

Geosynchronous Satellite - An earth satellite whose period of revolution is equal to the period of rotation of the Earth about its axis.

Harmful Interference - Interference that endangers the functioning of a radio navigation service or of other safety services or seriously degrades, obstructs, or repeatedly interrupts a radio communication service operating in accordance with [the ITU] Radio Regulations.

Inclination of an Orbit (of an earth satellite) - The angle determined by the plane containing the orbit and the plane of the earth's equator measured in degrees between 0° and 180° and in counter-clockwise direction from the earth's equatorial plane at the ascending node of the orbit.

Instrument Landing System (ILS) - A radio navigation system that provides aircraft with horizontal and vertical guidance just before and during landing and at certain fixed points indicates the distance to the reference point of landing.

Instrument Landing System Glide Path - A system of vertical guidance embodied in the instrument landing system that indicates the vertical deviation of the aircraft from its optimum path of descent.

Instrument Landing System Localizer - A system of horizontal guidance embodied in the instrument landing system that indicates the horizontal deviation of the aircraft from its optimum path of descent along the axis of the runway.

Interference - The effect of unwanted energy due to one or a combination of emissions, radiations or inductions upon reception in a radio communication system, manifested by any performance degradation, misinterpretation or loss of information that could be extracted in the absence of such unwanted energy.

Inter-Satellite Service - A radio communication service providing links between artificial satellites.

Marker Beacon - A transmitter in the aeronautical radio navigation service that radiates vertically a distinctive pattern for providing position information to aircraft.

Mean Power (of a radio transmitter) - The average power supplied to the antenna transmission line by a transmitter during an interval of time sufficiently long compared with the lowest frequency encountered in the modulation taken under normal operating conditions.

Mobile Earth Station - An earth station in the mobile-satellite service intended to be used while in motion or during halts at unspecified points.

Mobile Satellite Service - A radio communication service between mobile earth stations and one or more space stations, or between space stations used by this service, or between mobile earth stations by means of one or more space stations.

Multi-Satellite Link - A radio link between a transmitting earth station and a receiving earth station through two or more satellites, without any intermediate earth station.

> **NOTE:** *A multi-satellite link comprises one up-link, one or more satellite-to-satellite links and one down-link.*

National Telecommunications and Information Administration (NTIA) - An agency of the United States Department of Commerce that serves as the President's principal advisor on telecommunications and information policy issues. NTIA manages Federal use of the radio spectrum and coordinates Federal use with the FCC. NTIA sets forth regulations for Federal use of the radio spectrum within its Manual of Regulations & Procedures for Federal Radio Frequency Management (NTIA Manual).

Necessary Bandwidth - For a given class of emission, the width of the frequency band that is just sufficient to ensure the transmission of information at the rate and with the quality required under specified conditions.

Occupied Bandwidth - The width of a frequency band such that, below the lower and above the upper frequency limits, the mean powers emitted are each equal to a specified percentage Beta/2 of the total mean power of a given emission.

> **NOTE:** *Unless otherwise specified by the CCIR for the appropriate class of emission, the value of Beta/2 should be taken as 0.5%.*

Orbit - The path, relative to a specified frame of reference, described by the center of mass of a satellite or other object in space subjected primarily to natural forces, mainly the force of gravity.

Peak Envelope Power (of a radio transmitter) - The average power supplied to the antenna transmission line by a transmitter during one radio frequency cycle at the crest of the modulation envelope taken under normal operating conditions.

Period (of a satellite) - The time elapsing between two consecutive passages of a satellite through a characteristic point on its orbit.

Power - Whenever the power of a radio transmitter, etc., is referred to, it shall be expressed in one of the following forms according to the class of emission using the arbitrary symbols indicated:

1. Peak envelope power (PX or pX);
2. Mean power (PY or pY);
3. Carrier power (PZ or pZ).

Primary Radar - A radio determination system based on the comparison of reference signals with radio signals reflected from the position to be determined.

Radar - A radio determination system based on the comparison of reference signals with radio signals reflected, or retransmitted from the position to be determined.

> **AUTHOR'S NOTE:** *Acronym for Radio Detection and Ranging.*

Radiation - The outward flow of energy from any source in the form of radio waves.

Radio - A general term applied to the use of radio waves.

Radio Altimeter - Radio navigation equipment, onboard an aircraft or spacecraft, or the spacecraft above the Earth's surface or another surface.

Radio Beacon Station - A station in the radio navigation service whose emissions are intended to enable a mobile station to determine its bearing or direction in relation to radio beacon station.

Radio Communication - Telecommunication by means of radio waves.

Radio Direction-Finding - Radio determination using the reception of radio waves for the purpose of determining the direction of a station or object.

Radio Direction-Finding Station - A radio determination station using radio direction-finding.

Radio Location - Radio determination used for purposes other than those of radio navigation.

Radio Navigation - Radio determination used for the purposes of navigation, including obstruction warning.

Radio Navigation Land Station - A station in the radio navigation service not intended to be used while in motion.

Radio Navigation Mobile Station - A station in the radio navigation service intended to be used while in motion or during halts at unspecified points.

Radio Navigation Satellite Service - A radio determination-satellite service used for the purpose of radio navigation. This service may also include feeder links necessary for its operation.

Radio Navigation Service - A radio determination service for the purpose of radio navigation.

Radiosonde - An automatic radio transmitter in the meteorological aids service usually carried on an aircraft, free balloon, kite or parachute, and which transmits meteorological data.

Radio Waves or Hertzian Waves - Electromagnetic waves of frequencies arbitrarily lower than 3,000 GHz propagated in space without artificial guide.

Satellite - A body which revolves around another body of preponderant mass and has a motion primarily and permanently determined by the force of attraction of that other body.

Satellite Link - A radio link between a transmitting earth station and a receiving earth station through one satellite. A satellite link comprises one up-link and one down-link.

Satellite Network - A satellite system or a part of a satellite system, consisting of only one satellite and the cooperating earth stations.

Satellite System - A space system using one or more artificial earth satellites.

Semi-Duplex Operation - A method which is simplex operation on one end of the circuit and duplex operation at the other.

Simplex Operation - Operating method in which transmission is made possible alternatively in each direction of a telecommunication channel, for example, by means of manual control.

Single-Sideband Emission - An amplitude modulated emission with one sideband only.

Spread Spectrum Systems - A spread spectrum system is an information bearing communications system in which information is conveyed by modulation of a carrier by some conventional means and the bandwidth is deliberately widened by means of a spreading function over that which would be needed to transmit the information alone. In some spread spectrum systems, a portion of the information being conveyed by the system may be contained in the spreading function.

Spurious Domain (of an emission) - The frequency range beyond the out-of-band domain in which spurious emissions generally predominate.

Spurious Emission - Emission on a frequency or frequencies that are outside the necessary bandwidth whose level may be reduced without affecting the corresponding transmission of information. Spurious emissions include harmonic emissions, parasitic emissions, intermodulation products and frequency conversion products, but exclude out-of-band emissions.

Standard Frequency and Time Signal Satellite Service - A radio communication service using space stations on earth satellites for the same purposes as those of the standard frequency and time signal service.

> **NOTE:** *This service may also include feeder links necessary for its operation.*

Standard Frequency and Time Signal Service - A radio communication service for scientific, technical and other purposes, providing the transmission of specified frequencies, time signals, or both, of stated high precision, intended for general reception.

Standard Frequency and Time Signal Station - A station in the standard frequency and time signal service.

Station - One or more transmitters or receivers or a combination of transmitters and receivers, including the accessory equipment, necessary at one location for carrying on a radio communication service, or the radio astronomy service.

Suppressed Carrier Single-Sideband Emission - A single-sideband emission in which the carrier is virtually suppressed and not intended to be used for demodulation.

Survival Craft Station - A mobile station in the maritime mobile service or the aeronautical mobile service intended solely for survival purposes and located on any lifeboat, life-raft or other survival equipment.

Telephony - A form of telecommunication primarily intended for the exchange of information in the form of speech.

Transponder - A transmitter-receiver facility whose function is to transmit signals automatically when the proper interrogation is received.

Unwanted Emissions - Consist of spurious emissions and out-of-band emissions.

Index